| | | Ge | Si | GaAs |
|---|---|---|---|---|
| atoms per cm³ | | $4.4 \times 10^{22}$ | $5.0 \times 10^{22}$ | $4.4 \times 10^{22}$ |
| energy gap | $W_g$, eV | 0.7 | 1.1 | 1.3 |
| intrinsic electron concentration per unit volume | $n_i/\text{cm}^3$ $n_i^2/\text{cm}^3$ | $2.5 \times 10^{13}$ $6.3 \times 10^{26}$ | $1.5 \times 10^{10}$ $2.3 \times 10^{20}$ | $9.2 \times 10^6$ $8.5 \times 10^{13}$ |
| intrinsic conductivity | $\sigma_i$, mho/cm | $2.3 \times 10^{-2}$ | $4.4 \times 10^{-6}$ | $1.3 \times 10^{-8}$ |
| intrinsic electron mobility | $\mu_e$, cm²/V-s | 3900 | 1350 | 8500 |
| intrinsic hole mobility | $\mu_h$, cm²/V-s | 1900 | 480 | 450 |
| intrinsic diffusion coefficient for electrons | $D_e$, cm²/s | 101 | 35 | 221 |
| intrinsic diffusion coefficient for holes | $D_h$, cm²/s | 49 | 12.5 | 12 |
| effective mass ratio for electrons | $m_e^*/m_0$ | 0.55 | 1.1 | 0.06 |
| effective mass ratio for holes | $m_h^*/m_0$ | 0.37 | 0.59 | 0.5 |
| relative permittivity, dielectric constant | $\varepsilon_r$ | 16 | 12 | 11 |
| melting temperature | $t_m$, °C | 947 | 1410 | 1238 |

# INTRODUCTION TO ELECTRONIC
# SYSTEMS, CIRCUITS, AND DEVICES

**Donald O. Pederson**

**Jack J. Studer**

**John R. Whinnery**

*Department of Electrical Engineering*
*University of California, Berkeley*

# INTRODUCTION TO ELECTRONIC SYSTEMS, CIRCUITS, AND DEVICES

**McGraw-Hill Book Company**

*New York   San Francisco   St. Louis   Toronto   London   Sydney*

91536

621.38
P37/

**introduction to electronic systems, circuits, and devices**

# PREFACE

Three years ago the Electrical Engineering Department of the University of California, Berkeley, introduced a beginning course in electrical engineering at the sophomore level. The authors of this text had the assignment of starting the course and have since participated in its continuing development. This book represents the general point of view adopted by the department and implemented by the authors and other instructors of the course. A preliminary version was published in 1964 and used for three terms. This final version incorporates modifications resulting from the use of the preliminary edition and from suggestions by colleagues and several reviewers.

It is clearly impossible, without complete superficiality, to introduce any major part of electrical engineering in a one-term course. The breadth implied by the title thus represents a point of view rather than complete coverage. Engineering is concerned with systems. Systems are built of functional blocks, each of many circuits, and the circuits in turn are built of components. In this book, we examine this process and consider examples at several levels. In order to do this in depth as well as breadth—and quantitatively as well as qualitatively—certain components and principles must be treated in much more detail than others. The examples chosen for emphasis are not the only important ones, but they are some of the ones that illustrate a variety of functions from a few physical principles—principles which can be analyzed and understood from the level of physics and mathematics appropriate to the course.

Several boundary conditions exist at Berkeley which at first appeared to be constraints but which did permit much flexibility to be built into the text. The most important condition is that the department receives approximately half of its junior class as transfer students from other excellent publicly supported schools of higher education in California. Thus the course is available in the last half of the sophomore year for students at Berkeley, but students transferring without it should be able to take the course in the junior year concurrently with other electrical engineering courses. The course must be usable at the sophomore level by the other California public colleges that wish to adopt it. It must build upon the preparation provided by the basic physics and mathematics courses, taking into account the major revisions in these courses now occurring in high schools and universities. Finally, it must be of interest and use to students in fields other than electrical engineering, since a first course is frequently common to more than one curriculum.

In designing a course to meet these constraints, the decision was made to emphasize the basic electronic principles and interactions that lead to modern electronic devices like the transistor. This choice ties in well with the prerequisite physics courses, and the quantitative approach to the subject permits direct application of the mathematics studied concurrently. The introduction to electronics includes the important concepts of systems and of the signals to be processed by the devices, in order to place in context such matters as gain, bandwidth, and linearity or nonlinearity, which are studied for selected devices. Electronics is easy to study with some independence from other aspects of electrical engineering, and it is now an essential part of the understanding of electrical engineers and of other engineers who must use electronic instruments as basic tools.

Another decision was to continue the development of the students' facility with elementary circuit analysis from the base built in their first physics courses. Circuit analysis is thus reviewed and extended slightly in an early chapter; it is then used as required throughout the remainder of the text. There is no attempt, however, to make this a complete introduction to formal circuit theory, since that subject is left for a subsequent or con-current course. The present course should provide background and motivation for the thorough circuits course by showing the need for circuit theory. The text can also be used, of course, after a first course in circuit theory. The chapter on circuits can be omitted or used for review. Still other modifications can be made (such as the omission of the last two chapters and final sections of several chapters), and indeed some omissions are necessary, or some material must be treated as review material, when the text is used in a one-term course. We believe that, by selection, the result is a flexible text that can be given a variety of uses according to the specific background of the students.

The first three chapters introduce electronic systems, system building blocks, and electronic circuit functions, including signal description and processing and the review and extension of circuit analysis mentioned above. Chapter 4 reviews the basic laws of electron motion and introduces the physical behavior of charges in solids. Chapters 5 to 9 provide a first treatment of *pn*-junction devices, such as the *pn* diode and the junction transistor. The emphasis is on the development of an understanding of the basic electronic mechanisms of the devices and on the development of electrical circuit models for the devices. This material is applied to simple electronic circuits, such as switching and logic circuits and linear amplifiers. In Chapter 10, thermionic vacuum devices are introduced from the same point of view, but with more concise treatment. Chapter 11 introduces microwave devices in order to show some of the different problems that arise at high frequencies, and Chapter 12 introduces relatively new electronic devices with photon inputs or outputs, to show the open-ended character of our subject. Several appendixes are included to present reference data. Problems, developed and used in the course at Berkeley, are included with each chapter.

We have several times experimented with a final two-week assignment, in which details of the course are applied to the design or synthesis of portions of some simple but nontrivial system. Examples include an electronic seismograph, a sampling oscilloscope, and a hi-fi system, with stress on the overall system performance and design of a few key amplifiers, switches, or other functional blocks. The experiment has been successful enough to call to the attention of other instructors, although it has not seemed suitable for inclusion as text material.

With the ties between material provided, the book is approximately equally divided in emphasis among electronic systems and circuits (including the development and application of circuit models), basic charge motion and interactions in solids and vacuum, and electronic-device description. There are clearly other alternatives for a first course in electrical engineering, including the common first course in circuits. In the opinion of all the instructors of the course, the approach employed here has been successful in giving some view of the breadth and richness of electrical engineering, and at the same time, demonstrating the application of the basic tools being studied concurrently (especially physics and mathematics) to the quantitative study of real engineering problems.

It is impossible to list all the persons who made the course and this text possible. Professors R. S. Pepper, R. M. White, W. G. Oldham, and M. Gans deserve special credit for their work in presenting and helping to develop the course. We owe much gratitude to the students of the course for their comments, criticisms, and contagious enthusiasm, especially those of the first year, who were the "guinea pigs" of the original experiment. Criticisms from many reviewers of the preliminary edition were essential in the preparation of the final version; the comments of Professor A. R. Boothroyd of Queens University, Belfast, Northern Ireland, were especially detailed and helpful. The preliminary edition was prepared when one of the authors (DOP) was in Australia and another (JRW) in New Jersey. The former wishes to thank colleagues at the University of Melbourne and Monash University for many informative discussions at that time, and to express appreciation to the John Simon Guggenheim Memorial Foundation for fellowship support during that period. The latter acknowledges with pleasure similar help from the Bell Telephone Laboratories and colleagues at Murray Hill.

*D. O. Pederson*
*J. J. Studer*
*J. R. Whinnery*

# CONTENTS

## 12   photon-interaction devices

## A   complex numbers,

## B   atomic structures,

## C   continuity equation,

## D   cathode-ray tube phosphors,

## E   preferred values and color codes for *R* and *C* elements,

# SYMBOLS

| | |
|---|---|
| $\vec{a}$ | acceleration, m/s$^2$ |
| $A$ | area, m$^2$, cm$^2$ |
| $a_I$, $a_V$ | current (voltage) gain |
| $a_{I0}$, $a_{V0}$ | magnitude of current (voltage) gain at dc |
| $B$ | susceptance, mhos |
| $\vec{B}$ | magnetic flux density, Wb/m$^2$ = tesla = 10$^4$ gauss |
| $BW$ | bandwidth |
| $c$ | velocity of light |
| $C$ | capacitance, F |
| $C_j$ | space-charge capacitance of $pn$ junction |
| $C_{je}$, $C_{jc}$ | space-charge capacitance of emitter (collector) junction of transistor |
| $C_d$ | diffusion capacitance of $pn$-junction diode |
| $C_\pi$, $C_\mu$ | capacitances of active region circuit model of transistor |
| $C_B$ | base charging capacitance of transistor |
| $C_{cb}$ | capacitance due to base width modulation |
| $C_{ob}$ | output capacitance of c-b transistor |
| c-b | common-base connection of transistor |
| c-c | common-collector connection of transistor |
| c-e | common-emitter connection of transistor |
| $C_t$ | total equivalent input capacitance of c-e transistor |
| $C_x$, $C_y$, $C_z$ | stray and header capacitances of actual transistor |
| $C_E$ | emitter bypass capacitance |
| $C_K$ | cathode bypass capacitance |
| $C_{gp}$, $C_{gk}$, $C_{pk}$ | capacitances of vacuum triode circuit model |
| $D_e$, $D_h$ | diffusion constant for electrons (holes), cm$^2$/s |
| $D_b$ | diffusion constant for minority carriers in the base region of a transistor |
| dB | decibel |
| $e$ | base of natural logarithms |

xiv

| | |
|---|---|
| eV | electron volt |
| $\vec{E}$ | electric field intensity V/m, V/cm |
| $E$ | magnitude of electric field |
| $\vec{f}$ | force, newtons $= 10^5$ dyn |
| $f$ | frequency, Hz |
| $f_\beta$ | frequency, where $|\beta| = \beta_0/\sqrt{2}$ |
| $f_t$ | frequency where $|\beta| = 1$ |
| $f_{3\text{dB}}$ | frequency where a magnitude response is down $-3$ dB from reference value |
| $f_{0\text{dB}}$ | frequency where a magnitude response equals unity |
| $f_l$ | lower bandedge of frequency response |
| $f_u$ | upper bandedge of frequency response |
| $G, g$ | conductance, mhos |
| $g_d$ | incremental conductance of $pn$-junction diode |
| $g_m$ | transconductance |
| $G_p$ | power gain |
| $h_{ij}$ | $h$ (hybrid) parameters of a 2-port |
| $h_i, h_o, h_f, h_r$ | $h$ parameters of active device |
| $h_{fe}$ | $\beta$ of c-e transistor |
| $i, I, \boldsymbol{I}$ | instantaneous (dc, phasor) electric current, A |
| $I_s$ | saturation current of $pn$ junction |
| $I_{CO}, I_{EO}$ | saturation current of collector (emitter) junction with emitter (collector) open circuited |
| $I_{CS}, I_{ES}$ | saturation current of collector (emitter) junction with emitter (collector) shorted to base |
| $i_s, \boldsymbol{I}_s$ | short-circuit available current from a source |
| $I_B, I_E, I_C$ | base (emitter, collector) current into the transistor |
| Im | imaginary part of a complex number or expression |
| $I_f, I_r$ | forward (reverse) current of $pn$ diode |
| $I_P, I_G, I_K$ | plate (grid, cathode) current into the vacuum triode |
| $j$ | $= \sqrt{-1}$ |
| $\vec{J}$ | current density, A/m$^2$, A/cm$^2$ |
| $J$ | magnitude of current density |
| $J_e, J_h$ | magnitude of electron (hole) current density |
| $k$ | Boltzmann constant $1.38 \cdot 10^{-23}$ J/°K |
| $l_p, l_n$ | distance in $p$ region ($n$ region) from metallurgical junction to edge of space-charge region in an idealized $pn$ junction |
| $L$ | inductance, H |
| $L_e, L_h$ | diffusion length for electrons (holes) in an $n$ ($p$) region |
| $m$ | mass, kg, g |
| $m^*$ | effective mass |
| $N_a, N_d$ | acceptor (donor) impurity density, atoms/cm$^3$ |
| $n$ | electron density, electrons/cm$^2$ |

| | |
|---|---|
| $n_{b0}$ | electron density in base of *npn* transistor in thermal equilibrium |
| $n_i$ | intrinsic density of electrons |
| $n_n, n_p$ | majority (minority) electron density |
| $n_{p0}$ | electron minority-carrier density at space-charge edge of forward biased *pn* junction |
| $n_e$ | excess minority-carrier density, $n - n_p$ |
| $p$ | hole density, holes/cm$^3$ |
| $p_{b0}$ | hole density in base of *pnp* transistor in thermal equilibrium |
| $p_i$ | intrinsic density of holes |
| $p_p, p_n$ | majority (minority) hole density |
| $p_{n0}$ | hole minority-carrier density at edge of forward-biased *pn* junction |
| $p_e$ | excess minority-carrier density, $p - p_n$ |
| $P$ | power, W |
| $q$ | magnitude of electronic charge $= 1.602 \cdot 10^{-19}$ C |
| $q_e$ | charge of electron $= -q$ |
| $Q$ | charge |
| $Q_B$ | excess minority carrier stored charge in base of transistor |
| $R, r$ | resistance, $\Omega$ |
| $r_d$ | incremental resistance of *pn*-junction diode $= 1/g_d$ |
| $r_l$ | leakage resistance of *pn* device |
| $r_x, r_\pi, r_\mu, r_o$ | resistance elements of active-region circuit model of transistor |
| $r_b', r_c', r_e'$ | body resistances of transistor regions |
| $r_p$ | incremental plate resistance of vacuum triode |
| $R_s$ | resistance of signal source |
| $R_L$ | load resistance |
| $R_B, R_C, R_E$ | transistor bias resistors |
| $R_G, R_P, R_K$ | vacuum triode (pentode) bias resistors |
| Re | real part of a complex quantity |
| $t$ | time, s |
| $T$ | absolute temperature, °K |
| $T_d$ | delay time |
| $\vec{v}$ | velocity, m/s, cm/s |
| $v, V, V$ | instantaneous (dc, phasor) voltage, V |
| $v_s, V_s$ | open-circuit available voltage of a signal source |
| $V_{CE}, V_{BE}$ | collector-emitter (base-emitter) voltage of a transistor |
| $V_{GK}, V_{PK}$ | grid-cathode (plate-cathode) voltage |
| $V_T$ | $kT/q$ |
| $V_H$ | Hall voltage |

| | |
|---|---|
| $V_r$ | reverse bias voltage of $pn$ diode |
| $w$ | basewidth of transistor |
| $W$ | energy, J |
| $W_v$, $W_c$ | energy level of top (bottom) edge of valence (conduction) band |
| $W_g$ | energy cap of semiconductor or insulator |
| $W_f$ | Fermi energy level |
| $W_w$ | work function |
| $x,y,z$ | distance coordinates, m, cm |
| $x_j$ | $pn$-junction depth from surface |
| $X$ | reactance, $\Omega$ |
| $Y$, $y$ | admittance, mhos |
| $Z$, $z$ | impedance, $\Omega$ |
| $\alpha$ | short-circuit current gain of c-b transistor |
| $\alpha_0$ | magnitude of $\alpha$ at dc (low frequencies) |
| $\alpha_{r0}$ | magnitude of short-circuit gain of c-b transistor in inverse operation at dc |
| $\beta$ | short-circuit gain of c-e transistor, active device |
| $\beta_0$ | magnitude of $\beta$ at dc (low frequencies) |
| $\beta_{r0}$ | magnitude of $\beta$ of c-e transistor in inverse operation at dc |
| $\gamma_0$ | emitter efficiency of emitter junction of transistor |
| $\Delta\psi$ | potential barrier of unbiased $pn$ junction in thermal equilibrium |
| $\varepsilon_0$ | electric permittivity of free space $10^{-9}/36\pi$ F/m |
| $\varepsilon_r$ | relative permittivity, dielectric constant |
| $\eta$ | base-width modulation factor of transistor |
| $\mu$ | open-circuit voltage gain of an active device |
| $\mu$ | mobility, cm$^2$/v-s |
| $\mu_e$, $\mu_h$ | mobility of electrons (holes) |
| $\mu_0$ | magnetic permeability of free space, $4\pi \cdot 10^{-7}$ H/m |
| $\rho$ | charge concentration, C/cm$^3$ |
| $\rho$ | resistivity, $\Omega$-cm |
| $\sigma$ | conductivity, mho/cm |
| $\tau$ | time constant, pulse width |
| $\tau_d$ | delay time |
| $\tau_t$ | transit time |
| $\psi$ | magnetic flux, Wb |
| $\psi$ | electrostatic potential, V |
| $\omega$ | angular (radian) frequency $= 2\pi f$ |
| $\omega_\beta$ | $2\pi f_\beta$ |
| $\omega_t$ | $2\pi f_t$ |
| $\Omega$ | ohms |

**Currents and voltages of circuits and devices are designated as follows:**

instantaneous or incremental variables   lowercase symbols, with lower-case subscripts if used ($v_c$)

dc (static) variables   uppercase symbols, with upper-case subscripts if used ($V_C$)

bias potentials   uppercase symbols with double uppercase subscripts ($V_{CC}$)

phasor variable   uppercase, boldface symbols, with lowercase subscripts if used ($\boldsymbol{V_c}$)

peak values of sinusoidal quantities   uppercase symbols with an $m$ subscript ($V_m$)

**Abbreviations of standard units (from IEEE Spectrum, March, 1966, August, 1965)**

| Unit | Symbol | Unit | Symbol |
|------|--------|------|--------|
| ampere | A | hertz | Hz |
| angstrom | Å | joule | J |
| coulomb | C | meter | m |
| cycle per second | Hz | newton | N |
| degree Kelvin | °K | mho | mho |
| dyne | dyn | ohm | Ω |
| erg | erg | radian | rad |
| electron volt | eV | second | s |
| farad | F | time | t |
| gauss | G | volt | V |
| gram | g | weber | Wb |
| henry | H | webers/m² (tesla) | Wb/m² (T) |

**Recommended prefixes**

| Multiple | Prefix | Symbol |
|----------|--------|--------|
| $10^{12}$ | tera | T |
| $10^{9}$ | giga | G |
| $10^{6}$ | mega | M |
| $10^{3}$ | kilo | k |
| $10^{-2}$ | centi | c |
| $10^{-3}$ | milli | m |
| $10^{-6}$ | micro | $\mu$ |
| $10^{-9}$ | nano | n |
| $10^{-12}$ | pico | p |

# INTRODUCTION TO ELECTRONIC
# SYSTEMS, CIRCUITS, AND DEVICES

# chapter 1

# ELECTRONICS AND ELECTRONIC SYSTEMS

## 1.1 introduction

Electrical engineering, like the other major areas of engineering, is a broad field. It includes a number of major specialties, such as solid-state electronics, electronic computers, microwaves, electromechanical transducers, electronic circuitry, and control systems. In the broadest sense, electrical engineering is concerned with systems, particularly those involving the essentials of electric and magnetic phenomena. One of the largest, both in complexity and economic importance, is the power-generation and -distribution system used in the United States; this system is an example of one which has evolved over a long period of time. The United States antimissile defense system is another example of a huge and expensive system, but one, however, which had to be conceived, developed, and constructed in a minimum period of time. In addition, it had to make use of the most recent developments which had had little prior use in practice. Electronic computers, control systems, and communication systems are examples of other systems which are of intermediate levels of size and complexity. A number of the latter type act sometimes as complete systems in themselves; often, however, they are subsystems in a larger system, such as in the antimissile defense system referred to above.

On a percentage basis, few engineers will be concerned with the design of an overall, large, complex system, or with its operation, maintenance, and modification. At the opposite end of the range of technical responsibility, few engineers will be solely occupied with research in electronic phenomena in materials and media. The greater number of electrical and electronic engineers will be concerned with the research, design, development, or application of the electronic and electrical components, or building blocks (subsystems), which make up a larger system. On the one hand, this larger group must understand the physical behavior of the individual devices, circuits, and larger subsystems; and on the other, they must comprehend the problems and opportunities of interaction between the various components, building blocks, and subsystems. To discharge this responsibility requires knowledge of a wide range of physical principles, including the physics of electrons and other charged particles in the various materials and media of interest to electrical engineering. It also requires skill in the use of a wide range of mathematical tools. With this foundation in physics and with the logic and sophistication of mathematics, the electrical engineer will find the major tools of circuit and electromagnetic theory particularly useful.

This textbook is designed as a first course in electrical engineering for students in several of the engineering curricula. In this chapter, we take a broad look at electronics, specifically at representative electronic systems, to enable the reader to grasp the fundamental importance of electronic devices and their interconnection in circuits and systems. We then turn our attention in succeeding chapters to a range of fundamental principles and devices which are of crucial importance to electrical engineering practice.

## 1.2   systems engineering

The combining of elements and "functional blocks" into a practical working electronic system is a complicated matter. Generally, the systems engineer begins with a specific goal and considers broad alternative ways of achieving it. A few possibilities that appear plausible are set down in a series of connected functional blocks, in other words, a block diagram. The function represented by each block is assigned a tentative specification. A determination is then made as to whether or not the electrical specifications necessary to achieve the functions of the blocks or subsystems are feasible at the present state of the art. If not, that alternative is shelved. It sometimes happens, however, that a shelved subsystem must be reconsidered at a later time, since the proposed system of which it is a part is in other respects the most promising of the alternatives being investigated. A development program must then be undertaken to bring the key subsystems or components into practical being.

Once a few block-diagram methods of accomplishing the system goal are established, the engineer must examine each alternative carefully. Interactions within the system, as well as those between it and other systems, must be considered. He must study factors such as relative cost, weight, size, length of time for design and production, and reliability. Legal matters and customer preferences may represent other basic constraints.

A full consideration of all the above requires much fundamental knowledge and experience. In addition, the increasing number of more sophisticated tools that are being developed for the optimization of systems must be understood and utilized. Clearly, the job of the systems engineer is a challenging one. The following sections will illustrate the above points and show where the electronic devices, with which we are concerned, fit into the systems picture.

## 1.3  relay communication systems

The reader is probably aware that engineering electronics had its start in the last decade of the nineteenth century. There were two different directions of work which ultimately led to engineering electronics: one was taken by E. Marconi and by A. S. Popov in developing wireless communication; and the other was the work of electrophysicists who studied the electrical nature of material and media. Among the latter was J. J. Thomson, who proposed an experiment in which he conclusively proved that a charged particle, called the electron, was present and that its impact illuminated the fluorescent screen. This discovery also led to the invention of the cathode-ray tube.

Marconi and Popov[1], almost simultaneously, were able to show that communication over distance without wires could be accomplished using spark gaps and the electromagnetic waves that emanate from them. Transmission of information was accomplished by the presence or absence of the electromagnetic waves. Electronic wireless communication became possible with the discovery by A. Fleming in 1904, of the two-element thermionic diode, and with the subsequent invention of the thermionic triode by L. De Forest in 1907. In 1912, electronic communication took a very large step forward when E. Armstrong discovered the regeneration principle, which made possible oscillations involving the electronic triode. Convenient and controllable communications sources were then available so that the cumbersome, large spark-gap generators could be abandoned.

In 1918, Armstrong also discovered the principle of the superheterodyne receiver[2]. This discovery enabled the electronic engineer to build much

---

[1] C. Susskind, "Popov and the Beginnings of Radio-telegraphy," *Proc. IRE*, **50**:2036-2047 (October, 1962).

[2] Notable among Armstrong's many other discoveries were superregeneration in 1924 and frequency modulation in 1934. His four great discoveries place him among the greatest of the pioneers in engineering electronics.

more sensitive and much more stable receivers to pick up the waves now generated by electronic means.

With the development of good electronic oscillators and amplifiers, electronics also became useful for wire and telephone communication. It was now possible to insert amplifiers (called "repeaters" in telephone terminology) in the transmission lines, which removed the short-distance restriction on wire communication. Inevitably, the amount of information being transmitted increased and the distances to be spanned by communication systems became larger, giving rise to the problem of how to handle the growing volume of messages.

The term *communication channel* denotes a portion of a communication link used to transmit a particular message. A channel for information transmission in a communication system must be able to pass or transmit a portion of the frequency spectrum. In other words, the channel has to have a certain bandwidth of frequencies. Consider, for the moment, that each message needs a given bandwidth. For example, the bandwidth for television (TV) transmission is approximately 5 MHz,[1] which is 5 to 10 percent of the station frequency. A large bandwidth necessitates a high transmission frequency (sometimes called the "center" or "carrier" frequency). Since many messages are to be transmitted, a large portion of the frequency spectrum is required. The carrier frequency must be at least as large as the frequency range required for the information and usually is much larger. Thus very high frequencies must be used for long distance communication across the continent, when hundreds of telephone channels and many TV channels are to be transmitted on the same carrier. We find that for high frequencies the properties of the earth's atmosphere no longer provide the effective mirror needed for long-distance radio communication. Radio waves, like light, travel in straight lines unless particular means are taken or are available to reflect or refract them. At low frequencies, the charged particles in the ionosphere (a component of the upper atmosphere) act as a mirror to reflect the radio waves. At frequencies over several megahertz the radio waves are no longer reflected, but, instead, penetrate the ionosphere. For such frequencies, we are limited to "line of sight" transmission and reception.

A system of relay stations can be used for high-frequency, wideband radio transmission to handle a large volume of messages. In almost every locality, one can see large towers on which radio antennas are mounted and which are part of the relay operation. The longest continental relay system is Bell Telephone's TD-2 system, in which the radio waves have a frequency of approximately 4 GHz.[2] Signals are transmitted from tower to tower, or from tower to mountain peak in jumps of approximately

---

[1] 1 MHz = 1 megahertz = $10^6$ cycles per second; see list of symbols.
[2] 1 GHz = $10^9$ cycles per second.

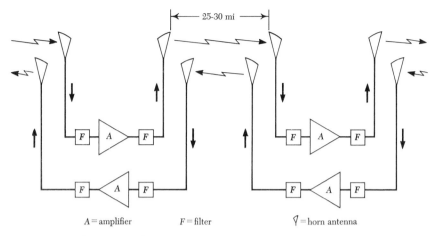

25-30 mi

A = amplifier        F = filter        ⊽ = horn antenna

**FIGURE 1.1** *Relay stations for systems of information transmission, showing channels for both directions of information flow.*

25 to 30 mi. A block diagram of a portion of such a system is shown in Fig. 1.1. Note that every station receives the incoming signal, processes and amplifies the signal, and finally transmits it on to the next station. The function of the blocks of such a station is explained in the next section.

Of course, the land-based relay system of Fig. 1.1 cannot be used for transmitting over the ocean. However, relay systems for that purpose now are possible using earth satellites as vehicles for electronic repeating stations. Several so-called "communication satellites" now in orbit have demonstrated the success of such relay systems.

A sensitive, selective receiver is one important component of a communication satellite. It must receive the signal from the ground transmitter station. The incoming signal is then processed and amplified, and the information is fed to a small transmitter in the satellite which then retransmits the signal back to a different ground station. This system is represented in a block diagram as shown in Fig. 1.2. In this figure, we have also emphasized some of the subsystems of the total system for a TV transmission network.

Before we discuss such a system in greater detail, we should mention several experiments which have proven the feasibility of communication satellites. The first active satellite experiment was the Bell System Telstar in 1962. This was followed by Relay which was developed for the National Aeronautics and Space Administration (NASA) by the Radio Corporation of America (RCA). Next, the Syncom communication system was developed for NASA by the Hughes Aircraft Company. The first two experiments are very similar in purpose and function. The Syncom satellite has a different feature and is particularly interesting because it is a syn-

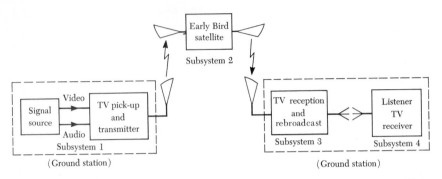

**FIGURE 1.2** *Information transmission system using Early Bird satellite; system block diagram using example of a TV broadcast between continents.*

chronous satellite. In this system, the satellite is placed at an altitude of approximately 22,300 mi from the surface of the earth. At this altitude, and with the correct velocity, the satellite will stay almost fixed with respect to a reference point on the surface of the earth, comparable to the ground relay stations used for land-based communication systems such as the TD-2. In principle, three relay stations of the Syncom variety properly positioned in orbit, as shown in Fig. 1.3, will provide communication from any one point to another on this planet.

The success of the Syncom satellite led to the adoption of an intercontinental communication system. This system, operated by the Communications Satellite Corporation, uses the Early Bird satellites, which are also stationary with respect to the surface of the earth. The Early Bird, made by the Hughes Aircraft Company, has the ability to handle simultaneously more than 240 two-way telephone channels between two continents (for instance between North America and Europe). This satellite can also carry two-way TV channels.

## 1.4  components of satellite relays

In the satellite communication system illustrated in Fig. 1.2, the satellite relay is only a component. In this section we concentrate on the relay

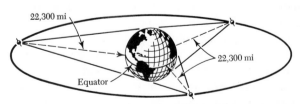

**FIGURE 1.3** *Syncom or Early Bird system using three satellites for global coverage.*

station itself, and note the functional blocks required for its performance.

The first function of the satellite is to receive the incoming signal. It then must process the signal, which principally involves amplification to increase its power level. Finally, it retransmits the signal. It is probably clear that the signal transmitted by the satellite is not at the same frequency as the incoming signal, for if it were, a portion of the output, which is at a high-power level, would interfere with the incoming signal. This would be an unstable situation.

In the case of Early Bird, the input signal is at 6.39 GHz (received from the United States), and the output signal to Europe is at 4.16 GHz. The use of the two different frequencies requires electronic equipment to provide *frequency conversion*. That is, we use the *superheterodyne principle* to move the information band of frequencies from one location in the frequency spectrum to another. In the satellite, two conversions, or converters, are used (see Fig. 1.4). The incoming signal is not converted directly

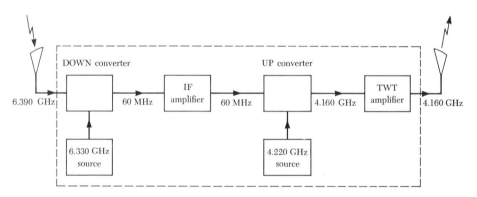

**FIGURE 1.4**   *Functional block diagram of Early Bird relay satellite.*

from 6.39 to 4.16 GHz; instead, it is converted to a frequency at which amplification can be more easily obtained. The resulting larger signal is then converted back to the final desired frequency. As shown in the block diagram of Fig. 1.4, the intermediate frequency (IF) at which a major portion of the amplification is provided is 60 MHz. Notice that a final power amplifier consisting of a traveling-wave tube (TWT) is used as the transmitter. In the IF amplifiers, junction transistors are the electronic devices that provide the amplification.

The precise conversion from one frequency to another requires precise electronic oscillators within the satellite. In the Early Bird satellite, two oscillators are needed, one oscillating at 6.33 GHz and the other at 4.22 GHz. In a later chapter we shall briefly investigate the electrical generation of new frequencies by combining two signals of different frequencies in a nonlinear element, such as a semiconductor diode, in a manner similar to the generation of audio harmonics and audio beat frequencies.

An important component of the satellite which is not shown in Fig. 1.4 is the basic energy-supply source, comprised of chemical batteries and the semiconductor solar cells that are used to charge them.

The performance of the individual blocks of the satellites depends on many special electronic devices to provide the different circuit functions. Semiconductor devices are used for satellites as much as possible because of their small weight and low power consumption. An exception occurs in the power amplifier of the satellite. Present semiconductor devices cannot provide the necessary output signal power over the band of frequencies at the desired center frequency. In this book, a great deal of attention is given to the study of semiconductor diodes and transistors such as those needed in the amplifiers, converters, and energy sources of the satellite. In addition, we shall study the motion of electrons under the application of electric and magnetic fields, which in turn leads us to the traveling-wave tube used here as the power amplifier. Further, we shall also investigate how a *pn* semiconductor diode can convert light energy into electrical energy as in the solar cells.

## 1.5   a control system for positioning a radio antenna

We are all familiar with certain *feedback* or *closed-loop* control systems in which a variable, such as position, temperature, etc., is controlled by using the difference between its measured value and a desired value as an error signal to actuate a controlling mechanism. The thermostat system for controlling room temperature is a common example. In this system temperature is measured and compared with a preset value of desired temperature. If the actual temperature drops more than an acceptable amount below the desired value, a signal is sent to the control motors, valves, or levers to provide more heat (fuel). When the temperature rises above an upper tolerance value, a signal is sent to turn off the heat or fuel source.

Nearly all physiological processes involve feedback control systems. In the complex process of driving a car, for example, the human sensors (primarily the eyes) are collecting data on road conditions, positions and velocities of other cars, speedometer and other indicator readings, and are feeding signals to the brain where comparison with stored experience initiates control signals to the hands on the wheel and the foot on the throttle or brake.

The familiar examples above illustrate that signals are generated in the process of control and that these signals must be processed by functional blocks in a manner similar to the communication signals described in the preceding sections. Moreover, the example of driving an automobile illustrates that we frequently must utilize stored information or "memory" in practical control systems. Both of these points will be made in more detail by considering two important control examples, one in this section and one in the next.

The necessity to point an antenna toward objects in space arises in many different situations. In radioastronomy one has to follow a radio source in space. In the case of satellites, the antenna must follow the space vehicle. This task can be very difficult because the antennas used have a very small beamwidth. For example, the NASA Advanced Antenna System at Goldstone, Calif., utilizes a paraboloid reflector antenna of 210 ft diameter. This yields a beamwidth of 0.1° at a frequency of 2.3 GHz. This antenna is shown in Fig. 1.5. A basic requirement of the antenna control system is that it must point the antenna axis within an uncertainty of one-tenth of the beamwidth. Another requirement is that the antenna must be able

**FIGURE 1.5** *Goldstone antenna of the Advanced Antenna System of NASA. (Courtesy JPL/NASA.)*

to follow the object in space. The Goldstone antenna can be moved with a maximum velocity of 0.5°/s, which is ample for tracking space vehicles on deep space missions.

The command for positioning the antenna is mostly made by a computer, which follows a given program for the object in space. We can think of the control system in basic terms as shown in Fig. 1.6a. The controller

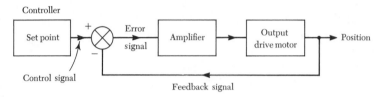

**FIGURE 1.6a**   *Simple position-control system.*

(in our example, the computer) establishes for each instant the set point needed. This information passes through an amplifier to the output drive motor. The antenna position is fed back to a summing point and subtracted from the required set point. The difference, if any, is called the *error signal* and, after amplification, is used to correct the antenna position. The signal may be positive or negative. Accordingly, the drive motors must be reversible and must move in the proper direction automatically. When the antenna axis has the proper position, the error signal is zero. For the control of the Goldstone antenna, hydraulic servo drives are used with a drive input of 200 hp per axis. In such a control system we have stability problems. By improper design or by a change in the characteristics of a component, it is possible that the error signal will overcorrect the antenna position. Thus the antenna is driven beyond the point where it should be at that time, and the antenna drive actually "hunts" about the desired position. We have, in essence, an oscillatory situation. For an acceptable control system, a careful design must be achieved which avoids hunting but which nevertheless produces as immediate a response as possible. For this we add additional components, e.g., electrical circuits, in the feedback path. By the proper design of such circuits, accurate corrective action for the dynamic behavior of the control system can be achieved.

Thus far we have considered only the basic building blocks for the feedback control system. Note that the character of the signal used is not uniform throughout the system. The output drive motor operates on an *analog* signal, which is continuous in time (although it is zero when the error is zero). The computer, on the other hand, may (and usually will) operate with *digital* signals, which are discontinuous and of the pulse type. Additional building blocks are included in the forward path for the conversion of digital-to-analog signals, as shown in Fig. 1.6b. A digital encoder

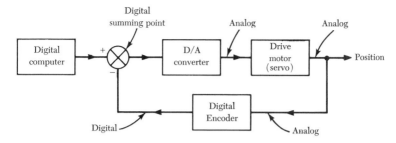

**FIGURE 1.6b**  *Computer-controlled antenna pointing system.*

is also added in the feedback loop to express the antenna position as a digital signal. Note that the summing point compares digital signals only.

## 1.6  a control system for attitude control of a satellite

The basic feedback control system illustrated in Fig. 1.6a is also used to control the attitude of satellites. For example, the Early Bird satellite has an antenna which must at all times point toward the earth, i.e., the antenna axis must be oriented perpendicular to the orbit. For this control system, the controller is located in the command ground station on earth. The forward path or link and the feedback path are transmission channels through space.

The Early Bird satellite is spin stabilized, the spin axis being coincident with the antenna axis. The spin is imparted to the satellite by the final rocket stage. Small control jets, which operate only during a fraction of the spin cycle, are used to change the velocity or attitude of the space vehicle. As a reference for the attitude of the spin axis, the satellite uses the "sun line" which is obtained by an optical system of slits and photodiodes

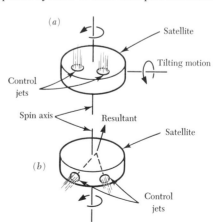

**FIGURE 1.7**  *Early Bird attitude control.* (a) *Orientation control* (*parallel to spin axis*); (b) *velocity control* (*perpendicular to spin axis*).

that give an electrical indication of the sun line and its angle with respect to the spin axis. This position signal is transmitted through the feedback link to the earth. If an error is detected in the satellite's attitude, an error signal is transmitted to the Early Bird, actuating the proper set of jets to correct the deviation. Figure 1.7a and b shows the control jets schematically and illustrates their action with respect to the spin axis of the satellite. Note that the error signal must be properly timed to make sure that the jets act during the correct fraction of the spin cycle.

## 1.7   instrumentation systems for scientific research: the mariner

As a final example for this chapter, we consider a very sophisticated and important system for scientific research—the Mariner Mars '64 system—in which a spacecraft was flown past the planet Mars to collect and transmit data back to earth from the following instruments:

1. Cosmic dust collector
2. Helium magnetometer
3. Plasma probe
4. Cosmic-ray telescope
5. Trapped radiation detector
6. Ion chamber
7. Television camera and picture storage

The spacecraft weighed 575 lb, had over 138,000 parts, and had an operational life of 6000 hr (250 days). The science instrumentation system weighed only 51.25 lb or 8.9 percent of the spacecraft. All experiments performed satisfactorily, except for the ion chamber, which ceased functioning 109 days after launch.

An overall functional block diagram of the spacecraft is shown in Fig. 1.8. Commands are received from transmitters on the earth, and signals are sent back to receivers on the earth over one of the two antennas. The low-gain antenna is used near the earth, and the high-gain antenna at greater distances. (The switchover from the low-gain to the high-gain antenna was commanded from the ground station about 80 days after launch.) The commands, in the form of coded radio signals, pass through a receiver of the radio subsystem and then on to the command subsystem where they are directed to their proper location. For example, a command to record information from one of the science experiments turns on the tape recorder and switches the proper information into it. Likewise, a command to turn on the main booster for changing the trajectory of the spacecraft goes to the propulsion subsystem. Other commands might release stored information from the computer, and so on. Data from the seven experiments in the science instrumentation subsystem can be either recorded for later

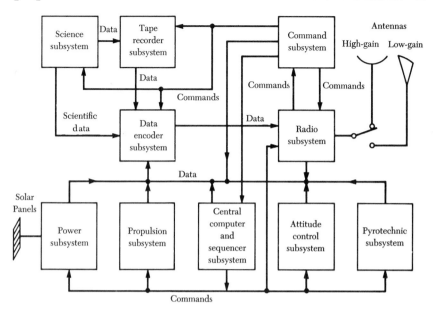

**FIGURE 1.8** *Mariner spacecraft functional block diagram. (From Frank L. Schutz, The Mariner Mars Science Subsystem, 1965 Wescon reprint, Session 4, August, 1965).*

coding and transmission, or may be coded when obtained and sent immediately through a transmitter in the radio subsystem back to earth. The onboard computer has information stored for automatically turning on and off certain experiments, or for controlling the spacecraft itself through changes in propulsion or attitude control at scheduled times. The large amount of preprogrammed information in the computer minimizes the number of commands that are sent over the command link.

The power subsystem includes the solar panels, a storage battery, converters to ac power, and power regulators. The pyrotechnic subsystem includes "squibs," or explosive bolts, which may be set off by command in order to extend solar panels or to actuate propulsion system valves.

The block diagram of Fig. 1.8 divides the system into very broad functions. Any one of the subsystems can be expanded further into a more detailed block diagram. For example, a block in the science subsystem could be shown for each of the seven experiments listed above, and in turn each of these could be shown in more detail. To illustrate this procedure, we consider a block diagram of the radio or telecommunication subsystem, as shown in Fig. 1.9. Signals from the earth enter the system at 2.116 GHz, and those to the earth are transmitted at 2.298 GHz. "Mode control" signals to the remote-controlled RF switches come from the command subsystem and may switch both receiver and transmitter to the

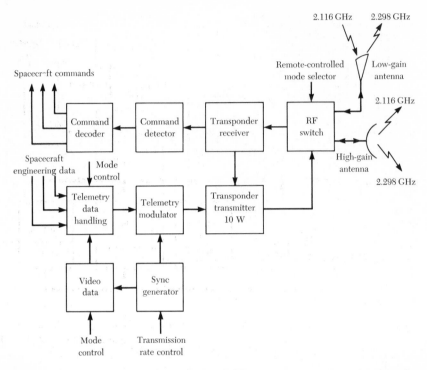

**FIGURE 1.9** *Mariner 1964 spacecraft telecommunication system.* (*From Richard P. Mathison, "Mariner Mars 1964 Telemetry and Command System," IEEE Spectrum, July, 1965, p. 76*).

high-gain antenna or to the low-gain antenna, or they may switch to an operational mode which transmits at high gain and receives at low gain. The received signals go through the receiver to the command detector and then to the command decoder. The decoder interprets the commands and directs them to their proper place, as described above. Spacecraft operational data, such as position, velocity, temperature, condition of battery charge, etc., are coded and sent to the modulator. The modulator impresses this information on the carrier, which is generated in the 10-watt transmitter, and it in turn transmits the information to the earth via the appropriate antenna. Scientific data from the several experiments are telemetered back to the earth in like manner, except that the video data from the television cameras are first stored on tape (see Fig. 1.8) and then transmitted back at a slow rate. This latter process will be discussed in Chap. 2. When commanded, recorded signals can be sent through the data link, with appropriate synchronism through the sync generator.

As mentioned above, any one of the blocks of the diagram of Fig. 1.9, such as the receiver, can also be broken down into more basic blocks, but we will not pursue the matter further here. The examples in this section

**FIGURE 1.10** *Mariner IV photo number 11 of the planet Mars. (Courtesy JPL/NASA.)*

serve to illustrate the variety of problems in communications and control that enter into a complex system. There is a clear need to study the various functional blocks and the nature of signals in a system, and this we do in the following chapter. We return to the Mariner television system at the end of Chap. 2, to illustrate the rate of information transmission. One of the exciting Mariner photos of Mars is shown in Fig. 1.10.

### REFERENCES

A. A. Roetken, K. D. Smith, and R. W. Friis, "The TD-2 Microwave Relay System," *Bell System Tech. J.*, **30**:1041–1077 (1951).

A. C. Dickieson et al., "The Telstar Experiment," *Bell System Tech. J.*, **42**:739–1908 (1963).

R. P. Mathison, "Mariner Mars 1964 Telemetry and Command System," *IEEE Spectrum*, **2**:76–84 (1965).

## PROBLEMS

**1.1** Give an example (not mentioned in the text) of a very large system and also of a smaller system that might enter into a much larger one.

**1.2** Find information about typical received power for a broadcast receiver and power desired for driving a speaker; estimate the overall power gain required in this amplification process.

**1.3** Give at least three examples of transducers.

**1.4** Using elemental block diagrams, illustrate the telephone link from a mobile phone in a car to an office phone in the same telephone exchange area.

**1.5** Illustrate by elemental block diagrams the similarities between the Early Bird Communication Relay System and the telephone link from a mobile phone in an automobile to an office phone in the same telephone exchange area.

**1.6** Why is the frequency of the received signal in a communication satellite different from that of the transmitted signal?

**1.7** Assuming that the Early Bird communication satellite moves in a circular orbit and remains stationary above a fixed point on the earth's surface, (a) find the height of the satellite; (b) find the time delay for a signal to travel from the earth's surface to the satellite and back.

**1.8** A cross-country microwave relay link utilizes many relay stations between the originating station and the ultimate receiving station. Indicate in broad terms how Fig. 1.1 might be extended to illustrate this situation.

**1.9** The thermostat temperature-control system in a home is a typical example of a simple closed-loop control system. Draw a block diagram similar to Fig. 1.6a identifying actual elements of the controlled heat system.

**1.10** A gravity-fed fuel tank is kept full by a feedback-controlled valve connected to a fuel reservoir. A transducer is used to check the fuel in the tank. The error signal is amplified and then used to drive a motor that closes or opens the valve as required. Draw a completely labeled block-diagram representation of the system.

**1.11** Describe the feedback loop that exists when a person picks up a pencil from a surface.

**1.12** An elevator has a closed-loop control system for positioning itself at each floor level. Draw a block diagram similar to Fig. 1.6a identifying actual elements of the controlled elevator system.

**1.13** A basic pulse radar system has a transmitter and receiver located in the same vicinity. (The transmitter and receiver usually use a common antenna with a switch but, for simplicity, assume separate antennas.) The oscillator of the transmitter is modulated by a sequence of pulses which may be radiated directly toward a target. The reflected wave from the target is received in the antenna and amplified in a receiver. Final display of the signal from the target, however, is usually visual, and in addition to strength, range is determined by measuring the time delay between transmitted and received pulses. Draw a block diagram of this system.

**1.14** The act of hitting a baseball involves elements of feedback control. Draw a block diagram of this feedback control "system" and identify each block.

**1.15** Show in block-diagram form the system used for black and white television broadcasting (transmission and receiving). Show video and sound channels separately.

chapter **2**

# SIGNAL WAVEFORMS AND PROCESSING

## 2.1 system building blocks and signals

The examples of electronic systems discussed in the previous chapter make evident two principal features of systems. First, the signals that enter and exist in a system are *processed* in many different ways. Second, the total system task is performed by various subsystems, which in turn use specific *building blocks*. The building block is the important basic system element which performs a specific processing function. Typical building blocks are amplifiers, oscillators, modulators, demodulators, detectors, transmission networks, filters, antennas, wave shapers, and memory units. Each of these building blocks processes the incoming signal to achieve a desired result; amplifiers, for example, amplify or increase the signal strength, whereas detectors extract the information from the signal. The building blocks consist of special electronic devices and associated circuits, and it is common to say that they perform an electronic circuit function or simply a *circuit function*.

To study a circuit function and to design a building block, we need to know what kind of a signal is to be processed by it. This leads us to ask what is meant by *signal*. The word "signal," derived from the Latin word meaning "mark," universally implies the communication of some information. The signal, then, contains information that is coded or otherwise arranged to be extracted meaningfully at a point different from its point of origin. For convenience, we will not at this stage differentiate between the signal and information content. We define the electrical signal as the electrical voltage or current

18

waveshape as a function of time flowing along a transmission path, or into and out of an electron device. Examples are the flow of electrical energy in a telegraph cable or the "flow" of radio energy (electromagnetic waves of radio frequency) in the atmosphere for radio or television transmission. Usually, the signal fed into and coming out of an electronic system is nonelectrical. Transducers are building blocks which transform the non-electrical signal into an electrical one. The performance of the transducer is that of an energy converter, which converts a nonelectrical energy form to electrical energy or vice versa. For an example consider a TV system. The visual signal is converted by the pickup tube to an electrical signal. At the TV receiver, which is the system output, the cathode-ray (CR) tube converts the electrical signal into a visual display.

## 2.2   signal waveforms — time domain

The expression "signal waveform" implies that the signal is a function of time, which we denote as $f(t)$. It can be said that we consider the signal in the *time domain*. We can view an electrical signal as a function of time by use of an oscilloscope. The signal is displayed on the face of the CR tube in rectangular coordinates, and the result can be interpreted as signal voltage versus time.

It is helpful to group signal waveforms into two broad categories as diagrammed in Fig. 2.1. One category includes *discrete* waveforms as represented by pulses or sine-wave packets. The second includes *continuous* waveforms. A discrete waveform is used to transmit information by the presence or absence of pulses as in telegraph codes and digital computer inputs or outputs. On the other hand, the electrical signal from a microphone (which is a transducer that converts acoustical energy to electrical) is usually continuous. Commercial radio systems usually employ continuous waveforms. Television systems, in contrast, use both continuous waveforms

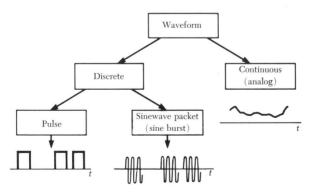

**FIGURE 2.1** *Classification of signal waveforms.*

(for video and audio information) and pulse waveforms (for sweep, synchronization, and control).

In order to deal effectively with signals and signal processing, we need to characterize signals in quantitative fashion. For this, we need a *mathematical model*. This matter is very important because it is necessary to establish how a signal waveform is affected when it is processed by a building block. The basic question can be stated in terms of an amplifier as follows: Does the amplifier leave the signal waveform undisturbed except to increase its magnitude. Or, if the waveform is modified, to what extent? Answers can be obtained by using appropriate mathematical models of the signals. Examples of the effect of a building block on a signal are given in the next chapter.

Rather than attempt to work with an arbitrary signal which is a function of time, we consider mathematical models for a few *ideal* waveforms, such as the ideal pulse and the sinusoid.

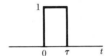

**FIGURE 2.2**    *Single pulse.*

**THE IDEAL PULSE**    An ideal pulse is shown in Fig. 2.2. This function is important, as noted above, and is characterized on a "piecewise" basis, as follows:

$$
f_1(t) = \begin{cases} 0 & \text{when} \quad -\infty < t < 0 \\ 1 & \text{when} \quad 0 \leqslant t \leqslant \tau \\ 0 & \text{when} \quad \tau < t < \infty \end{cases} \tag{2.1}
$$

**THE SINUSOID**    In the next section, we will see that the sinusoid (either a sine or a cosine function) appears as a basic constituent of general waveforms. Those familiar with resonant circuits and oscillations will realize that the sinusoid is a basic waveform resulting from simple harmonic motion and can be viewed as nature's basic constituent for complex waveshapes. Further, the sinusoid is a particularly simple function for use in dealing with integro-differential equations of linear circuits, since the integral or derivative of a sinusoid is also a sinusoid of the same frequency parameter. This aspect is brought out in the next chapter.

The mathematical description of a sinusoidal signal (for example, a voltage) is[1]

$$
v(t) = V_m \cos(\omega_1 t + \theta) \tag{2.2}
$$

[1]The notation for voltage and current symbols is described in the list of symbols, page xiv.

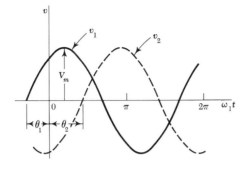

**FIGURE 2.3**   *Sinusoids with phase shift.*

where $\omega_1 = 2\pi/T$, $T$ is the period, and $\theta$ is a *phase angle* that depends on the choice of the time origin. The quantity $\omega_1$ is the frequency parameter of the sine wave and is discussed below. Equation (2.2) is plotted in Fig. 2.3. The peak or maximum value of $v(t)$ is $V_m$. The value of $v(0)$ is positive (as shown for $v_1$) if $-\pi/2 < \theta < +\pi/2$. The value of $v(0)$ becomes negative (as for $v_2$) if $-3\pi/2 > \theta > +\pi/2$. We say the dashed curve *lags* the first curve; alternatively, the solid curve *leads* the dashed curve. The time origin may often be arbitrarily chosen for a particular problem. If it is to occur at the zero of the cosine wave, for example, the sine wave results:

$$\cos\left(\omega_1 t - \frac{\pi}{2}\right) = \sin \omega_1 t \qquad (2.3)$$

It is helpful at this point to distinguish between *cyclic* or ordinary frequency and *angular* or radian frequency. The reciprocal of the period of a waveform is the cyclic frequency in cycles per second, expressed in hertz. Radian frequency is the displacement of the angle or phase per unit of time and is $2\pi$ times the cyclic frequency. In most equations involving frequency, radian or angular frequency is used in the form $\omega = 2\pi f$, expressed in radians per second.

**SUM OF SINUSOIDS OF THE SAME FREQUENCY**   In a typical system, processing involves the combination of signals. To illustrate, we choose simple sinusoidal signals. If the sinusoids are of the same frequency parameter, and if they are processed by a linear building block, the combining is a simple operation. In such a case, an alternative mathematical description for the combination of the signals can be obtained. To illustrate the combination of two sinusoidal voltages, $v_1$ and $v_2$, the following notation is used:

$$v_1 = V_1 \cos(\omega_1 t + \theta_1) \qquad (2.4a)$$

$$v_2 = V_2 \cos(\omega_1 t + \theta_2) \qquad (2.4b)$$

The sum of $v_1$ and $v_2$ is

$$v_1 + v_2 = (V_1 \cos \theta_1 + V_2 \cos \theta_2) \cos \omega_1 t$$

$$- (V_1 \sin \theta_1 + V_2 \sin \theta_2) \sin \omega_1 t \quad (2.4c)$$

To obtain (2.4c) we have used the identity $\cos (x + y) = \cos x \cos y - \sin x \sin y$. The summation is shown graphically in Fig. 2.4. The waveform of $v_1$, $v_2$, and of their sum, is given. For convenience, $\theta_1$ is assumed to be $-\pi/2$. Note that the sum is again a sinusoid of the same frequency $\omega_1$ but is shifted in phase with respect to the two components.

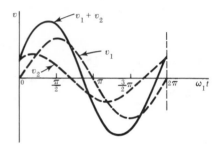

**FIGURE 2.4**  *Sum of sinusoids of the same frequency.*

**SUM OF SINUSOIDS OF DIFFERENT FREQUENCIES**   If two signals are combined in a building block which is linear and time-invariant, each signal component can be treated separately, as will be brought out in the next chapter. For the present, we are interested in establishing how the values of the parameters of the signal components affect the waveform of the composite signal.

For a first example, the composite signal is taken as $\cos \omega_1 t + \cos 2\omega_1 t$. Figure 2.5a shows the two components individually. Note that the magnitude of each component is unity. In Fig. 2.5b the components for another sum are shown: $\cos \omega_1 t + \frac{1}{2} \cos 2\omega_1 t$. For this situation, the second signal has a magnitude of one-half of the first. The composite waveforms for the two composite signals are given in Figs. 2.5c and d, respectively. Note that the periodicity in both cases is the same, namely, that of $\cos \omega_1 t$. The $\cos \omega_1 t$ term in both examples is called the *fundamental* and the $\cos 2\omega_1 t$ term is called the *second harmonic*.

Now we wish to find out if a change of phase of one of the components in the sum will influence the waveform. For simplicity, we take a phaseshift of 90° for the second term in each of the above sums. This converts the cosine term of the second harmonic to a sine term so that we have $\cos \omega_1 t - \sin 2\omega_1 t$ and $\cos \omega_1 t - \frac{1}{2} \sin 2\omega_1 t$. Figure 2.5e and f depict the corresponding waveforms of the composite signals. For both cases we see that the waveform is changed in comparison with the waveforms of Fig. 2.5c and d. The periodicity, however, is not affected.

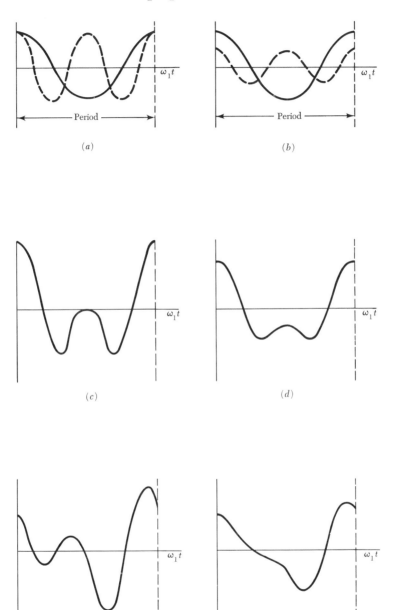

**FIGURE 2.5** *Sum of sinusoids of different frequencies.* (a) *cos* $\omega_1 t$ *and cos* $2\omega_1 t$ *(shown separately);* (b) *cos* $\omega_1 t$ *and* $\frac{1}{2}$ *cos* $2\omega_1 t$ *(shown separately);* (c) *composite of* a; (d) *composite of* b; (e) *cos* $\omega_1 t - sin\ 2\omega_1 t$ *(composite);* (f) *cos* $\omega_1 t - \frac{1}{2} sin\ \omega_1 t$ *(composite).*

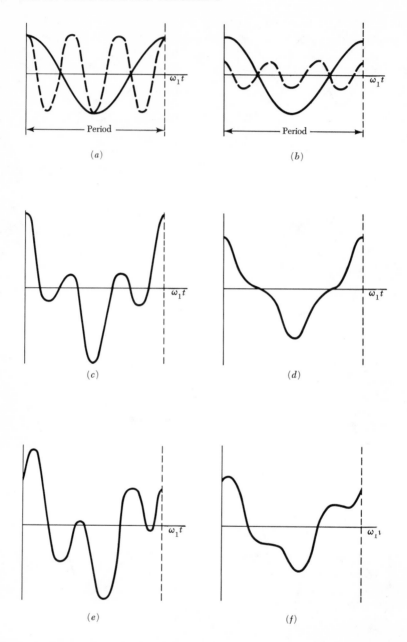

**FIGURE 2.6**  *Sum of sinusoids of different frequencies.* (a) *cos* $\omega_1 t$ *and cos* $3\omega_1 t$ *(shown separately);* (b) *cos* $\omega_1 t$ *and* $\frac{1}{3}$ *cos* $3\omega_1 t$ *(shown separately);* (c) *cos* $\omega_1 t$ + *cos* $3\omega_1 t$ *(composite);* (d) *cos* $\omega_1 t$ + $\frac{1}{3}$ *cos* $3\omega_1 t$ *(composite);* (e) *cos* $\omega_1 t$ + *sin* $3\omega_1 t$ *(composite);* (f) *cos* $\omega_1 t$ + $\frac{1}{3}$ *sin* $3\omega_1 t$ *(composite).*

**SUM OF A FUNDAMENTAL AND THIRD HARMONIC**    For another example, we choose a composite signal of the form $\cos \omega_1 t + \cos 3\omega_1 t$. The components are shown in Fig. 2.6a. Figure 2.6b shows the components for another sum also having just the fundamental and third harmonic, $\cos \omega_1 t + \frac{1}{3} \cos 3\omega_1 t$. The resultant composite waveforms are given in Fig. 2.6c and d. To obtain $\cos \omega_1 t + \sin 3\omega_1 t$ and $\cos \omega_1 t + \frac{1}{3} \sin 3\omega_1 t$ a phase shift of 90° is introduced in each second term, thus producing the modified composite waveforms shown in Fig. 2.6e and f. The periodicity remains that of the fundamental.

From the results of the two examples, it is clear that the waveform of a composite signal is affected by the values of each of the parameters of the two sinusoidal signals, i.e., the magnitude, phase, and frequency of the components. The periodicity of the composite waveform is that of the fundamental when the frequency components are harmonically related.

## 2.3  fourier analysis — frequency domain

In general, a classification of waveforms can be made as illustrated in Fig. 2.7. Waveforms are either *periodic* (having a recurring pattern) or they are *aperiodic* (no periodicity discernible). The single-pulse waveform in Fig. 2.2 is an example of an aperiodic waveform. For periodic waveforms

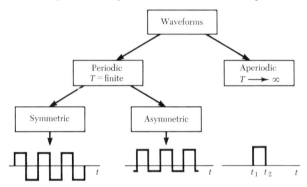

**FIGURE 2.7**    *Broad classification of waveforms.*

a series or sum of sinusoids can be used to describe the waveform. This representation was developed by the famous mathematician, J. B. Fourier, almost one and a half centuries ago.

**FOURIER SERIES FOR PERIODIC WAVEFORMS**    Fourier showed that a periodic signal $f(t)$ can be represented by a trigonometric series, which is now called a *Fourier series*. The criterion for a periodic function is

$$f(t) = f(t + T) \tag{2.5}$$

where $T$ is the period. Fourier showed that if a periodic function is "well-behaved," such as the signals in a typical electrical system,[1] it can be represented by, or transformed into, the following trigonometric series:

$$f(t) = a_0 + a_1 \cos \omega_1 t + a_2 \cos 2\omega_1 t + \cdots$$
$$+ b_1 \sin \omega_1 t + b_2 \sin 2\omega_1 t + \cdots$$
$$= a_0 + \sum_{n=1}^{\infty} a_n \cos n\omega_1 t + \sum_{n=1}^{\infty} b_n \sin n\omega_1 t \qquad (2.6)$$

where $\omega_1$ is a parameter and can be identified as the angular frequency of a sine wave having the period $T$,

$$\omega_1 = 2\pi f_1 = \frac{2\pi}{T} \qquad (2.7)$$

For a given function $f(t)$, the expressions for the coefficients of (2.6) are [2]

$$a_0 = \frac{1}{2\pi} \int_0^{2\pi} f(t)\, d(\omega_1 t) \qquad (2.8a)$$

$$a_n = \frac{1}{\pi} \int_0^{2\pi} f(t) \cos n\omega_1 t\, d(\omega_1 t) \qquad (2.8b)$$

$$b_n = \frac{1}{\pi} \int_0^{2\pi} f(t) \sin n\omega_1 t\, d(\omega_1 t) \qquad (2.8c)$$

where $n = 1, 2, \ldots$. Note that the normalized variable $\omega_1 t$ is used in the differentials of (2.8) rather than $t$ itself.

The key aspect of the above transformation is that we have characterized $f(t)$ by an infinite set of numbers, $a_0$, $a_n$, and $b_n$. These numbers and the value of $T$ (or $\omega_1$) contain all the information in $f(t)$. One advantage of this transformation is that often only a few of the constants are important and thus a simple, tractable expression for $f(t)$ can be obtained. More generally, knowledge of the important components in the frequency-domain representation is a help in designing networks or functional blocks to transmit or process the signal.

---

[1] Although this is not the place to discuss the mathematical base of the Fourier series, such questions are important to engineers. The condition for validity of the representation is one of *piecewise continuity*, or *bounded variation*. Although physical functions always satisfy such conditions, the approximations used for them might not.

[2] The coefficient $a_0$ is obtained by integrating (2.6) over a complete period, thus yielding $a_0$ as the average value of $f(t)$. The coefficient $a_n$ is obtained by multiplying both sides of (2.6) by $\cos n\omega_1 t$ and integrating over a period. All terms on the right integrate to zero except the term $a_n \cos^2 n\omega_1 t$, which gives $\pi a_n$. This leads to the expression (2.8b). Similarly, multiplication of (2.6) by $\sin n\omega_1 t$ and integration over a period leads to (2.8c).

In the previous section we found, when discussing the waveform of composite signals, that the magnitude, the phase, and the frequency of the constituents of the signal are of importance. Clearly, these parameters must be contained in the values of the Fourier coefficients. Both $a_n$ and $b_n$ involve magnitudes. Phase is represented by the fact that the cosine and sine terms of a given frequency are out of phase by 90°. The phase aspect becomes more evident if we use an alternate form of the Fourier series in which the magnitude and phase of the frequency components are used instead of the two coefficients $a_n$ and $b_n$. To obtain the alternate form, the two $n$th frequency components $n\omega_1$ of the series in (2.6) can be grouped together:

$$a_n \cos n\omega_1 t + b_n \sin n\omega_1 t \tag{2.9a}$$

Using $x$ instead of $n\omega_1 t$, for simplicity, we obtain

$$a_n \cos x + b_n \sin x \tag{2.9b}$$

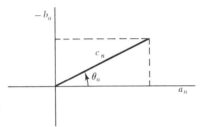

**FIGURE 2.8**  *Magnitude and phase angle of nth component.*

The multipliers of $\cos x$ and $\sin x$ may be taken as the axes of a rectangular coordinate system as in Fig. 2.8. In order to correspond with the sign convention of a commonly used exponential form of the Fourier series, the vertical axis is taken as $-b_n$ if the horizontal axis is $a_n$. The angular displacements in this diagram correspond to phase angles as in (2.4). In particular, the $\pi/2$ phase difference between $\sin x$ and $\cos x$ from (2.3) corresponds to the 90° angle between the coordinate axes.[1] From the polar representation of Fig. 2.8, the coefficients of (2.9b) are

$$a_n = c_n \cos \theta_n$$

$$-b_n = c_n \sin \theta_n \tag{2.9c}$$

Substituting these expressions in (2.9b), we obtain

$$c_n \cos \theta_n \cos x - c_n \sin \theta_n \sin x = c_n \cos (x + \theta_n) \tag{2.9d}$$

---

[1] This graphical representation can be thought of as a display in the complex number plane. The representations of sinusoids in this plane are called *phasors*. The subject is treated more thoroughly in Chap. 3.

The Fourier series can now be written

$$f(t) = c_0 + \sum_{n=1}^{\infty} c_n \cos(n\omega_1 t + \theta_n) \qquad (2.10a)$$

where
$$c_n = (a_n^2 + b_n^2)^{1/2} \qquad (2.10b)$$

$$\theta_n = \tan^{-1} \frac{-b_n}{a_n} \qquad (2.10c)$$

In this form the magnitude $c_n$ and phase $\theta_n$ for the frequency component $n\omega_1$ are directly evident. Finally, the frequency components of the Fourier series are often labeled as follows:

$n = 0$: dc or average value

$n = 1$: fundamental frequency

$n = 2$: second harmonic

$n = 3$: third harmonic

$n = n$: $n$th harmonic

On the basis of the Fourier series, the frequency spectrum of a signal wave can be displayed. That is, we can show the magnitudes of the $c_n$ versus the discrete frequency values $n\omega_1$. This plot or histogram is the *amplitude spectrum*. Separately, we can show a histogram of the values of the phase $\theta_n$ versus the discrete frequency values and obtain the *phase spectrum*. In other words, the signal can be completely represented in the *frequency domain* as an alternate to the representation in the time domain. Examples of this are brought out in the next section.

Note that under certain conditions either $a_n$ or $b_n$ becomes zero. When the signal is an even function, i.e., if

$$f(t) = f(-t) \qquad (2.11a)$$

the coefficients $b_n$ are all zero, since the sines are odd functions, and the series becomes considerably simpler. The single cosine function is a trivial example. When the function $f(t)$ is an odd function,

$$f(t) = -f(-t) \qquad (2.11b)$$

the cosine terms in the Fourier series drop out. In many cases the choice of the origin of the coordinate system is arbitrary. It should be chosen if possible to make the original function either an even or an odd function in order to simplify the Fourier series.

As a final point, for many practical signal waveforms, we need to consider only a few of the Fourier terms to obtain an adequate characterization or description of the waveform. This is usually the case if the coefficients decrease in magnitude sufficiently with increasing frequency. The examples below will make this point clear.

**FOURIER SERIES OF A RECTANGULAR WAVEFORM**   A *rectangular waveform* is shown as a function of time in Fig. 2.9a. Without loss of generality, we can choose the origin of the coordinate system so that an odd function results. Therefore, all the $a_n$'s are zero, including $a_0$ (because the waveform does not contain an average dc component). Although the Fourier series for this common waveform is readily available in mathematical tables or engineering handbooks, we evaluate the coefficients $b_n$ to show the procedure. Using (2.8c), we have to characterize the function $f(t)$ first in the time domain. For the fundamental period, the function is defined by

$$f(t) = \begin{cases} +1 & \text{when } 0 < \omega_1 t < \pi \\ -1 & \text{when } \pi < \omega_1 t < 2\pi \end{cases} \tag{2.12}$$

The coefficient $b_n$ is

$$b_n = \frac{1}{\pi} \int_0^\pi (+1) \sin n\omega_1 t \, d\omega_1 t + \frac{1}{\pi} \int_\pi^{2\pi} (-1) \sin n\omega_1 t \, d\omega_1 t$$

$$= \frac{1}{n\pi} \left[ (-\cos n\omega_1 t) \Big|_0^\pi + (\cos n\omega_1 t) \Big|_\pi^{2\pi} \right]$$

$$= \frac{1}{n\pi} (1 - 2\cos n\pi + \cos 2n\pi) \tag{2.13a}$$

The resulting value of $b_n$ depends on whether $n$ is even or odd. When $n$ is even

$$b_{n,\text{even}} = \frac{1}{n\pi} (1 - 2 + 1) = 0 \tag{2.13b}$$

When $n$ is odd

$$b_{n,\text{odd}} = \frac{1}{n\pi} (1 + 2 + 1) = \frac{4}{n\pi} \tag{2.13c}$$

This results in $b_1 = 4/\pi$, $b_3 = 4/3\pi$, $b_5 = 4/5\pi$, etc. The Fourier series is then

$$f(t) = \frac{4}{\pi} (\sin \omega_1 t + \frac{1}{3} \sin 3\omega_1 t + \frac{1}{5} \sin 5\omega_1 t + \cdots) \tag{2.14a}$$

Equation (2.14$a$) can be expressed as follows

$$f(t) = \sum_{k=1}^{\infty} \frac{4}{(2k-1)\pi} \sin(2k-1)\omega_1 t \qquad (2.14b)$$

If we wish the alternate form of the series using magnitude and phase components as given in (2.10$a$), we would obtain from (2.10$b$)

$$c_n = \begin{cases} b_n & \text{for odd values of } n \\ 0 & \text{for even values of } n \end{cases} \qquad (2.15a)$$

and

$$\theta_n = \tan^{-1}\frac{-b_n}{a_n} = -\frac{\pi}{2} \qquad (2.15b)$$

The use of these expressions in (2.10$a$) leads to (2.14$b$). As shown, the cosine term of (2.10$a$) is equal to a sine term so that we arrive at the same result for the Fourier series.

We show in Fig. 2.9$b$ the frequency spectrum for the amplitude (the amplitude spectrum), and in Fig. 2.9$c$ the phase spectrum. These two frequency-domain spectra now constitute an alternate description to the time-domain presentation of Fig. 2.9$a$. From Fig. 2.9$b$ and the Fourier series given above, it becomes evident that the Fourier coefficients decrease rapidly with increasing frequency. We conclude from this fact that the series can be terminated (or truncated) at some frequency without distorting the waveform too much. Therefore we can often use only a truncated

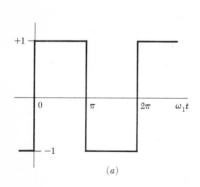

(a)

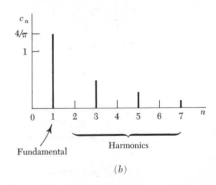

(b)

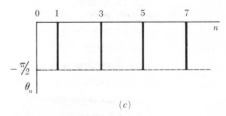

(c)

**FIGURE 2.9** *Rectangular waveform.* (a) *time domain;* (b) *frequency-domain amplitude spectrum;* (c) *frequency-domain phase spectrum.*

series in many applications. Figure 2.10 illustrates the effect of adding the successive terms and how the individual Fourier terms build up the rectangular waveform.

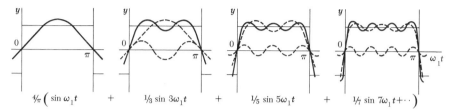

$$\tfrac{4}{\pi}\left(\,\sin\omega_1 t \quad + \quad \tfrac{1}{3}\sin 3\omega_1 t \quad + \quad \tfrac{1}{5}\sin 5\omega_1 t \quad + \quad \tfrac{1}{7}\sin 7\omega_1 t + \cdot \cdot\,\right)$$

**FIGURE 2.10** *Fourier components to represent a square wave.*

In the next chapter, we shall discuss the problem of filtering in greater detail. Briefly, filtering limits the extent of the frequency spectrum of a signal. For the example above, filtering might eliminate the higher harmonics. Because the amplitudes of the harmonics drop off so rapidly, the waveshape may not be changed appreciably after filtering if the "band of frequencies" which is retained is not too small. Figure 2.10 can be considered as a sequence of filtering operations to show the function of time which is obtained if the *fundamental* component only is retained; the fundamental and the third harmonic are retained; and finally the first four nonzero components are retained. It is clear that only a few terms of the series are needed to provide a good approximation of the original signal. On the other hand, only a crude representation results if too many terms are left out.

As a final point, we assumed for our example a unit magnitude of the rectangular wave. If the magnitude is multiplied by $A$, the series is multiplied by $A$.

**FOURIER SERIES FOR A SEQUENCE OF HALF-WAVE SINUSOIDS**    As a second example, consider the sequence of positive halfwave sinusoids shown in Fig. 2.11. The Fourier series for this waveform, that of a full wave rectifier, is

$$f(t) = \frac{2}{\pi}\left(1 + \frac{2}{3}\cos 2\omega_1 t - \frac{2}{15}\cos 4\omega_1 t \cdot \cdot \cdot\right) \tag{2.16}$$

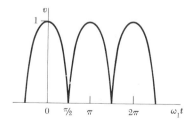

**FIGURE 2.11** *Full-wave rectifier wave.*

The time origin has purposely been chosen to make the function an even one, so the $b_n$ coefficients are all zero. In addition, only the $a_n$'s for even values of $n$ exist. The procedure to determine the coefficients is similar to that of the previous example and is not included.

The present example is interesting because it contains a dc term, $a_0$. Notice again the fast drop-off of the magnitudes of Fourier coefficients for increasing frequency.

**FOURIER INTEGRAL REPRESENTATION FOR APERIODIC WAVEFORMS** Of course, not all waveforms are periodic. For nonperiodic, or aperiodic, waveforms a frequency-domain representation can also be used. This involves the *Fourier integral*, which is sometimes called the Fourier transform. In essence, the series of discrete terms of the Fourier series becomes an integral of a *continuous* variable $\omega$ :[1]

$$f(t) = \frac{1}{2\pi} \int_{-\infty}^{\infty} [a(\omega) \cos \omega t + b(\omega) \sin \omega t] \, d\omega \tag{2.17}$$

The expressions for the coefficients also become integral expressions:

$$a(\omega) = \int_{-\infty}^{\infty} f(t) \cos \omega t \, dt \tag{2.18a}$$

$$b(\omega) = \int_{-\infty}^{\infty} f(t) \sin \omega t \, dt \tag{2.18b}$$

Similar to the procedure used for the Fourier series, we can replace $a(\omega)$ and $b(\omega)$ with magnitude and phase functions:

$$f(t) = \int_{0}^{\infty} F(\omega) \cos [\omega t + \theta(\omega)] \, d\omega \tag{2.19a}$$

where $F(\omega)$ is the magnitude, or amplitude, and $\theta(\omega)$ is the phase:

$$F(\omega) = \sqrt{a^2(\omega) + b^2(\omega)} \tag{2.19b}$$

$$\theta(\omega) = \tan^{-1} \frac{-b(\omega)}{a(\omega)} \tag{2.19c}$$

With these two functions of $\omega$, we can show amplitude and phase spectra versus the continuous variable $\omega$ for the Fourier integral of a given $f(t)$.

[1] Note that the $\frac{1}{2}\pi$ factor is included as a multiplier of the integral. For the Fourier series, the multiplier is associated with the coefficients $a_n$, $b_n$, or $c_n$. The latter procedure could also be followed above by associating $\frac{1}{2}\pi$ with $a(\omega)$ and $b(\omega)$. In electrical engineering problems, the definitions above are most often used. In many physics problems it is common to omit the $\frac{1}{2}\pi$ from (2.17) and introduce it into (2.18).

**FOURIER INTEGRAL FOR A PULSE**    As a first example of the Fourier integral we choose a single rectangular pulse of height $V$ as shown in Fig. 2.12. Note that the origin of the coordinate system is chosen so that an *even* function results, that is, $f(t) = f(-t)$. With this choice, $b(\omega) = 0$ in (2.17) so that only $a(\omega)$ must be considered. The pulse is characterized in the time domain by

$$f(t) = \begin{cases} V & \text{when } -\dfrac{\tau}{2} \leqslant t \leqslant +\dfrac{\tau}{2} \\ 0 & \text{for all other values of } t \end{cases} \tag{2.20a}$$

From (2.18a), we obtain

$$a(\omega) = \int_{-\tau/2}^{\tau/2} V \cos \omega t \, dt = \frac{V}{\omega}(\sin \omega t)\Big|_{-\tau/2}^{\tau/2} = \frac{2V}{\omega}\sin\frac{\omega\tau}{2} \tag{2.20b}$$

Multiplying and dividing by $\tau/2$, we obtain

$$a(\omega) = \tau V \frac{\sin(\omega\tau/2)}{\omega\tau/2} \tag{2.20c}$$

If in (2.20c) we let $x = \omega t/2$, we obtain the function $(\sin x)/x$. It is well known, and its values are given in handbooks. Essentially, except for a multiplier which is the area under the pulse, the function $(\sin x)/x$ is the representation of the pulse in the frequency domain (the amplitude spectrum). Notice that $a(\omega)$ becomes zero when $\omega\tau/2 = \pi$, $2\pi$, etc., that is, for $\omega = 2\pi/\tau$, $4\pi/\tau$, etc.

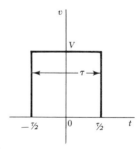

**FIGURE 2.12**    *Single rectangular pulse of height V.*

From Fig. 2.13 we can see that frequencies from zero to infinity are required to represent the pulse in the frequency domain. However, the most important contribution occurs over the frequency range 0 to $2\pi/\tau$. Therefore if a building block passes the frequencies ($f = \omega/2\pi$) from zero to $1/\tau$, we can expect a fair approximation of the pulse. In other words, a bandwidth for a building block of the order of $1/\tau$ is needed to pass a rectangular pulse of width $\tau$. For a numerical example, assume a value for

$\tau$ of 1 $\mu$s. Circuits which transmit this pulse should pass frequencies from zero to something of the order of 1 MHz.

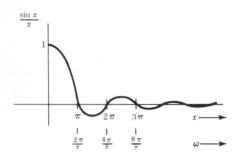

**FIGURE 2.13**   $(sin\ \mathrm{x})/\mathrm{x}$ *function.*

## 2.4   signal processing by building blocks

In the previous sections we were concerned principally with descriptions of the signal. In particular, we found that any complex signal waveform requires a *band of frequencies* if the signal is to be represented in the frequency domain. Now we return to the building blocks of a system introduced in Chap. 1, and examine the typical signal-processing functions of these blocks. Because of the conclusions above, we can first assume that the applied signal is a single-frequency sinusoid. To find what happens over a band of frequencies, we investigate the effects that occur if the signal frequency assumes different values in this band. We can obtain a simple estimate of how a signal is processed by a given building block if we know the range of frequencies required to represent the given signal.

**AMPLIFIERS**   The amplification function is all-important because losses in signal strength are inevitable in a system. An amplifier is shown in block-diagram form in Fig. 2.14. The basic characteristic of an amplifier is that it provides "gain." That is, the signal power obtained from the output of an amplifier is greater than the input signal power. We express this power gain as

$$G_p = \frac{\text{signal power out}}{\text{signal power in}} \tag{2.21}$$

Notice that we do not speak only of an *increase* of the signal voltage or the signal current since the mere translation of an input voltage to a higher voltage level is not sufficient in itself. Such an increase can be obtained from a transformer (a coupled set of coils). It is the *power* of the signal that is the important quantity, because it is the power that is needed to offset losses and to drive transducers. Power gain is also very frequently expressed in logarithmic measure, the common unit being the *decibel*. This is related to the ratio of (2.21) by

$$\text{Decibel power gain} = 10 \log_{10} G_p \qquad (2.22)$$

Thus, a power gain of unity·is 0 dB, a gain of ten is 10 dB, a gain of a hundred is 20 dB, a gain of a tenth is −10 dB, and so on.

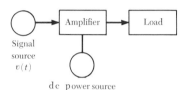

**FIGURE 2.14**  *Amplifier.*

We might wonder where the greater output power comes from. The answer is that a separate source of power must be provided. Usually, a dc power source such as a battery or a power supply is used, although some amplifiers utilize ac power sources. Figure 2.14 shows the separate power source. Another important aspect of an amplifier is its *bandwidth*; i.e., the width of its pass band. It should be able to preserve the frequency spectrum of the input signal. This spectrum may occur at low frequencies as in Fig. 2.15*a*. We then refer to the amplifier as a *lowpass amplifier*. If the amplifier is designed to preserve or pass a spectrum such as shown in Fig. 2.15*b*, we refer to the amplifier as a *bandpass amplifier*.

Unfortunately, any actual amplifier introduces *noise* into the signal waveform. The electrical noise is the result of statistical fluctuations of the currents within the active devices and the elements that form the complete amplifier. This noise sets a lower limit on the magnitude of the input signal which can be amplified. Thus, if an input signal is too weak, it will be "lost in the noise" of the amplifier, and the output will consist only of noise. The amount of noise (the noise power) in an amplifier, or any electronic circuit, is usually directly proportional to the bandwidth of the amplifier. Therefore, although we may need large bandwidth for an amplifier to preserve the frequency spectrum of the signal, from a noise

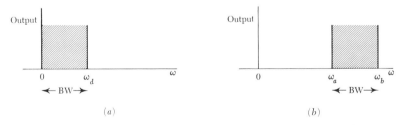

**FIGURE 2.15**  *Bandwidth of an amplifier.* (a) *Lowpass amplifier;* (b) *bandpass amplifier.*

viewpoint we want the smallest possible bandwidth. A compromise choice is usually made. This conflict is illustrated in the last section of this chapter.

Another important property of amplifiers is *linearity*. That is, the output signal should be a faithful replica of the input signal over a range of signal amplitudes. Linearity aspects are discussed in the next chapter.

**FILTERS**   When a building block truncates the frequency spectrum of a signal, we call the process a *filtering action*. When the high-frequency components of the frequency spectrum are eliminated or rejected, we call the building block a *lowpass filter*; conversely, a *highpass filter* truncates the low-frequency end of the spectrum. If both low-frequency and high-frequency components are rejected, leaving only a certain intermediate band of frequencies, the filter is called a *bandpass filter*.

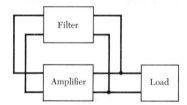

**FIGURE 2.16**   *Oscillator.*

**OSCILLATORS**   Now that we have at hand the critical aspects of both amplifiers and the frequency spectrum, it is a simple matter to introduce the basic aspects of oscillators. Assume that we have an amplifier, as in Fig. 2.16, which has part of its output fed back to its input through a filter. If the filter has a passband, such as shown in Fig. 2.15*b*, the input to the amplifier contains only these spectrum components. We next adjust the "gain around the feedback loop" to be equal to unity. The amplifier now has a sufficient input from itself to maintain equilibrium. If we next narrow the bandwidth of the filter sufficiently, the output to the load can have only a narrow spectrum. In fact, the output can be a close approximation to a pure sinusoid. The overall result is almost sinusoidal oscillation.

The feedback situation described above is not the only possible configuration to achieve oscillation. Devices which provide a negative resistance or a negative conductance across their terminals can also be used with a resonant circuit. An example of such a device is the tunnel diode, which is a special semiconductor diode. Oscillators providing nonsinusoidal outputs, as in computer and timing circuits, are also important, and some of these are related to electronic circuits to be met in later chapters.

**TRANSMISSION NETWORKS AND ANTENNAS**   A transmission network consists of lumped or distributed elements and is used for carrying the signal from one point to another. Often, we wish the *transmission* function of the network to modify the frequency spectrum of the signal as little as possible. However, most transmission networks or circuits contain unavoidable losses which usually vary with frequency and for which we must compensate by introducing *equalizers* and amplifiers. In addition, it is sometimes desirable to combine a transmission network with a filter to achieve a desired signal processing or to eliminate noise or other unwanted signals.

A transmitting antenna transforms electromagnetic energy confined to conductors into electromagnetic waves propagating through space. Of particular importance, as we saw in Chap. 1, are the directivity, beamwidth, and directional response of the electromagnetic waves after leaving the antenna. Similarly, a receiving antenna accomplishes the inverse process.

**OTHER FUNCTIONS**   The circuit functions presented above illustrate some of the important signal processing that takes place in a system. There are other important functions. Those concerned with placing information on a sinusoidal "carrier" signal (modulation), removing it from the carrier (demodulation or detection), and changing the frequency of the carrier (mixing) are so important that they will be treated separately in the following section.

## 2.5   signal processing for information transmission

In Chap. 1 we presented a number of systems applications in which it is desirable to impress an information signal, such as an audio, video, or telemetry signal, on a sinusoidal wave of different frequency, called the *carrier*. The process of impressing the information on the carrier is called *modulation*. As we shall see, the process results in a band of frequencies in the vicinity of the carrier frequency, and this new set of frequency components now carries the information. The various reasons for performing this function may be (1) to have an optimum frequency band for radiation and propagation over space; or (2) because a given band has been assigned to the particular service by the Federal Communications Commission (FCC), or (3) because amplification and other circuit building blocks may be easier to design in the new band, determined by the carrier, than in the original frequency band; and so on.

The carrier sinusoid of constant amplitude and phase by itself conveys no information; however, when we modify some parameter of the carrier sinusoid proportionally to the information signal, it then carries information. This is the process of modulation referred to above. A very common method of modulation is that of varying the amplitude of the sinusoid with the information signal; this is called *amplitude modulation* (AM). Another common method varies the frequency of the sinusoid with the

information signal and is called *frequency modulation* (FM). Still other
methods of modulation impress pulses on the carrier in order to convey
the information. Each of these methods will be discussed below.

**AMPLITUDE MODULATION**   Taking as an example a long-distance telephone
transmission, we assume that the carrier is a sinusoid at a microwave
frequency. A speech signal varies the amplitude of the carrier and we
have amplitude modulation. To show the nature of the modulated wave,
we assume the carrier to be of the form $V_c \sin \omega_c t$. Although the speech
signal comprises a band of frequencies, we consider for simplicity one
single frequency, $\omega_1$. The speech signal is then $V_1 \sin \omega_1 t$. The modulated
microwave carrier wave can then be expressed as

$$v(t) = V_c \left( 1 + \frac{V_1}{V_c} \sin \omega_1 t \right) \sin \omega_c t \tag{2.23}$$

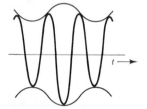

**FIGURE 2.17**   *Amplitude-modulated wave.*

A plot of (2.23) is shown in Fig. 2.17. The frequency spectrum of the
modulated wave is found by using the common trigonometric identity
$\sin x \sin y = \frac{1}{2} \left[ \cos (x - y) - \cos (x + y) \right]$; the result is

$$v(t) = V_c \sin \omega_c t + \frac{V_1}{2} \cos(\omega_c - \omega_1) t - \frac{V_1}{2} \cos(\omega_c + \omega_1) t \tag{2.24}$$

The frequency spectrum is shown in Fig. 2.18. Note that the modulation
process produces two *sideband frequencies* at $\omega_c - \omega_1$ and at $\omega_c + \omega_1$.
The information is contained only in these sideband frequencies. The
necessary bandwidth (BW) of the spectrum to preserve the signal information is at least $2\omega_1$.

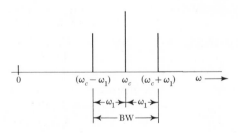

**FIGURE 2.18**   *Frequency spectrum
of AM wave.*

Common methods to achieve an output as in (2.23) or (2.24) usually involve a nonlinear addition of the two inputs, i.e., the carrier and the information, as shown in Fig. 2.19. For the telephone example, when all of the speech frequencies in a bandwidth of 3000 Hz, as shown in Fig. 2.20$a$, are involved in the modulation process, we obtain sidebands extending on both sides of the carrier frequency by 3000 Hz as shown in Fig. 2.20$b$. Comparing Fig. 2.20$a$ with 2.20$b$, we notice that we have *translated* the speech frequencies up to the microwave frequency range. Modulation can then be thought of as a process of *frequency translation.*

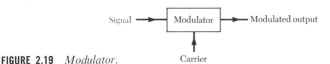

**FIGURE 2.19**   *Modulator.*

The frequency translator can also translate the information spectrum from one carrier frequency to another. This, as seen in Chap. 1, is used in superheterodyne receivers such as those used in the communication satellites. A frequency translator for this type of service is commonly called a *mixer.* The frequency components resulting from nonlinear elements used for demodulation or mixing are illustrated in Chap. 3.

**DEMODULATION**   In our example of telephone transmission we must, at the receiving end, shift the speech frequencies back to their original audible range. We need for this another frequency translation in which we demodulate the combined signal. This process is sometimes called *detection.* As with the modulator function, a nonlinear element, such as a semiconductor diode, is mostly used to accomplish demodulation.

**FREQUENCY MODULATION**   In frequency modulation, the basic modulator varies the frequency of the carrier according to the amplitude of the signal. Again it is helpful to use a single sinusoid as the assumed information

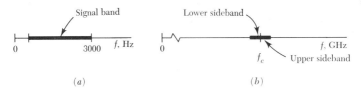

**FIGURE 2.20**   *Modulation by speech frequencies.* (a) *Speech frequencies* (*signal band*) *100 to 3000 Hz;* (b) *speech frequencies translated to microwave range* (*frequency scale is not the same as in* a).

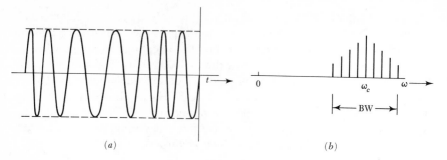

(a)                                        (b)

**FIGURE 2.21**  *Frequency modulation. (a) Waveform (typical); (b) frequency spectrum.*

signal. The form of an FM wave is shown in Fig. 2.21a. Its mathematical expression[1] is

$$v(t) = V_c \sin \left( \omega_c t + \frac{2\pi \Delta f}{\omega_1} \sin \omega_1 t \right) \qquad (2.25)$$

where $\omega_c$ is the carrier angular frequency, $\omega_1$ is the modulation frequency, and $\Delta f$ is the "frequency deviation." It is found that the expansion of this function produces an infinite series, so that a single modulating sinusoid produces an infinite number of sidebands for FM. This is in contrast to the two sidebands produced by a single sinusoid which amplitude modulates a carrier. An indication of the spectrum is shown in Fig. 2.21b. If the ratio $2\pi \Delta f / \omega_1$ (called the *modulation index*) is small, only two of the sidebands are of importance, but it is found that the chief advantage of FM is in noise reduction obtained with a large value of $2\pi \Delta f / \omega_1$. In this case a large number of the sidebands in the expansion of (2.25) may be important, and the bandwidth required may be appreciably greater than that required if the same signal were amplitude modulating a carrier. FM broadcasting, for example, utilizes bandwidths of 150 kHz for audio signals having frequencies up to 15 kHz. Carrier frequencies are around 100 MHz. The compensation for the large bandwidth is in very low noise reception when used under proper conditions.

**PULSE-MODULATION SYSTEMS**  The aforementioned modulation and demodulation schemes are applicable principally when the information is transmitted in analog (continuous) form. Another important possibility exists in the

---

[1]A common error is to write the form of an FM signal as

$$v(t) = V_c \sin[(\omega_c + \Delta \omega \sin \omega_1 t)t]$$

This appears to show the angular frequency as being modulated by $\sin \omega_1 t$, but careful study of this form shows that the period between zero crossings decreases with time on the average, instead of repeating periodically as in a true FM wave.

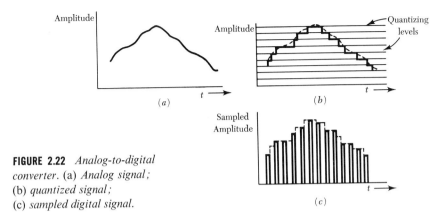

**FIGURE 2.22**  *Analog-to-digital converter.* (a) *Analog signal;* (b) *quantized signal;* (c) *sampled digital signal.*

use of discontinuous signals for information transmission by using pulses (or sine-wave packets). To use such pulse techniques when information is available in continuous form only, it must first be changed into digital form by using *analog-to-digital converters*. When an analog signal containing the information has the form given in Fig. 2.22*a*, the converter will produce an output as in Fig. 2.22*c*. In essence, two functions have been performed: quantizing and sampling. When the signal is *quantized*, the continuous waveform is approximated by a stepwise waveform as shown in Fig. 2.22*b*. This waveform is then *sampled*, which is the same as pulse modulation, and the result is the form shown in Fig. 2.22*c*. We now have the information in digital form, and this digital information can be transmitted by using one of several pulse-modulation schemes.

The most direct possibility is to transmit the sequence of pulses coming from the analog-digital converter. The pulses then have different amplitudes, but are equally spaced, as in Fig. 2.22*c*. This is called *pulse amplitude modulation* (PAM). Another method of pulse modulation is to keep the amplitude of the pulses constant and to change the width of the successive pulses according to the magnitude of the sampled signal. This is *pulse width modulation* (PWM). It has a form as shown in Fig. 2.23. The advantage

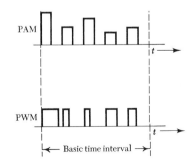

**FIGURE 2.23**  *Pulse width modulation (PWM) at bottom compared with pulse amplitude modulation (PAM) at top.*

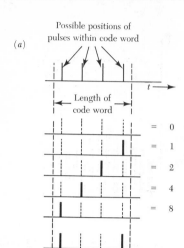
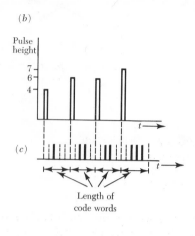

**FIGURE 2.24**  *Pulse code modulation.* (a) *Example of a code using four pulse positions within a code word length;* (b) *quantized and sampled pulses taken from Fig. 2.22c (first four pulses only);* (c) *encoded pulse heights of* b *(dotted lines mean pulse absent, heavy vertical lines mean pulse present within the code word).*

of this scheme is that one can transmit information even when the pulse heights would come through distorted.

A still more sophisticated system of pulse modulation is *pulse code modulation* (PCM). In this, the analog signal is sampled periodically, and each sample is value coded into a series of pulses. The principles for such coding will be made clearer in Sec. 2.6. As an example, an assumed code is shown in Fig. 2.24a. Within the length of one code word a pulse can be present or absent at four different positions. The numerical values 0 to 8 are shown in code form, and also, as an example, the numerical value 9. As an application of this coding scheme, the first few pulses from Fig. 2.22c are reproduced in Fig. 2.24b. The encoded form is shown in Fig. 2.24c. The coding scheme used in this example is a binary digital system, which is described in more detail in Sec. 2.6. This system has the advantage that neither height nor width distortions cause errors so long as the individual pulses are recognizable.

**MULTICHANNEL INFORMATION TRANSMISSION**  In practical applications, it is often possible to use the same major transmission channel to transmit information from several sources. In a space vehicle, for example, several transducers are used to measure temperature, nuclear particle densities, radiation, etc. The information from each transducer must be kept separate and therefore several separate information channels are needed. However, all the information in these channels must be transmitted by a single channel from the space vehicle to ground. The combination of several information channels in one transmission channel is called *multiplexing.* In practice, two possibilities are used, either time multiplexing or frequency multiplexing.

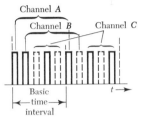

**FIGURE 2.25** *Time multiplexing of pulses.*

*Time multiplexing* can be obtained by combining several pulse trains as shown in Fig. 2.25. If the basic pulsewidth is narrow in relation to the basic period, several pulses can be inserted as shown, one for each "channel." Great care must be taken, of course, to space the pulse trains of each channel correctly so that not more than one train from any channel occurs at any instant of time. Such multiplexing permits us to send the information of several channels along one transmission path. Time multiplexing is extensively used in space communication.

*Frequency multiplexing* is commonly used in telephone systems. Let us say each telephone needs a channel bandwidth of 3000 Hz. Using amplitude modulation, we can shift the information of several separate channels

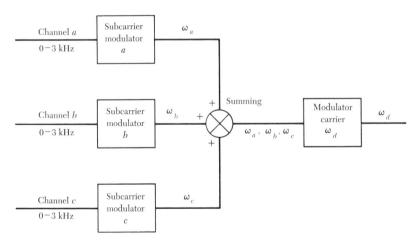

**FIGURE 2.26** *Frequency multiplexing (for simplicity transmission in one direction only is shown); carriers without sidebands are designated.*

to successive carrier frequencies. For example in Fig. 2.26, channel *a* is translated to carrier frequency $\omega_a$, channel *b* to a frequency $\omega_b$, etc. From the figure it is clear that all of the translated signals can be considered as one new information channel. The new channel must have a bandwidth wide enough to include all the carrier frequencies $\omega_a$, $\omega_b$, etc., with their sidebands.

## 2.6 information, noise, and channel capacity

Most electronic systems are used for processing and transmitting information. We must, therefore, know the requirements that electronic components or systems must meet in order that information can be handled and transmitted at a given rate.

When one person speaks to another, *language* is the vehicle and the code by which information is transmitted. The *words* are the basic information constituents and the number of possible words is very large. A good dictionary usually lists about 600,000 items, although we do not, of course, use that many in our usual information transmission. The items listed in the dictionary are an upper bound for practical purposes. For *written* communication, we use the 26 *letters* of the alphabet as the basic constituents. Notice that the number of building blocks is much less in the case of the written language. This leads us to the question, Is there a minimal building block for information? In other words, is there a unit of information? The answer is Yes, and it has been given by C. Shannon in his brilliant work on the information capacity of communication channels.[1]

Shannon showed that one can, in essence, reduce information to a *binary system* of "yes" or "no," representing a choice between equally likely alternatives. Electronic systems can easily handle information presented in binary form. The presence of a pulse, for instance, can denote one choice, the absence of a pulse the other choice. In terms of binary expressions, we can label one choice "1" and the other "0." This does not mean the 1 is represented by a pulse of 1 volt. Rather, 1 can represent any voltage level we wish to use, and 0 can be any other voltage level (it may be even negative). Instead of "yes" or "no," we now use the binary numbers 1 and 0 and call these binary units *bit*, for binary digit. The bit is the basic unit of information.

To illustrate the use of the bit in transmitting information, let us assume that we have a situation where four different choices are equally likely. Four bits are not needed to represent these choices; only 2 bits are. To understand this, assume that we use two pulses which we label as 1 and 0.

---

[1] For Shannon's original work see C. Shannon, "A Mathematical Theory of Communication," *Bell System Tech. J.*, **27**: 379-423 (July, 1948) or "Communication in the Presence of Noise," *Proc. IRE*, **37**: 10-21 (January, 1949).

By ordered coding we can represent the four alternatives. We can arrange these pulses as (00), (01), (10), and (11), as shown in Fig. 2.27. For example, the four choices may correspond to the four suits in a deck of cards as shown in Fig. 2.27. With 3 bits of information, one can represent eight

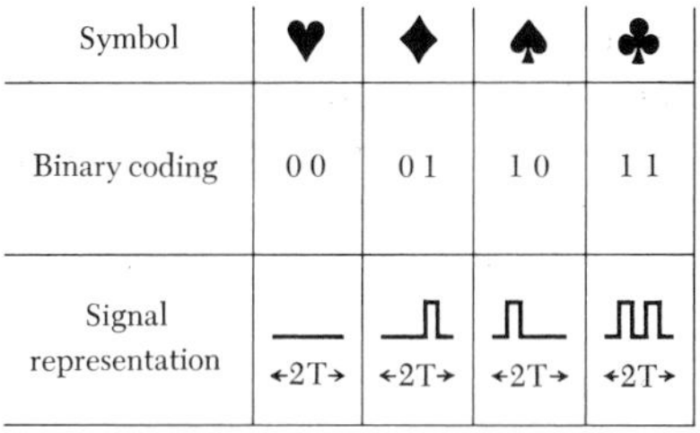

| Symbol | ♥ | ♦ | ♠ | ♣ |
|---|---|---|---|---|
| Binary coding | 0 0 | 0 1 | 1 0 | 1 1 |
| Signal representation | ‾‾ ←2T→ | _Π_ ←2T→ | Π_ ←2T→ | ΠΠ ←2T→ |

**FIGURE 2.27**  *Example of ordered coding with two pulses.*

equally likely choices; and, in general, with $n$ bits we can handle $2^n$ choices in a binary system. Reversing the above quantitative law, we see that if $n$ bits can denote $2^n$ items, $M$ items require $\log_2 M$ bits for designation. The information content in these $M$ items, if they are equally likely, is then

$$I = \log_2 M \qquad \text{bits} \qquad (2.26)$$

As an example, we assume that a gray scale with 10 intermediate shades of gray between black and white is to be represented by a binary system. We have to represent $M = 10 + 2 = 12$ levels (which includes black and white). In the binary system each decimal number is represented by powers of 2, as is shown in Table 2.1. From (2.26), the 12 levels contain $I = \log_2 12 = 3.58$ bits of information.

**TABLE 2.1**

| Powers of 2: | $2^3$ | $2^2$ | $2^1$ | $2^0$ |
|---|---|---|---|---|
| Decimal value→ ↓ | 8 | 4 | 2 | 1 |
| 0 | 0 | 0 | 0 | 0 |
| 1 | 0 | 0 | 0 | 1 |
| 2 | 0 | 0 | 1 | 0 |
| 3 | 0 | 0 | 1 | 1 |
| 4 | 0 | 1 | 0 | 0 |
| 5 | 0 | 1 | 0 | 1 |
| 6 | 0 | 1 | 1 | 0 |
| 7 | 0 | 1 | 1 | 1 |
| 8 | 1 | 0 | 0 | 0 |
| 9 | 1 | 0 | 0 | 1 |
| 10 | 1 | 0 | 1 | 0 |
| 11 | 1 | 0 | 1 | 1 |

In Table 2.1 we represent a total of 12 levels $(0 + 11 = 12)$. It is evident that we need 4 bits to represent 12 levels since we cannot divide digits. However, it is clear that with the 4 bits used, we could represent up to $M = 16$ levels, if required.

As another example, we return to the 600,000 items represented in a good dictionary of our language. How many bits would we need to represent this? From the above, $I = \log_2 (600,000) = 19.2 \sim 20$ bits.[1]

The above development illustrates how many bits (units of information) are needed to represent a given number of items (or levels). When we transmit information, the *transmission rate* $R$, in bits per second, is of importance. The question now is, What requirements are imposed on the system's building blocks so that they can handle a given information transmission rate?

When pulses are used in an electronic system, the binary system is often used for information transmission. In Sec. 2.3, which presented the time and frequency aspects of single (nonrecurrent) pulses, it was found that the required bandwidth for the building blocks increases as the pulse-width is made smaller. Further, a sequence of pulses, called a pulse train, is needed for information transmission. The pulse sequence has a certain periodicity which must be considered; alternatively, we can use a time period corresponding to the length of a binary "word." In the previous example of the representation of a gray scale, the "word" length was required to be 4 bits.

To transmit this pulse train faithfully, the system building blocks need to have an infinite bandwidth to correspond to the infinite number of Fourier components. However, as seen in Sec. 2.3, a reasonable approximation can be maintained with only a finite passband. To find the minimal bandwidth needed to transmit some semblance of this pulse train, we need a bandwidth $B = 1/\tau$ Hz, where $\tau$ is the width of the pulse.

The implication is that a limited bandwidth of the building blocks of a system force us to use values of $\tau$ of the basic pulse which cannot be arbitrarily small. This, in turn, means that the information transmission rate $R$ is bounded on the high end. In a usual telegraph system, for instance, we must operate the "key" at a slow rate because of the narrow bandwidth of the transmission channel. If too fast a rate is used, the "dots" are indistinguishable from the "dashes."

The discussions above refer to ideal situations in the absence of noise. When noise is present, as it always is in practice, the rate $R$ of information transmission is reduced. We know by experience that in calling home

---

[1] Many readers who have played the game "Twenty Questions" know that by judicious arrangement of the questions, one can pinpoint one of a tremendous number of items with only "yes" or "no" replies. We see that the twenty questions could actually cover all of the 600,000 items in an unabridged dictionary if each question divides the alternatives into two equally likely ones.

from an out-of-way place where, for example, the telephone lines are marginal at best, only a little extra interference rapidly cuts down the rate of information transmission. We must slow down our speech under such circumstances and repeat the message frequently. (Repetition is a case of "redundant coding" in communications jargon.)

To what extent does the presence of noise reduce the rate of transmission of information? To illustrate this problem we use an example of an analog signal $S$ which changes with time, as shown in Fig. 2.28. Note that the

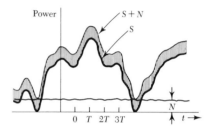

**FIGURE 2.28** *Signal transmission in the presence of noise.*

signal power is presented versus time.[1] The noise power $N$ is also shown, as is the total of signal plus noise $(S + N)$. Assume now that an analog-to-digital converter is used to detect and code the information contained in the signal. Because of the noise, an uncertainty is present and we cannot make choices between intermediate levels which are separated by less than the noise level. Therefore, we can operate with about $(S + N)/N$ distinguishable levels. The information content of each pulse representing one of those levels is then

$$I = \log_2 \left(1 + \frac{S}{N}\right) \quad \text{bits} \quad (2.27)$$

We define now the *channel capacity* for a transmission channel as the rate of transmission per second.

$$C = \frac{I}{T} \quad \text{bits/s} \quad (2.28)$$

where $T$ is the time to transmit a pulse and to keep it distinct from adjacent pulses. From our work above, we need a frequency bandwidth of $B \approx 1/T$ Hz to keep the pulses recognizable. Therefore, the channel capacity can be written

$$C = \frac{I}{T} = B \log_2 \left(1 + \frac{S}{N}\right) \quad \text{bits/s} \quad (2.29)$$

---

[1] Because noise is a random process, we must deal with mean square values or root-mean-square values. This corresponds to power, as is brought out in Chap. 9. For comparisons of signal and noise, we also use mean square or power values for the signal.

It should be noted that (2.29), which is called Shannon's equation, gives an ideal limit not often attained in actual communication channels. Shannon gave an exact proof for the formula; our development is only a plausibility argument.

**EXAMPLES: BROADCAST AND MARINER TELEVISION**   We now consider an example to illustrate the application of Shannon's equation. A television raster, as used for commercial TV in the United States, has 525 horizontal lines. This establishes the vertical picture resolution. Assuming the same horizontal resolution, we have to keep in mind that the picture width is larger than the height. The ratio of width to height, called the aspect ratio, is 4/3. Therefore, the number of picture elements (individual dots) scanned in the horizontal direction is $525 \cdot 4/3$ picture elements. All the picture elements constitute the picture frame which has $525 \cdot 525 \cdot 4/3 = 3.675 \cdot 10^5$ picture elements. In one second, the picture is scanned 30 times. The rate of scanned elements is, therefore, $3.675 \cdot 10^5 \cdot 30 = 1.1 \cdot 10^7$ elements per second. Each picture element has to reproduce a shade of the gray scale. Assuming eight shades, we would obtain, using (2.26), $\log_2 8 = 3$ bits per picture element. The result is that we must transmit $3 \cdot 1.1 \cdot 10^7 = 3.3 \cdot 10^7$ bits/s for this video system. A representative signal-to-noise ratio $S/N$ might be taken for convenience as 63. Equation (2.29) gives us the required bandwidth for the transmission channel of

$$B = \frac{C}{\log_2 (1 + S/N)} = \frac{3.3 \cdot 10^7}{\log_2 (1 + 63)} = \frac{3.3 \cdot 10^7}{6} = 5.5 \text{ MHz} \quad (2.30)$$

Actually, a bandwidth of 4 MHz is used for TV video channels. This example seems to show that the TV channel is used very effectively, but an actual picture has much less information than that calculated because of the slow change of the picture from point to point and from frame to frame (i.e., the "redundancy" of the picture transmission).

In special cases the ratio $S/N$ may be very unfavorable, meaning that the noise level is very high or that the signal level is very small. Such situations are encountered in communication between space vehicles and ground stations on earth. From Shannon's work, the bandwidth has to increase, in relation to a situation which has a high $S/N$ value, if a given information rate $C$ is to be maintained. This increase, however, is usually not an acceptable solution. Noise is ever present and is due to electrical random fluctuations in all electrical elements and media. An electrical resistor, for instance, produces random noise voltages which can be measured across its terminals. The noise increases with the absolute temperature $T$ of the resistor, and one finds that the noise is encountered throughout the entire frequency spectrum. Because of this last fact, the wider we make the bandwidth of our system, the more noise power is introduced. We have, therefore, conflicting requirements for signal rate, bandwidth, and noise. An engineering compromise must be made for each situation.

As an example to illustrate these compromises, consider the television transmission from a space vehicle, such as the Mariner, during passage near the planet Mars. The previous example of a TV signal under a favorable ratio $S/N$ gave a bandwidth of 5.5 MHz. If the $S/N$ ratio is more unfavorable than the value above we would, according to Shannon's expression, be tempted to increase the bandwidth, but as noted above, this would introduce more noise power. The bandwidth must actually be restricted to lower the noise, and the information rate must then be reduced. Thus, the TV information rate of the earlier example cannot be used. In the case of Mariner, two measures were taken to lower the information rate. First, a sequence of snapshots at short-time intervals was used. Each picture was actually a "still" picture. The resolution was reduced to 200 horizontal lines and each line had 200 picture elements, resulting in $200^2 = 4 \cdot 10^4$ picture spots. Each spot was assigned 64 levels, which corresponds to $\log_2 64 = 6$ bits per picture spot. The information content per picture frame is: (bits/picture spot)·(number of spots/frame) $= 6 \cdot 4 \cdot 10^4 = 2.4 \cdot 10^5$ bits. Secondly, the transmission of each picture was not made directly. Rather, each picture was stored in the Mariner's memory unit. The time taken to read out the information of one picture was 24 seconds, resulting in a readout information rate of $2.4 \cdot 10^5/24 = 10$ kbits/s. After readout, the picture was erased within another 24 sec to make ready for storing a subsequent "snapshot." (The memory as used was able to store 20 picture frames in digital form.) An analog-to-digital converter was used to convert the video information into suitable form for memory and transmission. In view of the very high noise level interfering with the information transmission from the vehicle's memory unit to the ground station on earth, over the distance of $260 \cdot 10^6$ km, and the limited signal power available on Mariner, a considerably reduced transmission rate of 8.3 bits/s was chosen as an engineering compromise. Thus, the transmission of the information content of one picture required a time duration of

$$t = \frac{\text{information/picture}}{\text{information rate}} = \frac{2.4 \cdot 10^5 \text{ bits}}{8.3 \text{ bits/s}} = 2.88 \cdot 10^4 \text{ seconds} = 8 \text{ hours}$$

It is interesting to compare this information transmission rate used for Mariner, namely 8.3 bits/s with that of the previously discussed example of "real time" TV, namely, $3.3 \cdot 10^7$ bits/s. This comparison illustrates well the tremendous reduction in bandwidth that had to be used in the case of Mariner to overcome the noise interference. The picture noted earlier, Fig. 1.10, was obtained through this procedure.

### REFERENCES

S. Goldman, "Frequency Analysis, Modulation, and Noise," McGraw-Hill Book Company, New York, 1948.

J. L. Marshall, "Introduction to Signal Theory," International Textbook Company, Scranton, Pa., 1965.

C. Shannon and W. Weaver, "The Mathematical Theory of Communication," University of Illinois Press, Urbana, Ill., 1949.

C. Cherry, "On Human Communication," Technology Press of the Massachusetts Institute of Technology, Cambridge, Mass., 1957.

### PROBLEMS

**2.1**  Give an example of nonelectrical signals which have analog waveforms. Name electrical signals (not mentioned in the text) which have discrete waveforms.

**2.2**  Express the waveform given in the accompanying illustration as a Fourier series and find the Fourier coefficients.

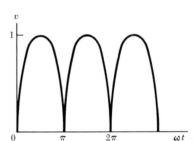

Problem 2.2

**2.3**  An amplifier has a voltage gain magnitude versus frequency characteristic like that shown here, with band-edge frequencies of $\omega_l$ and $\omega_u$. The band-edge frequencies correspond to a reduced magnitude value of $a_{vo}/\sqrt{2} = 0.707a_{vo}$. Suppose we design a hi-fi amplifier for which $f_l = \omega_l/2\pi = 20$ Hz and $f_u = \omega_u/2\pi = 30$ kHz. If the signal into the amplifier is of rectangular waveform, as shown in Fig. 2.9, what is the amplitude of the first two Fourier terms in the amplifier output? Use (2.14) and assume an amplitude of unity and a period of the fundamental frequency of $10^{-4}$ s.

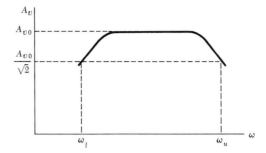

**Problem 2.3**

**2.4**  A fullwave-rectifier output signal of waveform shown in Fig. 2.11 is to be represented by a Fourier series (2.16). Assume that the maximum amplitude is 10 V. Find the amplitude of the first three terms of the series.

**2.5**  Consider the signal waveform of Prob. 2.4 and its Fourier series, which is now to be considered the input to a filter. At the filter output:

(*a*)  We obtain the first term of the Fourier series only; what is its meaning?

(*b*)  We obtain the first two terms only; interpret their significance.

**2.6**  A pulse is fed into an amplifier, which has a bandwidth from 20 Hz to 30 kHz. What is the approximate minimum pulse width that can be used if the output is to be a recognizable pulse.

**2.7**  Assume a sequence of rectangular pulses. Each pulse has a width of $\tau$ and repeats with a periodicity $T$, as shown in the sketch. The periodicity $T$ establishes a discrete value $\omega_1 = 2\pi/T$.

(*a*)  Find the $n$th Fourier coefficient $a_n$. Note that $a_n$ becomes zero at certain values of $n\omega_1$ and exists otherwise only at discrete frequencies $n\omega_1$.

(*b*)  Plot the contour of $a_n$ versus frequency and show that it corresponds to the form $(\sin x)/x$.

(*c*)  What bandwidth is needed to pass the pulse sequence? Make assumptions similar to those used in the text for the single pulse.

(*d*)  Assume $\tau = 1$ $\mu$s and $T = 10^{-4}$ s; what is the required bandwidth?

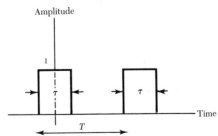

**Problem 2.7**

**2.8**   A dc signal is modulated by a 400-Hz chopper to obtain a rectangular wave with a repetition frequency of 400 Hz. The chopper is a mechanical switch having two stable switch positions, as shown in the accompanying diagram. Since the major requirement is the conversion of the dc signal to ac, the harmonics of the Fourier series are not needed and can be filtered out, retaining only the 400-Hz fundamental. What kind of a filter should be chosen for this task?

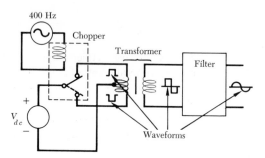

**Problem 2.8**

**2.9**   The illustration here shows the velocity-frequency characteristic for recording music on phonograph records. A mechanical transducer ("pickup") is used for playback. It provides an electrical signal of the same frequency characteristic as that used for recording.

(*a*) Ideally, we want a "flat" frequency characteristic. Give possible reasons why low frequencies are de-emphasized when recording and high frequencies are emphasized.

(*b*) For playback, we require an electrical signal into the loudspeaker which has a "flat" frequency characteristic. The deviations from such a uniform characteristic must be compensated for by using equalizers. In block diagram form, show the playback system, including equalizers, and sketch the frequency characteristic for each block.

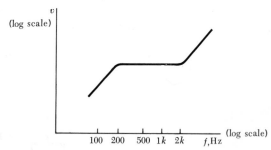

**Problem 2.9**

**2.10**   Give examples of mechanical systems that could be classified as oscillators.

**2.11**   Sketch the resulting amplitude-modulated wave if a carrier sinusoid of 10 Hz is modulated by a sinusoidal signal of 1 Hz.

**2.12**   A signal band of frequencies from 20 to 15,000 Hz is used to modulate a carrier frequency of 10 MHz.

(a) Show a frequency spectrum for the AM wave.

(b) What is the bandwidth required to pass the modulated wave?

(c) Express the bandwidth as a percentage of the carrier frequency.

(d) How would the percentage in part c change if the carrier is changed to 100 MHz?

**2.13** Explain why we use amplitude modulation for most radio broadcasting. Why is frequency modulation used for some radio broadcasting?

**2.14** Assume that ten continuous measurements are to be transmitted to a remote location. Each measurement is pulse coded. How could all ten measurements be transmitted through only one channel?

**2.15** In block-diagram form, design a teletype system to send and receive 26 letters, 10 numbers, 15 punctuation marks, and 13 other assorted characters. If the characters are coded, transmitted, and at the receiver, decoded, what is the minimum number of bits of information necessary to send any one of the characters?

**2.16** Suppose there are 1 billion telephones used in the world, therefore requiring nine-digit phone numbers (that is, 000,000,000 to 999,999,999). Each telephone utilizes a bandwidth of 6 kHz. At maximum usage, 10 percent of all the telephones are used simultaneously. What bandwidth is needed to transmit the maximum number of conversations over a single carrier frequency? If the information is modulated onto a $10^{15}$-Hz laser beam, what percentage of the laser center frequency is needed. Suppose we now wish to use a binary code to select, at the central exchange, any one of the 1 billion telephone numbers. How many bits of information are needed to determine the 1 billion telephone numbers?

**2.17** We wish to transmit 20 bits of information over a single carrier. Discuss which type(s) of coding (modulation) are applicable; sketch the waveforms.

**2.18** Suppose we wish to "save bandwidth" in TV broadcasting by storing the picture and altering only those picture spots that change from frame to frame. Assume a TV system with 525 lines, equal resolution horizontally, and an aspect ratio of 4:3. This results in $525 \cdot 525 \cdot 4/3 \approx 4 \cdot 10^5$ picture spots. We will transmit the address of each spot that changes and its new value 30 times per second.

(a) How many bits of information are required to address any spot?

(b) If 1 percent of the spots change each frame and we wish to distinguish eight light-intensity levels for each spot, how many bits must we send per frame? How many per second? (Consider this to include the addresses and the intensity of the spot.)

(c) Assuming a signal-to-noise ratio $S/N$ of 63, what bandwidth is required? (Assume the transmission channel and coding to be ideal.)

# chapter 3

# CIRCUITS AND CIRCUIT COMPONENTS

## 3.1 the circuit concept

We saw in Chap. 1 that a typical system is made up of a group of building blocks, each block having a specific purpose in the transmission or processing of a signal. Chapter 2 considered in more detail some of the processes, such as amplification, modulation, and filtering, that take place within the functional blocks. The powerful method of Fourier analysis was introduced so that arbitrary signals could be analyzed as a superposition of sinusoids of different frequencies. In this chapter, we wish to go farther by illustrating how circuit analysis techniques are utilized in the study and design of the functional blocks.

Circuit analysis is one of the important tools of electrical engineering, and students who go farther in this branch of engineering will study the subject in much more detail in later courses. This chapter is not intended to cover the subject, but only to extend the circuit information brought from beginning physics courses to a point applicable to the problems to be discussed in this text. The methods of analysis primarily needed follow directly from Kirchhoff's laws. It will be desirable to introduce the complex representation for sinusoids since that representation saves much work in handling linear circuits excited by sinusoidal sources. Students familiar with these matters may omit the chapter, or use it for a brief review.

A circuit is an interconnection by conductors of components or circuit elements, some of which will be discussed in the following section. To be specific, consider the example of Fig. 3.1. This pictures a signal source which provides an input to an amplifier. The source is represented or *modeled* by an ideal voltage generator in series with a source resistance, as shown in Fig. 3.2. The basis for such representation is the Thévenin theorem which is discussed in Sec. 3.2 and

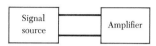

**FIGURE 3.1**   *Amplifier input from signal source.*

Chap. 9. For a very simple amplifier, let us assume that the absorption of signal power by the amplifier is represented by a resistor $R_a$, as shown in Fig. 3.3. The figure also shows a capacitor $C_a$ modeling the inevitable

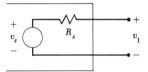

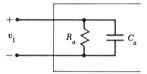

**FIGURE 3.2**   *Model of signal source.*          **FIGURE 3.3**   *Model of typical load.*

charge storage in the electronic devices and connecting elements. The inter-connection of source and amplifier leads to the overall circuit shown in Fig. 3.4. The problem in this example might be to find the transfer of power from the source to the amplifier as a function of frequency, considering the source voltage as a sinusoid. This particular circuit will be "lowpass," transmitting only the lower range of frequencies into the amplifier because of the interaction of capacitor $C_a$ with the two resistors. The general form of voltage magnitude response versus frequency is sketched in Fig. 3.5. Power transfer is proportional to the square of $v_2$.

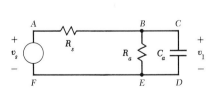

**FIGURE 3.4**   *Circuit model of signal source connected to a load.*

**FIGURE 3.5**   *Frequency response curve showing magnitude of voltage across load as a function of signal frequency.*

As in the above example, circuit modeling for a system building block consists in setting down an electrical circuit which can be analyzed to give, at least approximately, the behavior of that block. The considerable importance of this approach comes from the large body of organized technique which has been developed for the analysis and design of systems which are expressed in circuit form. Equally important are the physical pictures that one quickly develops which yield a qualitative feeling for performance from inspection of the circuit diagram. The technique is not applicable to all classes of electromagnetic systems. "Wave-type" systems, for example, often require more fundamental field laws. Even when applicable, other methods of modeling may be preferable, such as mathematical modeling which utilizes the representative equations of the phenomena directly without reference to a circuit.

Circuit analysis starts from the two Kirchhoff laws which are reviewed in Sec. 3.4. For the present we recall that these laws relate voltages and currents about a circuit, so the following section begins with a review of voltage-current relations for some of the idealized elements which are used in electrical circuits.

## 3.2   circuit elements

The most common circuit elements are the resistor, which dissipates electrical energy, and the inductor and capacitor, which store energy. All of these, if time invariant, are *passive* elements, meaning that they cannot act as sources of power. Other passive elements to be discussed include the switch and ideal diode, and 2-port devices (devices with an input pair and an output pair of terminals) such as the ideal transmission line and transformer. We will also discuss idealization of our signal sources or generators.[1] We are particularly concerned with the voltage-current relationships for each of these elements for use in circuit analysis.

**THE RESISTOR**   The resistor is an element which converts electrical energy to thermal energy when a current flows through it. The thermal energy is produced by internal "collisions" of charge carriers in motion within the solid as discussed in Chap. 4. For this chapter we note that most common resistors satisfy Ohm's law, which states that the voltage drop across the terminals of a resistor is directly proportional to the current flow through it. The symbol for the resistor is shown in Fig. 3.6a. For the resistor,

$$v(t) = Ri(t) \tag{3.1a}$$

---

[1] These generators are special cases of *active elements*, which can deliver power. Other classes of active elements will be met in later chapters.

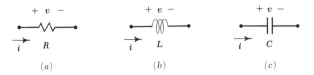

**FIGURE 3.6** *Circuit elements.* (a) *Resistance;* (b) *inductance;* (c) *capacitance.*

where $R$ is called the *resistance*, $v(t)$ denotes the voltage as an arbitrary function of time, and $i(t)$ denotes the current as a function of time. From here on we will drop the functional notation except where needed for clarity and use $v$ and $i$ alone to denote voltage and current in the time domain.

$$v = Ri \qquad (3.1b)$$

We can also write the relation in the inverse form

$$i = Gv \qquad (3.1c)$$

where $G = 1/R$ is called the *conductance*.

A *linear* resistor has a value of $R$ which is not dependent on $i$ or $v$, as shown in the solid curve in Fig. 3.7a. An alternate way of showing this is to plot the $vi$ relation of (3.1b or c). For a linear resistor, we obtain the linear curve shown in Fig. 3.7b. If the resistor is a function of $i$, as in the dashed curve in Fig. 3.7a, the $vi$ curve is not linear as indicated by the dashed curve of Fig. 3.7b.

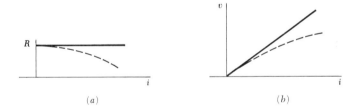

**FIGURE 3.7** *Characteristics of a resistor.*

**THE SWITCH AND IDEAL DIODE**   Two important elements are worth mentioning at this point. These are the *switch* and the *ideal diode* (ideal rectifier) both of which can be considered as special classes of resistors. The switch element is self-evident. A representation is shown in Fig. 3.8a. The ideal switch is either a perfect open circuit (infinite resistance) or a perfectly conducting path (zero resistance or infinite conductance). The switch is actuated by an external control signal or mechanism. The ideal diode is a highly nonlinear

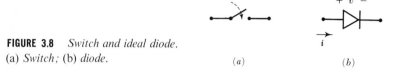

**FIGURE 3.8**   *Switch and ideal diode.*
(a) *Switch;* (b) *diode.*                    *(a)*                    *(b)*

resistor which is somewhat similar to a switch. It is a perfect open circuit to current flow in one direction, as well as a perfectly conducting path for current flow in the opposite direction. The representation of a diode is shown in Fig. 3.8*b*. The direction of the arrow is the "easy flow" direction. We usually show an *iv* characteristic[1] to describe the ideal diode as in Fig. 3.9. Note that for a negative voltage placed across the diode, zero current will flow. However, for a positive voltage, current of any value can flow in the positive direction. An actual diode has finite nonlinear resistances in both directions of current flow and has an *iv* characteristic as shown by the dashed line in Fig. 3.9. Diodes are extremely useful in signal processing and are realized by two-terminal electronic devices. We treat diodes in detail in Chaps. 5, 6, and 10.

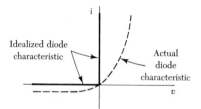

**FIGURE 3.9**   *Idealized and actual diode characteristics.*

**THE INDUCTOR**   An inductive element models the storage of magnetic energy which results from the flow of current in conductors. The conductor may have the form of a coil for increase of energy storage. Often a magnetic core is included. From Faraday's law, the voltage drop across an inductor is proportional to the rate of change of magnetic flux:

$$v = \frac{d\psi}{dt} \tag{3.2a}$$

where $\psi$ is magnetic flux. Flux is related to the current which flows by a proportionality constant called the *inductance*.

$$\psi = Li \tag{3.2b}$$

---

[1]We will use either an *iv* or a *vi* notation for a characteristic curve, the first quantity in the ordered pair denoting the dependent variable, or ordinate, and the second quantity denoting the independent variable, or abscissa.

where $L$ is inductance. If inductance is not a function of time,[1] we obtain the usual expression

$$v = L\frac{di}{dt} \tag{3.2c}$$

The symbol for the inductive element is shown in Fig. 3.6b. By definition, if the current increases in the direction of the current arrow, the voltage developed will have the positive polarity as shown. As a numerical example, a current building up at the rate of $10^{-3}$ A (1 mA) in $10^{-6}$ s (1 $\mu$s) through an inductance of $10^{-2}$ H (10mH) produces a voltage of 10 V.

**THE CAPACITOR** The capacitive element models the storage of electric energy. The representation of the capacitor is shown in Fig. 3.6c. The electrical relation for this element is developed from the proportionality of stored charge to voltage,

$$q = Cv \tag{3.3}$$

where $C$ is the *capacitance*. We obtain the $iv$ dynamical relation by using the fundamental relations

$$i = \frac{dq}{dt} = \frac{d}{dt}Cv \tag{3.4a}$$

$$i = C\frac{dv}{dt} \tag{3.4b}$$

The common form of (3.4b) is valid if the value of $C$ is time invariant.[2] Thus a voltage building up at the rate of $10^3$ V (1 kV) in $10^{-3}$ s (1 ms) through a capacitor of $10^{-8}$ F (0.01 $\mu$F) produces a current of 0.01A. A voltage increase in the sense of Fig. 3.6c yields positive current as shown.

**MODELS FOR REAL ELEMENTS** A physical component which is designed to provide one of the functions above (i.e., loss or storage of electric or magnetic energy) will to some extent involve one or more of the others. For example, an actual coil of wire, as illustrated in Fig. 3.10a, designed to serve as an inductor will certainly have some resistance associated with it. In addition, there will be a distributed capacitance between the turns of the wire. We therefore can model the coil in small increments, say turn by turn, as shown in Fig. 3.10b where the dotted line indicates a continuation of the structure. For a model which is easier to deal with, we can propose the

---

[1] Note that in addition to direct changes of $L$ with time, nonlinear characteristics may also cause it to be time variant. Thus if $L$ is a function of $i$, and $i$ changes with time, $L$ will also.

[2] As with inductance, nonlinear characteristics which cause $C$ to be a function of $v$ will also cause it to be a function of time when $v$ changes with time.

circuit shown in Fig. 3.10c. In this simplified model, one capacitor represents the gross capacitance, one resistor the total loss, etc. In designing an

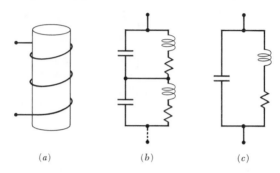

**FIGURE 3.10** *Inductor.* (a) *Coil;* (b) *circuit model;* (c) *another circuit model.*

inductor, we must pay particular attention to the minimization of losses and capacitance if we are to achieve an element which approximates an inductor sufficiently well over a given frequency spectrum. Of course, the same problems and considerations hold for other elements.

**THE IDEAL TRANSMISSION LINE** As one studies signal transmission along conductors at high frequencies, one finds that the inductive and capacitive effects are completely interrelated and a gross simplification, as in Fig. 3.10c, is not valid. This leads us to propose an *ideal transmission* line. This element is a *2-port* or *two-terminal pair* element. It has an input port or pair of terminals, and an output port or terminal pair. The equations of signal transfer will not be given here as this involves more electromagnetic wave theory than is appropriate to this text. Basically, however, such a "line" delays the signal traveling along it by the time required for the propagation of the signal at the velocity of light in the medium of the line. If we label the velocity of light $c$ and the length of line $l$, the time delay $\tau_d$ is

$$\tau_d = \frac{l}{c} \tag{3.5}$$

Such an ideal transmission line is illustrated in Fig. 3.11. Another important parameter for a transmission line is the ratio of voltage to current for a wave propagating in one direction along the line. This ratio is called the *characteristic impedance* $Z_0$.

**FIGURE 3.11** *Ideal transmission line.*

**IDEAL TRANSFORMERS** The last passive element considered here is the ideal transformer, which is also a 2-port element, as shown in Fig. 3.12. The

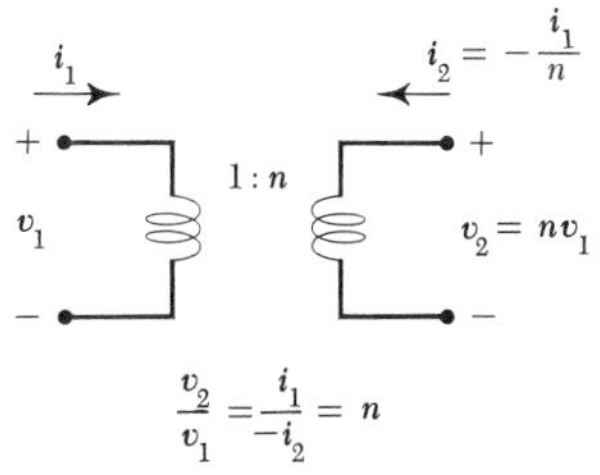

**FIGURE 3.12** *Transformer.*

$$\frac{v_2}{v_1} = \frac{i_1}{-i_2} = n$$

output voltage is $n$ times the input voltage; however, the output current $-i_2$ is $1/n$ times the input current flowing into the transformer. The direction for positive current flow at the output port is taken into the top node of the transformer by convention. Note that power flow is conserved in this element. The input power is

$$P_{\text{in}} = v_1 i_1 \tag{3.6a}$$

The output power is

$$P_{\text{out}} = v_2(-i_2) = n v_1 \left( \frac{1}{n} i_1 \right) = P_{\text{in}} \tag{3.6b}$$

There is no power amplification, only a scaling up of the voltage for $n > 1$, and a scaling down of the current. The current ratio is increased and the voltage ratio decreased by the transformer if $n < 1$. An ideal transformer can be approximated by an actual transformer consisting of closely coupled coils of wire with a turns ratio of $n$ turns in the output (secondary) coil to each turn in the input (primary) coil.

**THE IDEAL VOLTAGE SOURCE** In Sec. 3.1, an actual signal source was represented or modeled as a series connection of an ideal voltage source and a resistor. The ideal voltage source, by definition, has zero internal resistance as well as zero magnetic or electric stored energy. Irrespective of the load condition, the voltage across its terminals is fixed. It is useful to distinguish between constant voltage sources, e.g., a battery, and those that are time varying, e.g., a signal source. The constant or dc source is denoted by $V$ and the time-varying source by $v$ as shown in Fig. 3.13a and b, respectively. (The time-varying source may be denoted $v(t)$ when the functional notation is needed for clarity.) For both, we include plus and minus signs to indicate the

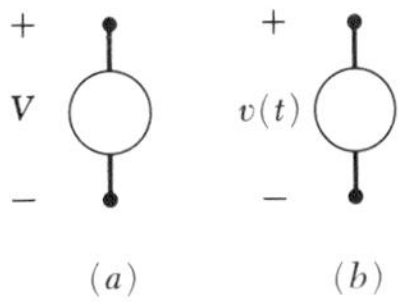

**FIGURE 3.13** *Symbols for ideal voltage sources (independent).*     (a)     (b)

assumed positive direction. For example, if $v$ is positive at a given instant, the top node in Fig. 3.13$b$ is positive with respect to the lower node at that instant, and vice versa if $v$ is negative. Later we will use the battery notation for the dc sources in electronic circuits to conform to common practice (see Chap. 6).

The constant or dc source in Fig. 3.13$a$ is usually an idealization of a battery, a fuel cell, a dc dynamoelectric generator, or a rectifier power supply. In these sources, energy comes from some other form, such as chemical or thermal energy, or from electromagnetic energy in a different form. The conservation-of-energy law, of course, holds for all sources. Time-varying sources are usually obtained when we model the output of a signal system. These model the signal energy or power coming to a circuit or building block from another portion of the system. The signal power may thus be many stages removed from an "original" source of energy.

The ideal voltage sources above are also referred to as *independent sources*. The voltage is not dependent on any voltage or current in the electronic circuit under study. In many electronic devices and circuits, however, it is helpful to model a voltage which is dependent on some other voltage or current in another part of the device or the circuit, but which is not dependent on the loading of the terminals of the source. We then have a *dependent voltage source*, as illustrated in Fig. 3.14, where

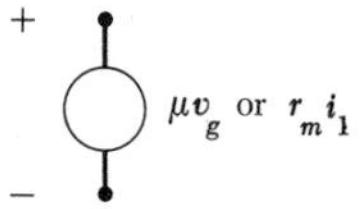

$$+$$
$$\mu v_g \text{ or } r_m i_1$$
$$-$$

**FIGURE 3.14**   *Dependent voltage source.*

$v_g$ and $i_1$ denote a voltage and current, respectively, in some other part of the circuit. Such dependent sources are common in circuit models for transistors and electron tubes.

**THE IDEAL CURRENT SOURCE**   We propose ideal current source models in a completely analogous manner. These are shown in Fig. 3.15$a$, $b$, and $c$. In Fig. 3.15$a$, the current into the top node and out of the bottom node is constant, irrespective of any loading. The arrow points in the direction of assumed positive current flow. The current source in Fig. 3.15$b$ is a time-varying source. A dependent current source is shown in Fig. 3.15$c$.

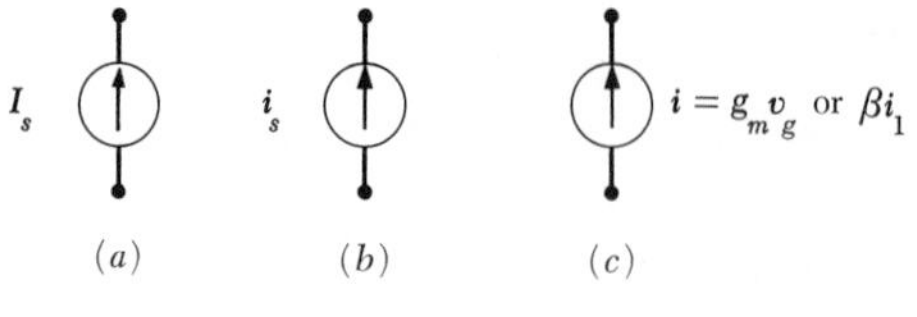

**FIGURE 3.15**   *Ideal current sources.*
(a) *A dc source;* (b) *an ac source;*
(c) *dependent current source.*

$$I_s \qquad i_s \qquad i = g_m v_g \text{ or } \beta i_1$$
$$(a) \qquad (b) \qquad (c)$$

The idea of a current source seems strange to some students. Batteries are commonly available, and an ideal constant voltage source is accepted without trouble. It should be remembered that we are modeling electrical phenomena with ideal elements. Thus, even though a common, almost constant current source is not as readily available as a battery, it is a most useful modeling element. For example, in Sec. 3.1, we could just as easily model the signal source with the current generator and conductance com-

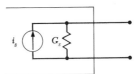

**FIGURE 3.16**  *Model of actual current source.*

bination shown in Fig. 3.16. The conductance $G_s$ represents the losses of the source, as does $R_s$ in Fig. 3.2. Therefore,

$$G_s = \frac{1}{R_s} \tag{3.7a}$$

If a short circuit is applied to the signal source, a current of $i_s$ flows. For a finite, nonzero value of load resistance the current $i_s$ splits between the load and the conductance $G_s$. If the load is an open circuit, the output voltage is $v = i_s/G_s = i_s R_s$. Clearly, the model of Fig. 3.16 is "equivalent" to that of Fig. 3.2 if (3.7a) applies and if

$$v_s = i_s R_s \tag{3.7b}$$

If a source is modeled as in Fig. 3.2, we commonly say that a "Thévenin equivalent" source is used. If Fig. 3.16 is used, we say that a "Norton equivalent" source is used. The basis for such equivalence will be expanded in Chap. 9. As a numerical value, a voltage generator having 100 V in series with $10^4$ Ω (10 kΩ) would be equivalent to a current generator of 0.01 A (10 mA) in parallel with a conductance of $10^{-4}$ mho.

## 3.3  linear and nonlinear circuits

In general, all actual circuits or circuit elements are nonlinear. Many circuits or circuit elements can nevertheless be well approximated as being linear. Linear circuits are thus extremely important, and it is well to review certain methods of establishing linearity.

In the last section, we saw that for a single resistor a plot of either the value $R$ or the $iv$ characteristic provides us with a technique for establishing linearity. This procedure can also be used in 2-port circuits consisting of resistors, such as shown in Fig. 3.17. The analysis of simple circuits is discussed in the next section. However, it is clear that we can solve for the

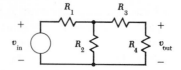

**FIGURE 3.17**   *2-port circuit.*

value of the output voltage in terms of the input voltage and plot this relation as in Fig. 3.18. If the curve is linear, we have a linear network. Note in particular that for an input voltage $v_1$ we obtain a particular "response" $v_2$ to the input. If $v_1$ is increased, say by a factor of 2, a linear circuit provides an output which is twice the previous value. This is not true for a nonlinear circuit.

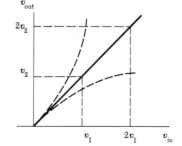

**FIGURE 3.18**   *Characteristics of linear 2-port (solid line) and nonlinear 2-ports (dashed lines).*

From the above follows the concept of *superposition*. To illustrate this concept, consider the situation where we have two inputs, $v_a$ and $v_b$, as shown in Fig. 3.19. A linear circuit provides a response (any current or voltage) which is the sum, i.e., the superposition, of the separate responses to each input.

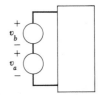

**FIGURE 3.19**   *Two voltage sources in series as circuit input.*

If the network contains energy-storage elements and is excited by time-varying sources, the static characteristic between input and output is not sufficient to determine linearity. Linearity in the general case is thus often determined by the form of the circuit equations. A circuit containing energy-storage elements is described electrically by differential equations. A nonlinear circuit is described by nonlinear differential equations, which are usually very difficult to solve except numerically. Linear differential equations, on the other hand, have standard methods for solution. In the next section, it will be clear that a simple analysis of even an elementary circuit is greatly simplified if the circuit is linear. To facilitate analysis we consequently often approximate a nonlinear element with a linear element, as will be seen frequently in later chapters. Here we consider two special techniques for nonlinear analysis.

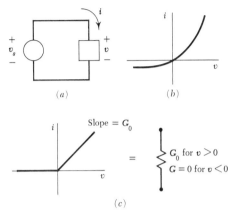

(a)          (b)

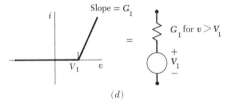

FIGURE 3.20 *Nonlinear circuit and piecewise linearization.* (a) *Connection;* (b) *characteristic;* (c) *piecewise linear characteristic;* (d) *alternate piecewise linear characteristic.*

Let us study the situation shown in Fig. 3.20a, which consists of an ideal voltage source and a nonlinear resistor (diode). We assume that the diode has the $iv$ characteristic shown in Fig. 3.20b. One approach is to approximate the curve with the two linear segments, each of which can be represented by a linear conductance as shown in Fig. 3.20c. For input voltages greater than zero, the linear conductance needed to model the diode is $G_0$. For $v < 0$, we assume a conductance of zero value, i.e., an open circuit. Depending on the value and range of the input voltage, we choose one or the other. If in a particular problem the input voltage has both positive and negative values, a *piecewise linear analysis* is used in which we move from one set of circuit-element values to another. Piecewise linear analysis is taken up in more detail in Chap. 6. Consider here the example for which the input voltage is a sine wave. No current then flows during the negative half cycles since we assume that the conductance $G = 0$. For the positive half cycles, we assume the conductance has a value $G_0$ and a current flows. The current thus has the waveform shown in Fig. 3.21. A Fourier-series analysis is easily obtained for this waveform:

$$i = \frac{I_m}{\pi}\left(1 + \frac{\pi}{2}\sin\omega_1 t - \frac{2}{3}\cos 2\omega_1 t - \frac{2}{15}\cos 4\omega_1 t + \cdots\right) \quad (3.8)$$

where $I_m$ is the peak value of the sinusoid. The generation of harmonics by the nonlinear element is shown by this expression.

The approximation of Fig. 3.20c may not provide the best fit for a particular operating range. Therefore a different linearization can be used, as shown in Fig. 3.20d. In the figure, the break point is placed at $V_1$. The circuit model for the diode must now consist of both a conductance and a dc voltage source (note Prob. 3.4).

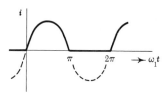

**FIGURE 3.21**  *Waveshape of current shown by solid line.*

As a final point, let us return to the original diode characteristic of Fig. 3.20b. If we want to investigate mathematically the effects of the non-linearity, we can propose an infinite series description of the curve:

$$i = a_0 + a_1 v + a_2 v^2 + \cdots \quad (3.9)$$

If the input is a sinusoid $v_s = V_m \cos \omega_1 t$, we can see that the nonlinear terms of the series will produce harmonics in the current response; for example, using the square term, we obtain

$$a_2 V_m^2 \cos^2 \omega_1 t = \frac{a_2 V_m^2}{2}(1 + \cos 2\omega_1 t) \quad (3.10)$$

From the description of (3.9), we can also easily substantiate the frequency-translation function described in the preceding chapter. Let the input be the sum of two sinusoids, each having a different frequency.

$$v_s = V_{m1} \cos \omega_1 t + V_{m2} \cos \omega_2 t \quad (3.11)$$

Again, using only the square term for simplicity, we obtain the following component of the current response:

$$\begin{aligned}
a_2 v_s^2 &= a_2 (V_{m1} \cos \omega_1 t + V_{m2} \cos \omega_2 t)^2 \\
&= a_2 V_{m1}^2 \cos^2 \omega_1 t + a_2 V_m^2 \cos^2 \omega_2 t \\
&\quad + a_2 V_{m1} V_{m2} \left[\cos(\omega_1 - \omega_2)t + \cos(\omega_1 + \omega_2)t\right] \quad (3.12)
\end{aligned}$$

Expansion of the first two terms by (3.10) yields second harmonics of both input frequencies. In addition, we obtain components that have the difference (beat) frequency $\omega_1 - \omega_2$ and the sum frequency $\omega_1 + \omega_2$. By proper filtering, we can reject all except these last two components. If we then consider $\omega_1$ as the carrier and $\omega_2$ as the information signal, it is clear (by comparing with results of Sec. 2.5) that we have obtained a modulated waveform from the nonlinear element.

In summary, linear circuits permit superposition and may be solved by a variety of techniques applicable to linear differential equations. Non-linear circuits must be treated graphically, by series methods, or by breaking up into portions of the characteristic for which linearity may be assumed. Analysis of the nonlinear circuits is generally more complicated, and superposition does not apply. Nonlinear circuits generally yield harmonics of an applied signal of a given frequency, and sum and difference frequencies of a signal consisting of sinusoids of different frequencies. This last result permits the use of nonlinear circuits for frequency changers, modulators, or demodulators.

## 3.4  kirchhoff's laws and a simple circuit example

We return now to the problem of analyzing a simple electrical circuit in order to establish its response to a given excitation. In this section we review Kirchhoff's laws and apply them to a simple example. In following sections we consider two special systematic treatments, *loop analysis* and *nodal analysis*, respectively. As noted earlier, we will treat only those circuit tools to be employed in the basic electronic circuits of later chapters and will leave general circuit theory to other books.

KIRCHHOFF'S LAWS  The two Kirchhoff laws are commonly stated as follows:

*1.* The sum of voltages about any loop of a circuit is zero:

$$\sum_{\text{loop}} v = 0 \qquad (3.13)$$

*2.* The sum of currents flowing into any node of the circuit is zero:

$$\sum_{\text{node}} i = 0 \qquad (3.14)$$

In interpreting the above, a loop is any closed path of a circuit, as *ABEF* or *BCDE* of Fig. 3.4, and a node is the point of interconnection of several circuit elements, as *B* of Fig. 3.4. It is necessary to assume a sign convention in using (3.14). For example, if we assume that a positive current is one that flows toward the node, a negative sign denotes a current flowing out of the node. Similarly, in (3.13), if voltage rises, as discussed below, are considered positive, a negative sign in that equation denotes a voltage drop. A common equivalent statement to (3.13) is

$$\sum (\text{voltage rises}) = \sum (\text{voltage drops}) \qquad (3.15)$$

The sign relations of elements given in Sec. 3.2 have considered sources as voltage rises, and the voltages across passive elements as drops. Signs often cause much difficulty to beginning students, but the use should become clearer from the examples to follow.

The Kirchhoff current law (3.14) is recognized as the expression for continuity of charge, since any charge flowing into a node must flow out as a current in one or more of the current paths entering that node. The voltage law (3.13) is simply the conservation of energy when we are concerned with dc currents, since a charge moved around a closed path in static fields requires no work. For time-varying fields, the derivation is more complicated, but it can be said that the voltage-current relations of ideal elements discussed in Sec. 3.2 were defined to satisfy this law. Approximations are required for these laws in the general time-varying case, and when the approximations are not well satisfied, more fundamental field laws must be used. This subject also will be left for other courses.

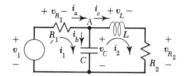

**FIGURE 3.22**   *RLC circuit.*

**CIRCUIT EQUATIONS**   As an example for this section, the circuit of Fig. 3.22 is chosen. We assume that all the element values are constants. We thus have a linear, time-invariant circuit. The problem is to establish the current $i_2$ through $R_2$, resulting from the input voltage $v_1$. The first step in the analysis is to establish a set of *circuit equations*. This is done using Kirchhoff's laws and the electrical, dynamical relations of the elements from Sec. 3.2. If Kirchhoff's voltage law (3.15) is applied to the loop containing $v_1(t)$, we obtain

$$v_1 = v_{R1} + v_C \qquad (3.16)$$

That is, the voltage rise $v_1(t)$ is equal to the sum of the voltage drops $v_{R1}$ and $v_C$ as in (3.15). The signs on each voltage denote the arbitrarily chosen directions for positive voltages. For the second loop

$$v_C = v_L + v_{R2} \qquad (3.17)$$

Applying Kirchhoff's current law (3.14) to the node $A$, we obtain

$$i_a = i_b + i_c \qquad (3.18)$$

That is, the current into node $A$ is equal to the sum of the currents leaving the node. Note that here we show by the arrows the chosen positive direction of each of these currents. We do not use Kirchhoff's current law for the lower node because no new information is available; we would only obtain (3.18) again. Introduction of the dynamical relations of the elements from Sec. 3.2 into (3.16) and (3.17) yields

$$v_1 = R_1 i_a + \frac{1}{C} \int i_b \, dt \qquad (3.19a)$$

$$\frac{1}{C} \int i_b \, dt = L \frac{di_c}{dt} + R_2 i_c \qquad (3.19b)$$

The integrals, obtained by integrating (3.4b), are shown as indefinite integrals without limits. This will be the usual convention of the text except where we are concerned with a transient buildup from conditions at $t = 0$, in which case the limits will be shown.

Next, if we solve (3.18) for $i_b$, identify $i_a = i_1$ and $i_c = i_2$, and use these in (3.19a) and (3.19b), we obtain

$$v_1 = R_1 i_1 + \frac{1}{C} \int (i_1 - i_2) \, dt \qquad (3.20a)$$

$$0 = -\frac{1}{C} \int (i_1 - i_2) \, dt + L \frac{di_2}{dt} + R_2 i_2 \qquad (3.20b)$$

The two equations, (3.20a) and (3.20b), contain the two unknown currents $i_1$ and $i_2$, and may in principle be solved for these currents, if $v_1$ is given. Some methods of solution will be studied in the next few sections. Let us note here only the conditions which yield constant (that is, dc) values of all quantities. By inspection of the circuit of Fig. 3.22, we see that the capacitor should become charged and that no current flows for a steady dc source, and the inductor will have no voltage drop across it for a steady current, so there remain $R_1$ and $R_2$ in series with the dc source voltage. Letting $i_1 = I_1$, $i_2 = I_2$, $v_1 = V_1$, all constants, we then have

$$V_1 = (R_1 + R_2) I_1 = (R_1 + R_2) I_2 \qquad (3.21)$$

where $I_1 = I_2$ in the steady limit. This solution can also be obtained formally from (3.20a) and (3.20b) by substituting the constant values of voltage and the currents in those equations (Prob. 3.7).

## 3.5 the loop analysis of circuits

In the simple example of Fig. 3.22 which we discussed in Sec. 3.4, voltage equations were written about closed loops using the Kirchhoff voltage law, (3.13) or (3.15). Branch currents were first utilized, and the resulting equations, (3.19), contained three unknown branch currents $i_a$, $i_b$, and $i_c$ in the two simultaneous equations. These were reduced to two unknowns through the use of Kirchhoff's current law, (3.14), and the unknowns were identified as *loop currents*, $i_1$ and $i_2$. The loop currents can be assigned initially and the resulting analysis is referred to as the *loop analysis* of circuits.

To illustrate loop analysis in a slightly more general fashion, consider the three-loop circuit of Fig. 3.23. The various branch currents need not

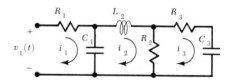

**FIGURE 3.23**   *Three-loop circuit.*

be shown, but the three loop currents $i_1$, $i_2$, and $i_3$ may be designated directly. Note that the arrow on each loop current is chosen by convenience to show the convention for positive current for that loop. The choice of these senses is arbitrary, for any current flowing opposite to the arrow simply comes out with a minus sign.

Writing now the voltage equation for the first loop, we follow the direction of the current arrow and set the sum of voltage rises equal to the sum of voltage drops, using the sign conventions for the elements as in Sec. 3.2. Note that the current flowing through $C_1$ in the direction of the arrow is $(i_1 - i_2)$ and the voltage equation is

$$v_1 = i_1 R_1 + \frac{1}{C_1} \int (i_1 - i_2)\, dt \qquad (3.22a)$$

Repeating the process for the remaining two loops, we obtain

$$0 = L_2 \frac{di_2}{dt} + R_2(i_2 - i_3) + \frac{1}{C_1} \int (i_2 - i_1)\, dt \qquad (3.22b)$$

$$0 = R_3 i_3 + \frac{1}{C_3} \int i_3\, dt + R_2(i_3 - i_2) \qquad (3.22c)$$

Kirchhoff's current law, (3.14), is automatically satisfied by the use of loop currents (Prob. 3.6). With a given form of applied voltage $v_1(t)$, and the initial conditions of the circuit (charges on capacitors and currents in inductors at $t = 0$), the three equations, (3.22a), (3.22b), and (3.22c) are sufficient, in principle, to determine all currents of the circuit. Voltages across any element may be obtained from the known currents if desired. We now consider some examples of such solutions.

**EXAMPLE OF DC CIRCUITS WITH BATTERIES AND RESISTORS**   As a first simple example, consider the circuit of Fig. 3.24. The two loop equations are

$$V_1 = I_1 R_1 + (I_1 + I_2) R_2 \qquad (3.23a)$$

$$V_2 = I_2 R_3 + (I_1 + I_2) R_2 \qquad (3.23b)$$

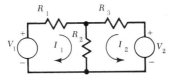

**FIGURE 3.24**   *Two-loop dc circuit.*

These two simultaneous equations may be solved to give the currents

$$I_1 = \frac{(R_2 + R_3) V_1 - R_2 V_2}{R_1 R_2 + R_2 R_3 + R_3 R_1} \qquad (3.24a)$$

$$I_2 = \frac{-R_2 V_1 + (R_1 + R_2) V_2}{R_1 R_2 + R_2 R_3 + R_3 R_1} \qquad (3.24b)$$

These results could also be obtained by superposition for this linear circuit as explained in a preceding section. That is, the currents arising from $V_1$, with $V_2 = 0$ (that is, shorted), may first be obtained and then there may be added the currents arising from $V_2$ with $V_1 = 0$. As a numerical example, if $R_1 = 2\ \Omega$, $R_2 = 5\ \Omega$, $R_3 = 3\ \Omega$, (3.24a) and (3.24b) give

$$I_1 = \frac{8}{31} V_1 - \frac{5}{31} V_2 \qquad (3.25a)$$

$$I_2 = \frac{-5}{31} V_1 + \frac{7}{31} V_2 \qquad (3.25b)$$

**EXAMPLE OF A SINGLE-LOOP RC SERIES CIRCUIT WITH STEP FUNCTION VOLTAGE**   As a next example, consider a circuit which demonstrates a *transient* current change when a voltage is suddenly applied. Consider the single-loop *RC* circuit of Fig. 3.25a. The loop equation for this figure, following the method sketched earlier in the section, is

$$v_1 = R i_1 + \frac{1}{C} \int i_1 \, dt \qquad (3.26)$$

A straightforward method of solving this linear equation starts with the solution of the corresponding homogeneous equation, obtained by setting the source equal to zero:

$$0 = R i_1 + \frac{1}{C} \int i_1 \, dt \qquad (3.27)$$

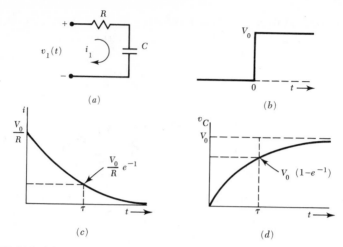

**FIGURE 3.25**   (a) *RC circuit;* (b) *step function applied voltage;* (c, d) *current and voltage waveshapes for RC circuit.*

A solution of (3.27) is obtained by assuming an exponential form

$$i_1 = I_1 e^{pt} \tag{3.28}$$

Substitution of (3.28) in (3.27) yields

$$0 = RI_1 e^{pt} + \frac{1}{pC} I_1 e^{pt}$$

from which we obtain

$$p = -\frac{1}{RC} \tag{3.29}$$

Thus (3.28) with (3.29) yields

$$i_1 = I_1 e^{-t/RC} \tag{3.30}$$

To the solution of the homogeneous equation (3.27), one normally adds a *particular-integral* (PI) solution of the inhomogeneous equation (3.26), but the form (3.30) is sufficient for a problem starting with a finite current $I_1$ at $t = 0$. Let us take the capacitor uncharged at $t = 0$, and suddenly apply a constant voltage $V_0$ as in Fig. 3.25b. Thus at $t = 0$ the uncharged capacitor has no voltage so that all the applied voltage appears across $R$. The initial current is $V_0/R$, which must be $I_1$ in (3.30). The current expression is then

$$i_1 = \frac{V_0}{R} e^{-t/RC} \tag{3.31}$$

The capacitor voltage as a function of time is found by integrating (3.31).

$$v_C = \frac{1}{C}\int_0^t \frac{V_0}{R} e^{-t/RC}\, dt = -\frac{V_0}{RC}(RC\, e^{-t/RC})\Big|_0^t$$

$$v_C = V_0(1 - e^{-t/RC}) \tag{3.32}$$

The current function, (3.31), and the capacitor voltage function, (3.32), are plotted in Fig. 3.25c and d, respectively. We see the decay of the former and the buildup of the latter as the capacitor charges through the resistor. A convenient *time constant* for the process is defined as the time for current to decay to $1/e \simeq 37$ percent of its initial value. From (3.31) the time constant for this example is

$$\tau = RC \tag{3.33}$$

The voltage builds up to $(1 - 1/e)\, V_0 \simeq 0.63\, V_0$ in time $\tau$. This time measure is shown on both the current and capacitor voltage curves. Note if $R = 1\ \text{M}\Omega\,(10^6\ \Omega)$ and $C = 1\ \text{pF}\,(10^{-12}\ \text{F})$, then $\tau = 1\ \mu\text{s}\,(10^{-6}\ \text{s})$.

**EXAMPLE OF TWO-LOOP CIRCUIT WITH SINUSOIDAL VOLTAGE**    Consider next the two-loop circuit of Fig. 3.26 with an applied voltage $V_m \cos \omega t$. Selecting loop currents

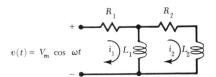

**FIGURE 3.26**  *Two-loop circuit with applied sinusoidal voltage.*

$i_1$ and $i_2$ as shown, we can write the voltage equations for the two loops as discussed above,

$$V_m \cos \omega t = R_1 i_1 + L_1 \frac{d}{dt}(i_1 - i_2) \tag{3.34a}$$

$$0 = R_2 i_2 + L_2 \frac{di_2}{dt} + L_1 \frac{d}{dt}(i_2 - i_1) \tag{3.34b}$$

To solve this equation, we may expect that the steady-state current will also be of sinusoidal form of the same angular frequency $\omega$, but not necessarily in phase with the applied voltage. That is, both sines and cosines will be required in the solution. Therefore we assume

$$i_1 = A \cos \omega t + B \sin \omega t \tag{3.35a}$$

$$i_2 = C \cos \omega t + D \sin \omega t \tag{3.35b}$$

We may substitute these forms in (3.34a) and (3.34b).

$$V_m \cos \omega t = R_1(A \cos \omega t + B \sin \omega t)$$
$$+ \omega L_1[(C - A) \sin \omega t + (B - D) \cos \omega t] \qquad (3.36a)$$

$$0 = R_2(C \cos \omega t + D \sin \omega t) + \omega L_2(-C \sin \omega t + D \cos \omega t)$$
$$+ \omega L_1[(A - C) \sin \omega t + (D - B) \cos \omega t] \qquad (3.36b)$$

Since the sine and cosine functions are linearly independent functions, the multipliers of each of these must separately be equal on the two sides of the equation. Thus for the cosine functions in (3.36a) we obtain

$$V_m = R_1A + \omega L_1(B - D) \qquad (3.37a)$$

and for the sine functions,

$$0 = R_1B + \omega L_1(C - A) \qquad (3.37b)$$

For the cosine and sine functions of (3.36b) we obtain, respectively,

$$0 = R_2C + \omega L_2D + \omega L_1(D - B) \qquad (3.37c)$$

$$0 = R_2D - \omega L_2C + \omega L_1(A - C) \qquad (3.37d)$$

The four equations (3.37a), (3.37b), (3.37c), and (3.37d) may be solved simultaneously to give the amplitudes $A$, $B$, $C$, and $D$. We will not complete this moderately laborious step because the phasor form to be presented in Sec. 3.7 provides a much easier method of solution. Nevertheless, we see that the problem is solvable by a straightforward approach as above.

## 3.6   the nodal analysis of circuits

An alternative circuit formulation to that of Sec. 3.5 stresses Kirchhoff's current law, (3.14). This method is known as the *nodal* analysis of circuits. Any circuit may be solved by either the loop or nodal methods, but one or the other may save work for a given problem. The nodal method is usually preferable when there are current sources and many parallel elements; the loop method is probably better with voltage sources and many series connections. Combinations of the two may also be used after one develops a feeling for the two methods separately.

To illustrate nodal analysis, consider the circuit of Fig. 3.27 which is

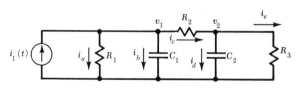

**FIGURE 3.27**   *Circuit illustrating nodal analysis.*

driven by a current generator $i_1(t)$. The Kirchhoff current law (3.14) for node 1 yields

$$i_1 = i_a + i_b + i_c \tag{3.38}$$

But the branch currents may be written in terms of the voltages $v_1$ and $v_2$ of nodes 1 and 2, respectively, with respect to a reference for zero voltage. In this example the bottom node is taken as the reference.

$$i_a = \frac{v_1}{R_1} \tag{3.39a}$$

$$i_b = C_1 \frac{dv_1}{dt} \tag{3.39b}$$

$$i_c = \frac{v_1 - v_2}{R_2} \tag{3.39c}$$

The nodal equation for node 1 is

$$i_1 = \frac{v_1}{R_1} + C_1 \frac{dv_1}{dt} + \frac{1}{R_2}(v_1 - v_2) \tag{3.40}$$

The corresponding equation for node 2 is

$$\frac{v_1 - v_2}{R_2} - C_2 \frac{dv_2}{dt} - \frac{v_2}{R_3} = 0 \tag{3.41}$$

With a given form of $i_1$, and initial conditions when required, the two nodal equations, (3.40) and (3.41), permit the solution for $v_1$ and $v_2$, at least in principle.

It may be noted that a separate equation need not be written for the reference node, for continuity at nodes 1 and 2 ensures continuity there. That is

$$-i_1 + i_a + i_b + i_d + i_e = -i_1 + i_a + i_b + i_c = 0 \tag{3.42}$$

Two examples of the nodal method are given below. Other examples are given later after the introduction of the phasor concept for sinusoids.

**EXAMPLE OF DC CIRCUIT WITH CURRENT GENERATORS AND RESISTORS**   For the circuit of Fig. 3.28 with dc current sources $I_1$ and $I_2$, nodes 1 and 2 are selected and voltages $V_1$ and $V_2$ are defined for these nodes. The nodal equations

**FIGURE 3.28**   *A dc circuit with resistors and two current generators. Values of G are conductances.*

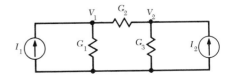

for nodes 1 and 2 are

$$I_1 = V_1 G_1 + G_2(V_1 - V_2) \tag{3.43a}$$

$$I_2 = V_2 G_3 + G_2(V_2 - V_1) \tag{3.43b}$$

Solution for the voltages $V_1$ and $V_2$ yields

$$V_1 = \frac{(G_2 + G_3) I_1 + G_2 I_2}{G_1 G_2 + G_2 G_3 + G_3 G_1} \tag{3.44a}$$

$$V_2 = \frac{G_2 I_1 - (G_1 + G_2) I_2}{G_1 G_2 + G_2 G_3 + G_3 G_1} \tag{3.44b}$$

An interesting point comes from the comparison of this result with that of the dc example of Fig. 3.24. Equations (3.43) are of the same form as (3.23), and the solutions (3.44) are of the same form as (3.24), if voltages and currents are interchanged, if the signs of $V_2$ and $I_2$ are reversed, and if each resistance is replaced by a corresponding conductance. Two circuits having this relationship are said to be *duals*, one of the other.

To obtain a numerical result, let $G_1 = 10^{-3}$ mho, $G_2 = 2 \cdot 10^{-3}$ mho, and $G_3 = 4 \cdot 10^{-3}$ mho. We obtain from (3.44a) and (3.44b)

$$V_1 = (\tfrac{6}{14} I_1 + \tfrac{2}{14} I_2) \, 10^3 \tag{3.44c}$$

$$V_2 = (\tfrac{2}{14} I_1 - \tfrac{3}{14} I_2) \, 10^3 \tag{3.44d}$$

**EXAMPLE OF RC PARALLEL CIRCUIT EXCITED BY STEP FUNCTION CURRENT**   A second example, similar to the voltage buildup example of Fig. 3.25, is that shown in Fig. 3.29a, with the applied current shown in Fig. 3.29b. There is only one node, and the current equation for this is easily written

$$i_1(t) = \frac{v_1}{R} + C \frac{dv_1}{dt} \tag{3.45}$$

As in the example of Sec. 3.5, we first find the solution of the corresponding homogeneous equation with no source current

$$0 = \frac{v_1}{R} + C \frac{dv_1}{dt} \tag{3.46}$$

Next we assume an exponential form for current

$$(v_1)_{\text{homogeneous}} = A_1 e^{pt} \tag{3.47a}$$

This is substituted in (3.46) to give

$$0 = \frac{A_1}{R} e^{pt} + pC A_1 e^{pt} \tag{3.47b}$$

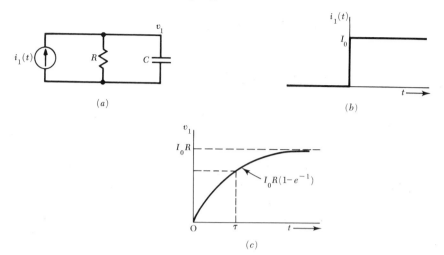

**FIGURE 3.29** (a) *Parallel RC circuit driven by current generator with suddenly applied current;* (b) *functional form of current;* (c) *voltage build up across capacitor, showing time constant* $\tau = RC$.

or
$$p = -\frac{1}{RC} \qquad (3.47c)$$

Thus
$$(v_1)_{\text{homogeneous}} = A_1 e^{-t/RC} \qquad (3.47d)$$

Since the voltage $v_1$ must be zero at $t = 0$ if the capacitor is initially uncharged, the solution given by (3.47d) cannot be sufficient, for this would require $A_1 = 0$, leading to zero current for all time. We must add to (3.47d) the particular-integral solution of the inhomogeneous equation. Inspection of (3.45) with $i_1 = I_0$, a constant, shows that the steady-state solution is a constant

$$(v_1)_{\text{PI}} = I_0 R \qquad (3.48)$$

Addition of (3.47d) to (3.48) yields

$$v_1 = I_0 R + A_1 e^{-t/RC} \qquad (3.49)$$

This satisfies the initial condition of $v_1 = 0$ at $t = 0$ if $A_1 = -I_0 R$. The final result is

$$v_1 = I_0 R(1 - e^{-t/RC}) \qquad (3.50)$$

This voltage buildup is illustrated in Fig. 3.29c, with the time constant $\tau = RC$ giving the time to build up to $(1 - 1/e) \simeq 63$ percent of the final value. Note that although this example is similar to that of Fig. 3.25, it is not the dual, and does have differences in the solution because the constant or steady-state solution of the inhomogeneous equation must be included. The relationship of the time constant to $R$ and $C$ is the same as in (3.33).

## 3.7 phasor representation of sinusoids

In Sec. 3.5 a straightforward solution of the two-loop circuit with applied sinusoidal voltage yielded four simultaneous equations. For an $N$-loop circuit, there would be correspondingly $2N$ such equations, and it would be difficult to treat circuits of many loops in this manner. Since we have seen the sinusoidal case to be so important, it is fortunate that there is a shortcut through the use of complex exponentials. The simplicity of the exponential form comes about since derivatives and integrals of exponentials are the same exponentials together with a multiplier. The exponential form can then be canceled from all terms of the equation. This is in contrast with the earlier example which used sinusoidal functions directly, where derivatives and integrals change sine functions to cosine functions and cosines to sines.

The relation between sinusoids and complex exponentials comes through the Euler relation (see Appendix A for a review of complex numbers)

$$\cos x + j \sin x = e^{jx} \tag{3.51}$$

where $j = \sqrt{-1}$. In order to make use of this, one may recall the super-position principle for linear circuits discussed in Sec. 3.3. If there is an actual voltage $V_{m1} \cos \omega t$ applied to the circuit of Fig. 3.22, we can (mentally) add an imaginary voltage $jV_{m1} \sin \omega t$, and by (3.51) we have the complex exponential form

$$V_{m1} \cos \omega t + jV_{m1} \sin \omega t = V_{m1} e^{j\omega t} \tag{3.52}$$

This superposition of the real and imaginary voltages is indicated in Fig. 3.30. With this excitation, currents of the circuit will also be complex, but for linear circuits the real portion of the current function will be that arising from the real part of the applied voltage, so this may be separated from the imaginary part to give the desired result. As we shall see, the actual process of separating real and imaginary parts of the solution is not always done explicitly, since the desired magnitude and phase information are contained in the complex multipliers of $e^{j\omega t}$. These com-

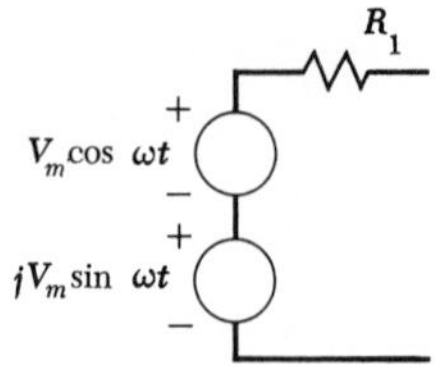

**FIGURE 3.30** *Two-signal sources in series.*

plex multipliers thus become important in themselves and are called *phasors*.

To continue with the example of Fig. 3.22, we utilize the two loop equations of the circuit, (3.20a) and (3.20b),

$$v_1 = R_1 i_1 + \frac{1}{C} \int (i_1 - i_2)\, dt \qquad (3.53a)$$

$$0 = -\frac{1}{C} \int (i_1 - i_2)\, dt + L\frac{di_2}{dt} + R_2 i_2 \qquad (3.53b)$$

If the applied voltage is of the form (3.52), currents $i_1$ and $i_2$ will also be complex and may be written

$$i_1 = I_{m1} e^{j(\omega t + \theta_1)} = (I_{m1} e^{j\theta_1})\, e^{j\omega t} \qquad (3.54a)$$

$$i_2 = I_{m2} e^{j(\omega t + \theta_2)} = (I_{m2} e^{j\theta_2})\, e^{j\omega t} \qquad (3.54b)$$

The coefficients multiplying $e^{j\omega t}$ are the important complex multipliers which we called phasors, and are denoted in the remainder of the text by boldface type. (The student may use the printer's designation for this when necessary by showing a wavy line under the symbol: $I_1 = \underset{\sim}{I_1}$. After one becomes familiar with phasors, they are clear from the context and one does not use special notation.)

$$\mathbf{I}_1 = I_{m1} e^{j\theta_1} \qquad (3.55a)$$

$$\mathbf{I}_2 = I_{m2} e^{j\theta_2} \qquad (3.55b)$$

The definitions (3.55), substituted in (3.54), then give

$$i_1 = \mathbf{I}_1 e^{j\omega t} \qquad (3.56a)$$

$$i_2 = \mathbf{I}_2 e^{j\omega t} \qquad (3.56b)$$

Substitution of (3.56a), (3.56b), and (3.52) in (3.53a) yields

$$V_{m1} e^{j\omega t} = R_1 \mathbf{I}_1 e^{j\omega t} + \frac{1}{j\omega C}(\mathbf{I}_1 - \mathbf{I}_2)e^{j\omega t} \qquad (3.57a)$$

Similar substitution in (3.53b) gives

$$0 = -\frac{1}{j\omega C}(\mathbf{I}_1 - \mathbf{I}_2)e^{j\omega t} + j\omega L\mathbf{I}_2 e^{j\omega t} + R_2 \mathbf{I}_2 e^{j\omega t} \qquad (3.57b)$$

The exponentials may be canceled from all terms, leaving the two *algebraic* equations

$$V_{m1} = \left(R_1 + \frac{1}{j\omega C}\right)\mathbf{I}_1 - \frac{\mathbf{I}_2}{j\omega C} \qquad (3.58a)$$

and
$$0 = -\frac{I_1}{j\omega C} + \left(\frac{1}{j\omega C} + j\omega L + R_2\right)I_2 \qquad (3.58b)$$

After familiarity with the method is gained, the forms (3.58) are written directly without the intermediate step of (3.57). Notice that derivatives are equivalent to simple multiplication by $j\omega$ and integrals to multiplication by $1/j\omega$.

The two algebraic equations in (3.58) can now be solved for $I_1$ and $I_2$ in terms of voltage magnitude $V_{m1}$. For an example we solve for $I_2$,

$$I_2 = \frac{V_{m1}}{R_1(a + jb)} \qquad (3.59a)$$

where
$$a = 1 + \frac{R_2}{R_1} - \omega^2 LC \qquad (3.59b)$$

$$b = \omega\left(R_2C + \frac{L}{R_1}\right) \qquad (3.59c)$$

The phasor current $I_2$ may be written to display magnitude and phase as in the form (3.55),

$$I_2 = \frac{V_{m1}}{R_1\sqrt{(a^2 + b^2)}}e^{j\theta_2} = I_{m2}e^{j\theta_2} \qquad (3.60a)$$

where
$$I_{m1} = \frac{V_{m1}}{R_1\sqrt{(a^2 + b^2)}} \qquad (3.60b)$$

$$\theta_2 = -\tan^1\frac{b}{a} \qquad (3.60c)$$

Since the actual applied voltage is the real part of (3.52), the actual current is the real part of (3.56b) for this linear circuit:

$$v_1(t) = \operatorname{Re}(V_{m1}e^{j\omega t}) = V_{m1}\cos\omega t \qquad (3.61a)$$

$$i_2(t) = \operatorname{Re}(I_{m2}e^{j(\omega t + \theta_2)}) = I_{m2}\cos(\omega t + \theta_2) \qquad (3.61b)$$

with $I_{m1}$ and $\theta_2$ given by (3.60b) and (3.60c).

As a numerical example, let $R_1 = 2\,\Omega$, $R_2 = 2\,\Omega$, $C = 2\,\text{F}$, $L = 1\,\text{H}$, $V_{m1} = 1\,\text{V}$, and $\omega = 2\,\text{rad/s}$. From (3.59b) and (3.59c), $a = -5$ and $b = 10$. From (3.60b) and (3.60c), $I_{m2} = 0.1785\,\text{A}$ and $\theta_2 = -116.6° = -2.03\,\text{rad}$. Thus the phasor current may be written

$$I_2 = 0.1785\,e^{-j2.03}\text{ ampere} \qquad (3.62)$$

and the actual current as a function of time is

$$i_2(t) = \operatorname{Re}(I_2e^{j\omega t}) = 0.1785\cos(2t - 2.03)\text{ ampere} \qquad (3.63)$$

The voltage and current waveshapes are plotted in Fig. 3.31. The sinusoid for $i_2$ lags the voltage sinusoid by a phase angle of 116.6°.

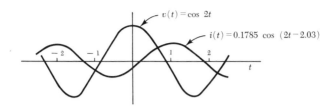

**FIGURE 3.31**   *Voltage and current waveshapes for a specific example.*

Note that the desired information on magnitude and phase is actually contained in the phasor form (3.62). As a consequence, one frequently interprets the results directly from this phasor without going on to the specific time function (3.63). In addition, the complex phasors may be displayed on a complex number plane, as shown in Fig. 3.32 for the above numerical example. Since the desired information on magnitude and phase is contained in the phasor (3.62), the phasor may be considered the "solution" of the problem. In this form, it may be considered a solution in the *frequency domain* in contrast to the actual form (3.63), which is a solution in the *time domain*. Figure 3.32 is a graphical representation of the frequency-domain solution.

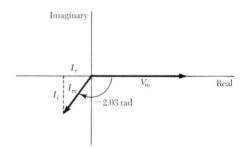

**FIGURE 3.32**   *Representation of phasor voltages and currents in complex plane.*

The phasor may be expressed in terms of its real and imaginary parts as an alternative to magnitude and phase, as shown in Fig. 3.32. Thus (3.55*b*) may be written

$$I_2 = I_{m2}e^{j\theta}{}_2 = I_{r2} + jI_{i2} \qquad (3.64a)$$

where

$$I_{r2} = I_{m2} \cos \theta_2 \qquad (3.64b)$$

$$I_{i2} = I_{m2} \sin \theta_2 \qquad (3.64c)$$

The actual current in terms of these components is then

$$i_2(t) = \text{Re}\left[(I_{r2} + jI_{i2})\,e^{j\omega t}\right]$$

$$= \text{Re}\left[(I_{r2} + jI_{i2})(\cos \omega t + j \sin \omega t)\right]$$

$$= I_{r2} \cos \omega t - I_{i2} \sin \omega t \qquad (3.65)$$

From this form we see that $I_{r2}$ gives the part of current $i_2(t)$ which is in phase with voltage $v_1(t)$, and $I_{i2}$ gives the component which is 90° out of phase with the applied voltage. For the numerical example given above

$$I_{r2} = I_{m2} \cos \theta_2 = 0.1785 \cos(-116.6°) = -0.0846 \text{ ampere}$$

$$I_{i2} = I_{m2} \sin \theta_2 = 0.1785 \sin(-116.6°) = -0.162 \text{ ampere}$$

**NODAL EXAMPLE WITH PHASORS**   To illustrate the nodal method with phasors let us return to the example of Fig. 3.27, where we assume a current generator of sinusoidal form $i_1(t) = I_{m1} \cos \omega t = \text{Re}(I_{m1}e^{j\omega t})$. The equations for nodes 1 and 2, using phasors, are

$$I_{m1} = G_1 V_1 + j\omega C_1 V_1 + G_2(V_1 - V_2) \qquad (3.66a)$$

$$G_2(V_1 - V_2) - j\omega C_2 V_2 - G_3 V_2 = 0 \qquad (3.66b)$$

These are the phasor equivalents of (3.40) and (3.41). Conductances have been used in place of resistances, $G_1 = 1/R_1$, $G_2 = 1/R_2$, and $G_3 = 1/R_3$. Solution for $V_2$ yields

$$V_2 = \frac{G_2 I_{m1}}{G_1 G_2 + G_1 G_3 + G_3 G_2 - \omega^2 C_1 C_2 + j\omega[C_1(G_2 + G_3) + C_2(G_1 + G_2)]}$$

$$(3.67)$$

This may readily be interpreted in terms of magnitude and phase, as in the preceding example.

## 3.8   impedance and admittance of circuits with sinusoidal excitation

Let us now apply the phasor method to a single-loop circuit with $R$, $L$, and $C$ excited by a sinusoidal voltage as in Fig. 3.33. The circuit equation is

$$v = Ri + L\frac{di}{dt} + \frac{1}{C}\int i\,dt \qquad (3.68)$$

The applied voltage $V_m \cos \omega t$ is augmented by the imaginary portion $jV_m \sin \omega t$ and current is assumed to have the form of a complex phasor multiplied by $e^{j\omega t}$ as in the preceding section.

$$v = V_m e^{j\omega t} = V e^{j\omega t} \tag{3.69a}$$

$$i = (I_m e^{j\theta}I) e^{j\omega t} = (I_r + jI_i) e^{j\omega t} = I e^{j\omega t} \tag{3.69b}$$

Substitution of (3.69) in (3.68), with cancellation of the $e^{j\omega t}$ factors, yields

$$V = \left( R + j\omega L + \frac{1}{j\omega C} \right) I \tag{3.70a}$$

This may be written

$$V = ZI \tag{3.70b}$$

where $Z$, called the *impedance* of the circuit, is

$$Z = R + j\omega L + \frac{1}{j\omega C} \tag{3.70c}$$

In the above example of the series connection of the three elements, the impedance is seen to be the sum of impedances for the individual elements. Thus the impedance of a resistor is just the resistance $R$; that

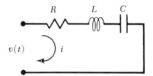

**FIGURE 3.33**    *RLC series circuit.*

for an ideal inductor has an imaginary value equal to $j\omega L$, and that for the capacitor is $1/j\omega C$. These values are summarized in Table 3.1. The

**TABLE 3.1**

| ELEMENT | $Z$ | $Y$ |
|---|---|---|
| $R$ | $R$ | $G = \dfrac{1}{R}$ |
| $L$ | $j\omega_1 L = \omega_1 L e^{j(\pi/2)}$ | $\dfrac{1}{j\omega_1 L} = \dfrac{1}{\omega_1 L} e^{-j(\pi/2)}$ |
| $C$ | $\dfrac{1}{j\omega_1 C} = \dfrac{1}{\omega_1 C} e^{-j(\pi/2)}$ | $j\omega_1 C = \omega_1 C e^{j(\pi/2)}$ |

total impedance may be written either in real and imaginary parts, or in magnitude and phase,

$$Z = R + jX = |Z|e^{j\theta_z} \tag{3.71a}$$

$$X = \omega L - \frac{1}{\omega C} \tag{3.71b}$$

$$|Z| = \sqrt{R^2 + X^2} \tag{3.71c}$$

$$\theta_Z = \tan^{-1}\frac{X}{R} \tag{3.71d}$$

In the above, $R$ is the resistance, $X$ is the *reactance*, $|Z|$ is the magnitude of impedance, and $\theta_Z$ is the phase of the impedance. The phasor current, from (3.70b), is

$$I = \frac{V}{Z} = \frac{V_m}{|Z|\,e^{j\theta_z}} = \frac{V_m}{|Z|}e^{-j\theta_z} \tag{3.72}$$

As a numerical example, take $R = 100\ \Omega$, $L = 1$, mH $= 10^{-3}$ H, $C = 1\mu F = 10^{-6}$ F, and frequency $= 10$ kHz, so that $\omega = 2\pi \cdot 10 \cdot 10^3 = 6.28 \cdot 10^4$ rad/s,

$$X = 6.28 \cdot 10^4 \cdot 10^{-3} - \frac{1}{6.28 \cdot 10^4 \cdot 10^{-6}}$$

$$X = 62.8 - 15.9 = 46.9\ \Omega$$

$$|Z| = \sqrt{(100)^2 + (46.9)^2} = 110.5\ \Omega$$

$$\theta_Z = \tan^{-1}\frac{46.9}{100} = 25.1° = 0.44\ \text{rad}$$

If the applied voltage is $V_m = 1$ kV $= 10^3$ V, the phasor current is

$$I = \frac{1000}{110.5}e^{-j0.44} = 9.05\,e^{-j0.44}\ \text{amperes} \tag{3.73a}$$

which corresponds to an actual function of time

$$i(t) = \text{Re}(Ie^{j\omega t}) = 9.05\cos(6.28 \cdot 10^4 t - 0.44)\ \text{amperes} \tag{3.73b}$$

As noted in Sec. 3.7, we often interpret magnitude and phase of the current from the phasor form (3.73a), and the actual time function (3.73b) is not written.

Impedance is a most important concept and is applied to many combinations of linear elements, giving the ratio of phasor voltage to phasor current when a sinusoidal voltage is applied to a given combination. Thus the interconnection of elements shown in Fig. 3.34*a* might be represented by the single complex impedance as illustrated in Fig. 3.34*b*, insofar as response to a sinusoidal input excitation is concerned. The relations (3.71*a*), (3.71*c*), and (3.71*d*) apply to any general impedance.

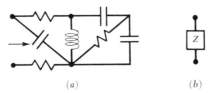

(a)　　　　　　　　(b)

**FIGURE 3.34** (a) *Interconnection of elements;* (b) *input viewed as impedance Z.*

The reciprocal of impedance is *admittance* and gives the ratio of phasor current to phasor voltage for a 1-port network, such as Fig. 3.34*a*, when excited by a sinusoidal input. Thus

$$I = YV \tag{3.74a}$$

$$Y = |Y|e^{j\theta_Y} = G + jB = \frac{1}{Z} \quad \text{mhos} \tag{3.74b}$$

$$|Y| = \sqrt{G^2 + B^2} = \frac{1}{|Z|} \quad \text{mhos} \tag{3.74c}$$

$$\theta_Y = \tan^{-1}\frac{B}{G} = -\theta_Z \tag{3.74d}$$

The real part of admittance, $G$, is known as conductance and the imaginary part $B$, as *susceptance*. $|Y|$ is magnitude of admittance and is the reciprocal of impedance magnitude. The angle $\theta_Y$ is the phase of admittance and is just the negative of impedance phase angle. The admittance for the numerical example used above is simply

$$Y = \frac{1}{110.5e^{j0.44}} = 9.05 \cdot 10^{-3} e^{-j0.44} \text{ mho} \tag{3.75}$$

This would give the same value of current as (3.73) if used with (3.74*a*).

The admittances of ideal elements are also shown in Table 3.1. One of the important uses of admittance is with circuits having many elements in parallel because the admittance of several parallel elements is just the sum of the admittances for the individual elements. This is easily seen from

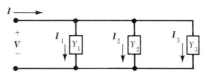

**FIGURE 3.35** *Parallel connection of three elements.*

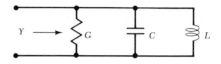

**FIGURE 3.36** *GLC parallel circuit.*

Fig. 3.35, since currents in this parallel connection add directly in the input and the same voltage is applied to all elements. Thus

$$I = I_1 + I_2 + I_3 = Y_1 V + Y_2 V + Y_3 V = (Y_1 + Y_2 + Y_3) V \qquad (3.76)$$

For the specific case of a conductor, an inductor, and a capacitor in parallel as shown in Fig. 3.36, the total admittance is

$$Y = G + j\omega C + \frac{1}{j\omega L} = G + j\left(\omega C - \frac{1}{\omega L}\right) \qquad (3.77a)$$

The susceptance $B$ is the imaginary part of $Y$,

$$B = \omega C - \frac{1}{\omega L} \qquad (3.77b)$$

This expression may be used with (3.74c) and (3.74d) to determine magnitude and phase of the admittance if desired.

The complex values of impedance or admittance may be plotted in the complex plane, thus displaying graphically the real and imaginary parts, or magnitude and phase, just as was shown for phasors in Sec. 3.7. Figure 3.37a shows an impedance $1 + j2$, with the corresponding admittance $0.2 - j0.4$, displayed on such a plane. Figure 3.37b shows a phasor voltage $1 + j0$ displayed on the complex plane as explained in Sec. 3.7. The corresponding phasor current for the impedance is $I = 0.2 - j0.4$ and is also shown on the plane.

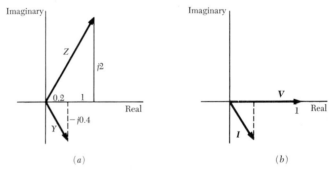

**FIGURE 3.37** (a) *Complex impedance and corresponding admittance;* (b) *phasor voltage* $(1 + j0)$ *and phasor current* **I** *corresponding to impedance of* a.

## 3.9   transmission-circuit examples

We saw in Chap. 2 that general signals may be represented by a sum of sinusoids of different frequencies. Thus the frequency characteristics of a transmission circuit are important in telling the frequency components that are passed and the consequent faithfulness of reproduction of the original signal. The frequency characteristics of amplifiers are stressed in later chapters. Here we illustrate the use of phasor methods for analyzing the frequency response of certain simple transmission circuits. Some of these examples are circuit models of transistor or electron-tube amplifiers, as will be seen in later chapters.

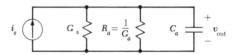

**FIGURE 3.38**   *Lowpass circuit.*

**LOWPASS CIRCUIT**   Let us consider the circuit of Fig. 3.38 excited by a sinusoidal current source. This circuit utilizes parallel elements, so the admittance formulation of Sec. 3.8 is used.

$$I_s = Y V_{out} \tag{3.78a}$$

where
$$Y = G_s + G_a + j\omega C_a \tag{3.78b}$$

Thus the ratio of $V_{out}$ to source current $I_s$ is just the impedance of the circuit

$$\frac{V_{out}}{I_s} = Z = \frac{1}{Y} = \frac{1}{(G_s + G_a) + j\omega C_a} \tag{3.79}$$

If we use the polar form,

$$Z = |Z|e^{j\theta}$$

$$|Z| = \frac{1}{\sqrt{(G_s + G_a)^2 + (\omega C_a)^2}} = \frac{1}{(G_s + G_a)\sqrt{1 + (\omega/\omega_1)^2}} \tag{3.80a}$$

where we have defined a parameter $\omega_1$, which has the dimension of radian frequency,

$$\omega_1 = \frac{G_a + G_s}{C_a} \tag{3.80b}$$

This circuit is seen to provide maximum magnitude response at the output for zero frequency and to give decreased response at high frequencies, as illustrated in Fig. 3.39a. The circuit is useful for signals with frequency components no greater than $\omega_1$ (approximately). Frequency

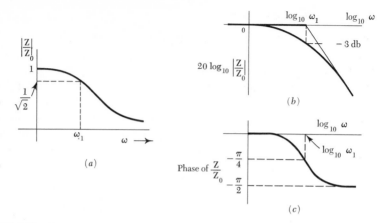

**FIGURE 3.39** *Frequency response of lowpass circuit.* (a) *Magnitude of* $Z$; (b) *logarithm of magnitude versus log* $\omega$; (c) *phase versus log* $\omega$.

components much above this are appreciably attenuated. The circuit is consequently called a *lowpass* circuit.

It is frequently convenient to plot the magnitude response curve as either a semilog plot or a log-log plot. In both cases, the abcissa is $\log_{10} \omega$ and is used to show a greater range of frequency than is possible if $\omega$ is used directly. Similarly, the logarithm of magnitude response may be used to provide a greater range in magnitude.[1] When this is done, it is common to adapt the decibel measure defined in Sec. 2.4 for power ratios. Instead of (2.22), we now define the dB measure of voltage or current ratios as:

$$dB = 20 \log_{10} x \tag{3.81}$$

where $x$ is a ratio of two voltages or two currents (or other amplitudes such as velocity or pressure in acoustics). Applying (3.81) to (3.80a) and dividing by the dc value $Z_0 = 1/(G_s + G_a)$, we have

$$dB = 20 \log_{10} \frac{G_s + G_a}{(G_s + G_a)\sqrt{1 + (\omega/\omega_1)^2}} \tag{3.82a}$$

A plot of this function versus $\log_{10} \omega$ is shown as the solid curve in Fig. 3.39b.

The straight lines of Fig. 3.39b are the low-frequency and high-frequency asymptotes. For low frequencies, $\omega \ll \omega_1$, the response approaches the constant $-20 \log_{10} 1 = 0$. For high frequencies, $\omega \gg \omega_1$, (3.82a) approaches

$$dB = 20 \log_{10} \frac{\omega_1}{\omega} = -20 \log_{10} \omega + 20 \log_{10} \frac{\omega_1}{\omega} \tag{3.82b}$$

[1]Plots with a logarithmic or decibel measure of magnitude response versus log $\omega$ are frequently known as Bode plots.

This high-frequency asymptote is thus a straight line on the decibel versus log frequency plot, the straight line having a slope of $-6$ dB per octave or $-20$ dB per decade. (An octave represents a doubling of frequency, and a decade an increase by ten times in frequency.) The parameter $\omega_1$ defined in (3.80$b$) is seen from the figure to be the intersection of the low-frequency and high-frequency asymptotes, and is consequently given the name *break frequency*. Response of the actual curve is seen to be decreased by $1/\sqrt{2}$ at the break frequency. In decibel measure this is $20 \log_{10} 2^{-1/2} \simeq -3$dB.

The phase response, from (3.74$d$) and (3.79), is

$$\theta = -\tan^{-1} \frac{\omega C_a}{G_s + G_a} = -\tan^{-1} \frac{\omega}{\omega_1} \qquad (3.82c)$$

The phase response versus frequency is sketched in Fig. 3.39$c$. The phase is seen to be $-\pi/4$ at the break frequency.

**HIGHPASS CIRCUIT**   Consider next the simple series circuit shown in Fig. 3.40. The ratio of phasor output voltage to input voltage is

$$\frac{V_o}{V_s} = \frac{R_L I}{V_s} = \frac{R_L}{R_s + R_L + 1/j\omega C} \qquad (3.83a)$$

This can be written

$$\frac{V_o}{V_s} = \frac{R_L}{R_s + R_L} \frac{j(\omega/\omega_1)}{1 + j(\omega/\omega_1)} \qquad (3.83b)$$

where
$$\omega_1 = \frac{1}{C(R_s + R_L)} \qquad (3.83c)$$

The plot of the magnitude of this response is shown in Fig. 3.41$a$, and we see that this circuit has its maximum magnitude response at high frequency, approaching zero output for zero frequency. This is expected since the capacitor produces an effective open circuit (infinite reactance) at zero frequency. The quantity $\omega_1$ is again the break frequency for this problem giving the angular frequency for which response is down by $1/\sqrt{2}$ i.e.,

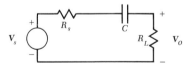

**FIGURE 3.40**  *Highpass circuit.*

$-3$dB, from the maximum value. For very low frequencies, $\omega << \omega_1$, response is proportional to $\omega$, and thus decreases 6 dB each time frequency

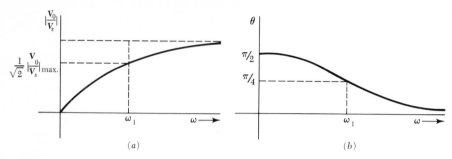

**FIGURE 3.41**   *Frequency response of highpass circuit.*

is halved in this range. The phase response, from (3.83b), is plotted in Fig. 3.41b,

$$\theta = \frac{\pi}{2} - \tan^{-1}\frac{\omega}{\omega_1} \qquad (3.83d)$$

**TWO-LOOP LOWPASS CIRCUIT**   As a next example, we take the circuit of Fig. 3.22, which is analyzed in Sec. 3.7. The ratio of output to input voltage for this case, using (3.59a), is

$$\frac{V_2}{V_1} = \frac{R_2 I_2}{V_1} = \frac{R_2}{R_1(a + jb)} \qquad (3.84)$$

where $a$ and $b$ are defined by (3.59b) and (3.59c). The magnitude response is

$$\left|\frac{V_2}{V_1}\right| = \frac{R_2}{R_1\sqrt{a^2 + b^2}} = \frac{R_2/R_1}{[(1 + R_2/R_1 - \omega^2 LC)^2 + \omega^2(R_2 C + L/R_1)^2]^{1/2}} \qquad (3.85)$$

The magnitude response of this circuit is seen to be a maximum at $\omega = 0$. It decreases with increasing frequency. The magnitude response for very high frequencies in this example is

$$\left|\frac{V_2}{V_1}\right|_{\omega \to \infty} \to \frac{R_2}{R_1 \omega^2 LC} \qquad (3.86)$$

This decreases as $\omega^2$, or a decrease of about 12 dB per octave.

**EXAMPLE OF PULSE APPLIED TO A LOWPASS CIRCUIT**   The frequency components in a rectangular pulse of width $\tau$ were found in Sec. 2.3 and shown in Fig. 2.13. If such a pulse is applied to a lowpass circuit such as that of Fig. 3.39, it is clear that the higher frequency components are decreased in magnitude and shifted in phase by the circuit. The pulse, as a consequence, is reproduced inexactly. If most of the important frequency components lie within the range of nearly constant response for the circuit (the nearly flat, low-frequency portion of Fig. 3.39b), the pulse is reproduced well and the main effect will be a slight rounding of the sharp pulse edges. If more of the important frequency components extend into the range where response varies appreciably with frequency, the distortion will be greater and perhaps intolerable for certain applications. The principle here is just that illustrated for periodic waveshapes in Fig. 2. 10 The rectangular pulse has appreciable frequency components extending to frequencies a few times $(1/\tau)$, as shown in Fig. 2.13. Since the circuit response is almost flat for frequencies lower than the break frequency $\omega_1$, the condition for good reproduction of the pulse by the circuit of Fig. 3.38 is

$$\omega_1 >> \frac{1}{\tau} \qquad (3.87)$$

The mathematical analysis of a Fourier integral spectrum passing through an actual network is more complicated than is appropriate to give here. It is helpful to show some known results for an important idealization of the lowpass filter. Let a unit pulse be applied to the 2-port transmission network of Fig. 3.42a. The response of this 2-port is approxi-

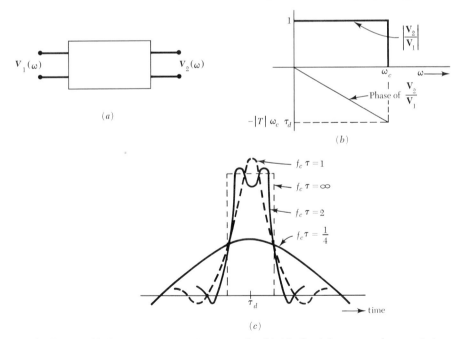

(a)

(b)

(c)

**FIGURE 3.42**   (a) *Lowpass transmission network;* (b) *idealized frequency characteristics of the network;* (c) *output waveshape when input is a rectangular pulse of width* $\tau$. (*From S. Goldman, "Frequency Analysis, Modulation and Noise," p. 83, McGraw-Hill Book Company, 1948.*)

mated by the idealized results of Fig. 3.42$b$ in which magnitude response is constant up to a certain cutoff frequency, $\omega_c$, and is zero beyond this point. The phase response is linear with frequency up to $\omega_c$. The overall response of the network is thus expressed by a *transfer function* $H(\omega)$ which gives the ratio of an output voltage phasor to an input voltage phasor for angular frequency $\omega$. For the idealized conditions stated, this transfer function is

$$H(\omega) = \frac{V_2}{V_1} = \begin{cases} Ae^{-j\omega T_d} & \omega < \omega_c \\ 0 & \omega > \omega_c \end{cases} \tag{3.88a}$$

where $T_d$ is a constant for which a physical interpretation is given below. The frequency components of the input pulse of unit area are, by (2.20$c$),

$$V_1(\omega) = \frac{\sin(\omega\tau/2)}{\omega\tau/2} \tag{3.88b}$$

The frequency spectrum of the output is then given by multiplying the frequency spectrum of the input, (3.88$b$), by the transfer function, (3.88$a$):

$$V_2(\omega) = H(\omega)V_1(\omega) = \begin{cases} \dfrac{A\sin(\omega\tau/2)}{\omega\tau/2}e^{-j\omega T_d} & \omega < \omega_c \\ 0 & \omega > \omega_c \end{cases} \tag{3.88c}$$

The result (3.88$c$) gives magnitude and phase of the various frequency components of the output, which is the representation of the output in the frequency domain. To find the corresponding output voltage $v_2(t)$ in the time domain, the results may be substituted in the Fourier integral (2.17) of the preceding chapter.[1] The integration will not be carried out, but Fig. 3.42$c$ shows results for several values of $f_c\tau$ where $f_c = \omega_c/2\pi$. The curve for $f_c\tau = 1$ (cutoff frequency of the idealized filter $= 1/\tau$) shows that the output pulse is appreciably rounded, but usable as a representation of the input for many purposes. As $f_c\tau$ increases above unity, the pulse becomes an increasingly better representation of the original. As $f_c\tau$ decreases

---

[1] A complex form of the Fourier integral is more useful for working purposes than the real forms given in Chap. 2. Although we do not use them in the text, they will be stated here for convenience. This form utilizes a complex function $G(\omega)$, which conveys both magnitude and phase information, and is

$$f(t) = \frac{1}{2\pi}\int_{-\infty}^{\infty} G(\omega)\, e^{j\omega t}\, d\omega$$

where

$$G(\omega) = \int_{-\infty}^{\infty} f(t)\, e^{-j\omega t}\, dt$$

below unity, the output signal is spread out and becomes a decreasingly poorer representation of the input.

It is also interesting to note that the center of the output is delayed by the constant $T_d$ appearing in the phase response of the idealization (3.88a). To interpret, note Prob. 3.42.

## 3.10 conclusion

In this chapter we have considered a few of the basic tools of circuit analysis. Examples have been given to show the use of these tools, with emphasis on the matter of the frequency response of networks. As we stressed in Chap. 2, matters of frequency response are of fundamental concern in determining the fidelity with which signals can be transmitted by the building blocks of electronic systems.

The circuit tools of this chapter will be applied in succeeding chapters to some circuits which are associated with active electronic devices. Loop and nodal analysis, in phasor and time-varying form, will thus be needed for the study of simple transistor amplifiers, diode pulse circuits, and the like.

The methods of analysis developed here will also be useful in studying a variety of physical problems. For example, the methods of solution of simple differential equations will be applied to the problem of current flow in solids in the following two chapters. The concept of time constant for functions which decay exponentially with time is also important in these chapters.

As noted at the beginning of the chapter, only a small part of the large body of circuit theory can be included in this text. Two additional general matters, the use of the Thévenin and Norton theorems and the subject of impedance matching for optimum transfer, will be considered in Chap. 9. The application of all these tools to the problems of this text should give some view as to the power of the subject, and may provide motivation for further study.

### REFERENCES

M. E. Van Valkenburg, "Network Analysis," 2d ed., Prentice-Hall, Inc., Englewood Cliffs, N.J., 1964.

H. H. Skilling, "Electrical Engineering Circuits," 2d ed., John Wiley and Sons, Inc., New York, 1965.

N. Balabanian, "Fundamentals of Circuit Theory," Allyn and Bacon, Inc., Boston, 1961.

## PROBLEMS

**3.1**   To aid in visualizing the behavior of circuit elements, find as functions of angular frequency the equivalent reactances of the purely reactive circuit elements shown, and sketch their forms on a plot. Determine and indicate on the plots the frequency $\omega_r$ at which the reactances pass through zero and the frequency $\omega_a$ at which the reactances become infinite (these are sometimes referred to as *resonant* and *antiresonant* frequencies, respectively). The inductance is given as an example in figure $a$. (Refer to Sec. 3.8 for the definition of reactances.)

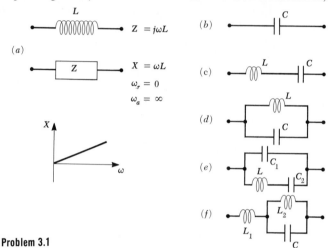

**Problem 3.1**

**3.2**   The following measurements were carried out on four different boxes containing interconnected electrical elements:

| Box | $v_{in}(t)$ | $v_{out}(t)$ |
|-----|-----------|------------|
| 1 | $\sin \omega t$ | $2 \sin 2\omega t$ |
| 2 | $\sin \omega t$ | $\cos (\omega t + \phi)$ |
| 3 | $2 \sin \omega t$ | $4 \sin (\omega t + \phi)$ |
|   | $3 \sin \omega t$ | $6 \sin (\omega t + \phi)$ |
| 4 | $\sin \omega t$ | $\sin \omega t,\ 2n\pi < \omega t < (2n + 1)\, \pi$ |
|   |   | $0,\ (2n + 1)\, \pi < \omega t < (2n + 2)\, \pi$ |

Are the elements in boxes 1, 2, 3, and 4 linear or nonlinear? Why?

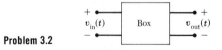

**Problem 3.2**

**3.3**   Consider the left-hand circuit shown, which consists of the linear time-invariant elements $R$, $L$, and $C$.

(a) Assume a voltage input $v_{in} = 4 \sin \omega_1 t$; what is the frequency of the output signal?

(b) If the input signal is changed from $v_{in} = 4 \sin \omega_1 t$ to $v_{in} = 12 \sin \omega_1 t$, what can you say about the change in the output voltage?

(c) If the termination shown in figure b is connected to terminals 3 and 4, what can be said about the frequency of the output voltage across the terminals?

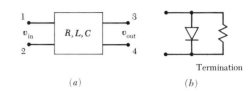

**Problem 3.3**          (a)          (b)

**3.4**   Show that the piecewise linear characteristic of Fig. 3.20d is modeled by a resistor and battery in series, as shown.

**3.5**   Substitute constant values of voltage and current in (3.20a) and (3.20b) to obtain the steady-state solution (3.21) for the circuit of Fig. 3.22.

**3.6**   Using the circuit of Fig. 3.23 as an illustration, show that the use of loop currents $i_1$, $i_2$, and $i_3$ automatically satisfies the Kirchhoff current law at all nodes of the circuit.

**3.7**   Write Kirchhoff's laws for the circuit shown here.

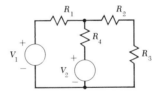

**Problem 3.7**

**3.8**   Solve the equations of Prob. 3.7 and find the current through $R_3$ given the following values:

$$V_1 = 100 \text{ V} \qquad V_2 = 10 \text{ V} \qquad R_1 = 10 \text{ }\Omega$$

$$R_2 = \quad 2 \text{ }\Omega \qquad R_3 = \quad 3 \text{ }\Omega \qquad R_4 = \quad 5 \text{ }\Omega$$

**3.9**   Since the circuit of Prob. 3.7 is linear, superposition holds. Illustrate this by solving for the current through $R_3$ with $V_1$ alone (assuming $V_2$ shorted), then with $V_2$ alone (assuming $V_1$ shorted), and finally adding. Why do we short the unused source instead of open circuiting it?

**3.10**   For the circuit of Fig. 3.24, show that currents as given by (3.24a) and (3.24b) may be obtained by superposition.- That is, find the currents with $V_1$ nonzero and $V_2 = 0$, then add to them the currents with $V_2$ nonzero and $V_1 = 0$.

**3.11**   The definition of linearity is given in terms of the physical concept of superposition. What requirements does this place on the coefficients of the differential or algebraic equations resulting from Kirchhoff's laws? Answer for both a linear time-invariant circuit and for one which is linear but has time-varying elements.

**3.12** Write the circuit equations for the circuit shown and solve for $v_2$ ($A_1$ and $A_2$ are constants).

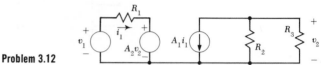

**Problem 3.12**

**3.13** It is sometimes necessary to solve electric-circuit problems graphically. Graphical solutions are useful when the circuits contain nonlinear elements such as semiconductor or vacuum diodes.

(a) Consider the linear circuit shown in a. The resistances $R_1$ and $R_2$ are linear resistances. The voltage across $R_2$, obtained by application of Kirchhoff's law, is simply

$$V_2 = \frac{V_1 R_2}{R_1 + R_2}$$

This result can be obtained graphically as follows:

(1) Write the voltage loop equation:

$$V_1 - IR_1 - IR_2 = 0 \tag{1}$$

(2) Write the equation for the unknown voltage:

$$V_2 = IR_2 \tag{2}$$

(3) From equation (1), $V_2$ is also given by:

$$V_2 = V_1 - IR_1 \tag{3}$$

(4) Plot equations (2) and (3) on the same graph [$I$ versus $V_2$ (figure b)]. The value of $V_2$ corresponding to the intersection of the two curves is a solution to the problem. Note that equation (2) is a straight line passing through the origin, having a slope $1/R_2$. Equation (3) is a straight line having a negative slope $1/R_1$; at $I = 0$, $V_2 = V_1$ and at $V_2 = 0$, $I = V_1/R_1$. Assuming $V_1 = 10$ V, $R_1 = 100$ $\Omega$, and $R_2 = 25$ $\Omega$, find $V_2$ graphically, showing the construction.

(b) Consider now the circuit of figure c containing a linear resistor and a nonlinear resistor, as shown. For the nonlinear resistor the characteristic equation is $I = kV_3^2$, where $k$ is a constant. Assuming $R_1 = 1$ $\Omega$, $V_1 = 6$ V, and $k = \frac{1}{10}$, use the same procedure as in part a to find $V_3$ graphically.

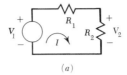

(a)

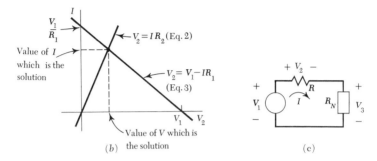

(b)

(c)

**Problem 3.13**

**3.14**   Find the form for current as a function of time in a circuit with a resistor $R$ and inductor $L$ in series, when a constant voltage $V_0$ is applied at $t = 0$. What is the time constant of this circuit, defined as the time for current to build up to $e^{-1}$ of its final value? Calculate the time constant for $R = 1$ k$\Omega$, $L = 1$ mH.

**3.15**   Explain why the Kirchhoff voltage law is automatically satisfied in the nodal method of analysis described in Sec. 3.6.

**3.16**   Use Kirchhoff's laws to write the circuit equation in integro-differential form for the circuit shown.

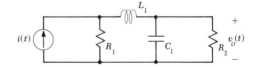

**Problem 3.16**

**3.17**   Consider the low-frequency circuit model of a transistor, as shown. Note that the current generator $\beta_0 i_i$ (where $\beta_0$ is a constant) is a *dependent-current generator*, i.e., the current is proportional to the current $i_1$ defined as shown. Find $v_o$ as a function of $R_1$, $r_i$, $\beta_0$, $R_2$, and $i_s$.

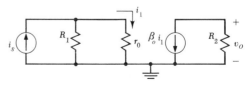

**Problem 3.17**

**3.18**   Find the form for voltage as a function of time across a circuit with a resistor $R$ in parallel with an inductor $L$. The circuit is driven by a constant current $I_0$ applied at $t = 0$. Explain physically the role of the two elements in the transient process.

**3.19**   Interpret the following expressions:

    (a) $\text{Re}(e^{j(\omega t + \theta)})$

    (b) $\text{Re}[(V_r + jV_i)\,e^{j(\omega t + \theta)}]$

    (c) $\text{Im}(e^{j(\omega t + \theta)})$

**3.20**   A current is represented by $i_1 = I_{m1}e^{j(\omega t + \theta)}$. Find the phasor in this expression.

**3.21**   A current representation $i_2 = I_{m2}e^{j\omega t}$ is added to the current given in Prob. 3.20.

    (a) Find the sum of the currents using phasors.

    (b) Express the sum in the exponential form.

**3.22**   What properties of sinusoids are particularly important in the analysis of linear circuits and systems.

**3.23**   Convert the following complex numbers into the polar form $Z = |Z|e^{j\theta} = |Z|\underline{/\theta}$ :

    (a) $1 + j2$    (b) $1 - j2$    (c) $-1 + j2$    (d) $-1 - j2$

    (e) $\dfrac{1}{1 + j2}$    (f) $\dfrac{1}{1 - j2}$    (g) $\dfrac{1}{-1 + j2}$    (h) $\dfrac{1}{-1 - j2}$

**3.24**   Convert the following complex quantities to the polar form $Z = |Z|e^{j\theta} = |Z|\underline{/\theta}$ :

    (a) $R + j\omega L$    (d) $\dfrac{j\omega C}{G + (1/j\omega L)}$    (e) $\dfrac{1}{j\omega L + (1/G)} + \dfrac{1}{j\omega L}$

    (b) $R + \dfrac{1}{j\omega C}$    (f) $\dfrac{-8.62}{1 + (3 + j\omega 2.7)/(9 + j\omega 3.6)}$

    (c) $\dfrac{R_1 + j\omega L_1}{R_2 + j\omega L_2}$    (g) $\dfrac{3 - j\omega 2.9}{1/(j\omega 5 + 0.2) + j\omega 9} \quad \dfrac{2 + j\omega 3}{9}$

**3.25**   Convert the following complex numbers to cartesian form:

    (a) $2e^{j3}$    (b) $\dfrac{4e^{j2.5}}{4 + j3}$    (c) $2e^{j\pi}$    (d) $3e^{j(\pi/4)}$

**3.26**   Assume an admittance $Y = G + jB$, through which a current $i(t)\ \text{Re}(Ie^{j\omega t})$ is applied. Find the expression for the voltage $v(t)$, utilizing the complex exponential for the intermediate steps.

**3.27**   Repeat Prob. 3.26 for $Y = |Y|e^{j\phi}$.

**3.28** A sinusoidal voltage of magnitude 100 V and frequency 10 MHz is applied to a 10-kΩ resistor in series with a 0.1-mH inductor. Show, in the complex plane, the complex impedance and the phasor voltage and phasor current of the circuit. (Adjust scales for impedance, voltage, and current independently, in order to display values clearly.)

**3.29** Repeat Prob. 3.28, assuming that the resistor and inductor are in parallel.

**3.30** Repeat Probs. 3.28 and 3.29, assuming that the inductor is replaced by a capacitor with capacitance of 10 pF.

**3.31** Find the input admittance $Y_{in} = I_1/V_1$ of the circuit shown.

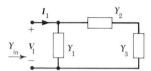

Problem 3.31

**3.32** Find the currents $i_1$ and $i_2$ in the circuit of Fig. 3.26 by the use of phasors. Compare with the result found by completing the direct solution of Sec. 3.5, solving for the four constants $A$, $B$, $C$, and $D$.

**3.33** Use Kirchhoff's laws to obtain equations for the circuit shown. Solve for $v_o(t)$, assuming $v(t) = 2 \sin 2t$, and $R_1 = 2 \ \Omega$, $R_2 = 1 \ \Omega$, $L_1 = 1 \ H$, $C_1 = 2 \ F$.

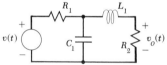

Problem 3.33

**3.34** (a) For the circuit of Prob. 3.16, use Kirchhoff's laws to write the circuit equations.

(b) Assume $i(t) = I_m \sin \omega t = \text{Im} \ (I_m e^{j\omega t})$ and solve for $v_o(t)$ using complex exponential notation. The final answer should be in the following form:

$$v_o(t) = V_m(\omega) \sin \left[ \omega t + \phi_1(\omega) \right]$$

where $V_m(\omega)$ and $\phi_1(\omega)$ are functions of $\omega$.

(c) Write the solution of part b in the form

$$v_o(t) = V_m(\omega) \cos \left[ \omega t + \phi_2(\omega) \right]$$

**3.35** Write Kirchhoff's equations for the circuit shown. Solve for $v_o(t)$, assuming $i(t) = 3 \cos 3t$, and $R = 1 \ \Omega$, $C = 1 \ F$, $L = 2 \ H$.

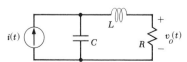

Problem 3.35

**3.36** Given the circuit shown in figure $a$,

(a) Transform the $v_s, R_s$ source to the left of terminals 1-2 into an equivalent current $i_s$, $R_s$ source, as shown in figure $b$; what are $i_s$ and $R_s$ for this current source? [Refer to (3.7a) and (3.7b).]

(b) Using nodal analysis, write the equations for nodes 1 and 3 in integro-differential form, taking the reference node as 2 in figure $b$.

(c) If the source is sinusoidal, rewrite these equations in phasor form (i.e., time-independent form), and solve for $V_o(\omega)$.

(d) The behavior of this network may be expressed by the use of a transfer function $H(\omega) = V_o(\omega)/I_s$. Find the magnitude of the transfer function $|H(\omega)|$ and evaluate $|H(0)|$.

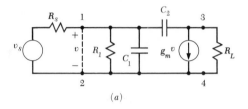

(a)

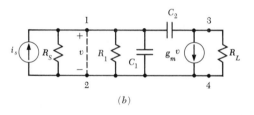

(b)

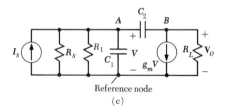

Reference node

(c)

**Problem 3.36**

**3.37** Consider the circuit model for an electronic device, as shown. Note that the voltage generator $\mu v$ is a dependent-voltage generator where $\mu$ = constant.

(a) Using *nodal analysis* write the equations for nodes $a$ and $b$ in integro-differential form.

(b) Assuming a sinusoidal excitation, rewrite these equations in time-independent (phasor) form. (*Note:* In parts $a$ and $b$, use the notation $v$ for a time-varying quantity and $V$ for a phasor.

(c) Assume $v = \sin \omega t$, $\omega = 2\pi f$, $f = 2 \cdot 10^6$ Hz, $C_1 = C_3 =$ 10 pF, $C_2 = 0$, $R_L = 10$ kΩ, $r = 5$ kΩ, and $\mu = 20$. Evaluate $i_L(t)$ and express it in the form $|I_L| \sin(\omega t + \phi)$.

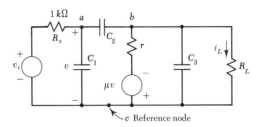

**Problem 3.37**

$c$ Reference node

**3.38**   In the circuit shown, the source voltage contains two different frequencies. $v(t) = 10 \sin 10t + 10 \sin 1000t$ (note that the amplitudes for both frequencies are the same). Assume that linearity holds for the circuit.

(a) What kind of a transmission circuit is it?

(b) Solve for $v_o(t)$.

(c) Show a "Bode" diagram for magnitudes only (i.e., a response curve in log-log coordinates), using asymptotes, and explain the answer obtained in part b.

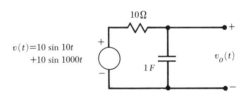

$v(t) = 10 \sin 10t$
$+10 \sin 1000t$

$v_o(t)$

**Problem 3.38**

**3.39**   A lowpass and a highpass circuit are given in figures $a$ and $b$, respectively. Assume that they have the same break frequency $\omega_1$.

(a) Show that $V_o/V_i$ as a function of frequency can be expressed as

$$\frac{V_o}{V_i} = \frac{1}{1 + j(\omega/\omega_1)}$$

for the circuit in figure $a$, and

$$\frac{V_o}{V_i} = \left( j\frac{\omega}{\omega_1} \right) \frac{1}{1 + j(\omega/\omega_1)}$$

for the highpass circuit of figure $b$.

(b) Show a "Bode" diagram (magnitude only), use asymptotes and a normalized frequency $\omega/\omega_1$ (logarithmic scale). Show how the frequency response of the circuit of figure $b$ is obtained from the Bode diagram of the circuit in figure $a$.

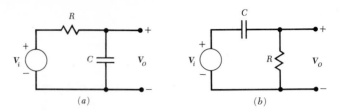

**Problem 3.39**

**3.40**   Given the circuit shown, note that it is a combination of a low-pass and a highpass transmission circuit. It has, therefore, two break frequencies, a highpass break frequency $\omega_1$ and a lowpass break frequency $\omega_2$. Assume $\omega_1 < \omega_2$.

(a) Find the impedance $Z$, seen by the voltage source.

(b) What is the value of $Z$ at $\omega = 0$ and at $\omega = \infty$?

(c) Show the frequency response of the circuit $|V_o/V_s|$ using a log-log plot of the asymptotes.

(d) What is the bandwidth of the passband between break frequencies?

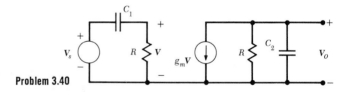

**Problem 3.40**

**3.41**   Utilizing the curves of Fig. 3.42c as guides, estimate the forms of the output for a pulse of width $\tau = 0.1$ $\mu$s when passed through an ideal filter having the response of Fig. 3.42b. Consider cutoff frequencies $f_c$ of 1 MHz, 10 MHz, and 100 MHz.

**3.42**   Explain why the linear phase variation $-(\omega T_d)$ introduced into the idealized filter response of Eq. (3.88a) leads to a constant time delay $T_d$ in the form of the pulse. (Argue either physically or from the Fourier integral given in the footnote on page 92.)

**3.43**   For the functions $e^{-t/T}$ and $(1 - e^{-t/T})$ show that the linear extension of the slope at $t = 0$ of each function intercepts at $t = T$ the line equal to the final value of the function.

chapter **4**

# CURRENT FLOW IN SOLIDS

## 4.1 introduction

We have found that a number of circuit functions, such as amplification, detection, and switching, are required for typical systems such as those studied in Chap. 1. In addition to the passive circuit elements utilized in Chap. 3, active electronic devices such as transistors and tubes are needed for these functions. Essentially, all electronic devices depend on the flow of charges and on the control of those charges by electric or magnetic fields in solids, gases, or in vacuum. Thus, electrons are controlled by fields in vacuum electronic devices. Electrons and "holes" (the latter to be defined in Sec. 4.7) are controlled by fields in semiconductors. Both electron and ion flow may be important in some gas discharge devices, such as those used in switching.

For many application purposes, it is often sufficient to be primarily interested in overall characteristics of a device, usually expressed in the form of equations or curves giving the current-voltage relationships for that device. However, to gain an understanding of the device, we need to study the nature of electronic motion in vacuum and in solids. This understanding serves not only for personal satisfaction, but it also permits us to propose and design devices that perform a specified circuit function.

Because of the importance of modern semiconductor devices, the next several chapters place particular stress on them. Vacuum tubes are still vital, as exemplified by the traveling-wave tubes in communication satellites as mentioned in Sec. 1.4, but the detailed study of such elements will be delayed until Chap. 10. We thus stress in this chapter the nature of current flow in solids, especially in semiconductors. In the following section we review briefly some matters concerning motion of isolated charges. We then turn to the more complicated subject of charge motion in solids.

## 4.2 motion of isolated electrons

Because the charged particle of concern in most electronic devices is the electron, let us begin by studying the motion of electrons in electric and magnetic fields. Two basic properties of the electron are its electrical charge $q_e$ and its mass $m$. The numerical values for these quantities are

$$q_e = -q = -1.602 \cdot 10^{-19} \text{ coulomb}$$
$$m = 9.107 \cdot 10^{-31} \text{ kg}$$

(4.1)

Dimensions of the electron are so small compared with those of practical devices that it may be considered as a point charge in all of the following. The mass given is the rest mass. Relativistic effects modify this at high velocities, but they are not of main concern to the electronic devices studied in this book. We also recognize that there is a gravitational force on the electron arising from its finite mass, but that force is negligible compared with the field forces to be considered for any reasonable values of field (Prob. 4.2).

**FORCE FROM ELECTRIC FIELDS**   An electric field, characterized by the symbol $\vec{E}$, is a force field arising from other charges of the system. The arrow denotes that it is a vector, and by definition $\vec{E}$ is the force in magnitude and direction on a unit charge at a point. If an electric field acts on charge $Q$, the force is $Q$ times the force that acts on a unit charge,

$$\vec{f} = Q\vec{E}$$

(4.2)

In the vector equation (4.2), the direction of $\vec{E}$ is the direction of force for a positive charge, and the charge moves in that direction. For an electron, $Q$ is $q_e$ and is negative. Therefore, the force on an electron is in the opposite direction from that of the $\vec{E}$ field. (That is, the $\vec{f}$ and $\vec{E}$ vectors are parallel but oppositely oriented.) An electron moves in the opposite direction from that of the electric field. The directional relations for positive and negative charges are illustrated in Fig. 4.1a.

The magnitude of force, from (4.2), is just the charge multiplied by magnitude of electric field. The latter is denoted simply $E$, and has the units of volts per meter. (Electric fields expressed in volts per centimeter are also common, and the conversion for use in the equations is straight-

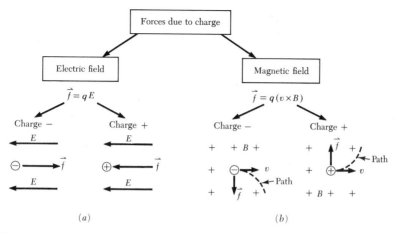

**FIGURE 4.1**  *Forces due to charge.*

forward.) As a numerical example, consider an electron moving in a weak field of magnitude 1 V/m (0.01 V/cm). From (4.1) and (4.2), the resulting force magnitude is $1.6 \cdot 10^{-19}$ newtons.

**FORCE FROM MAGNETIC FIELDS**    A magnetic field expresses the force field which arises from currents and moving charges of the system. It is characterized by the symbol $\vec{B}$ and has the units of webers per square meter (also called tesla). The $\vec{B}$ field, which is also a vector field, produces a force only on a moving charged particle. Therefore it is necessary to take into consideration in a force calculation the vector directions of the field and of the moving electron. The direction of the resulting vector force is illustrated in Fig. 4.1b. If the magnetic-field vector points into the paper and if $\vec{v}$, the velocity vector, is perpendicular to $\vec{B}$ and to the right as shown in the figure, the force vector $\vec{f}$ is down and vertical. In general, the vector force on a charge $Q$ can be expressed as follows:

$$\vec{f} = Q(\vec{v} \times \vec{B}) \qquad (4.3)$$

In (4.3), a *cross product* of $\vec{v}$ and $\vec{B}$ is used.[1] The magnitude of this product is $|v|\,|B| \sin \alpha$, where $\alpha$ is the angle between $\vec{v}$ and $\vec{B}$. In Fig. 4.1b, $\alpha$ is 90°. Note from (4.3) that no force results if the velocity of the particle is zero or if the velocity vector is parallel to $\vec{B}$.

For an electron, $Q = q_e = -q$ in (4.3); the direction of force is illustrated in Fig. 4.1b. The figure also illustrates the direction of force for a moving positive charge.

[1] The vector cross product $\vec{v} \times \vec{B}$ is perpendicular to the plane containing $\vec{v}$ and $\vec{B}$, and is in the direction of advance of a right-hand screw if $\vec{v}$ is rotated into $\vec{B}$ through the smallest angle.

**ENERGY RELATIONS IN STATIC FIELDS**   We turn now to a simple but important example involving a constant $\vec{E}$ field. (In a later section, a corresponding example for a constant magnetic field is included.) Assume that an electron is located in a region in which there is a nonuniform electric field which is not varying with time. The principle of the conservation of energy can be used to establish the nature of the electron motion. Initially, the electron is chosen to lie at a point $P_1$ with a velocity of $\vec{v_1}$. Its initial kinetic energy is then $\frac{1}{2}\,mv_1{}^2$. With time, it is acted on by the $\vec{E}$ field and moves to point $P_2$, where it has a new velocity $\vec{v_2}$ and a kinetic energy of $\frac{1}{2}\,mv_2{}^2$. Since energy must be conserved, the change in kinetic energy must equal the change in potential energy. The difference of potential energy at points $P_1$ and $P_2$ can be expressed in terms of a line integral, i.e., an integral taken along the path of the electron.

$$\int_{P_1}^{P_2} \vec{f}\cdot \vec{dl} = \frac{1}{2}\,mv_2{}^2 - \frac{1}{2}\,mv_1{}^2 \tag{4.4a}$$

The dot product in the integral of (4.4a) is equal to the product of the magnitude of the force $|\vec{f}|$, the length of the incremental vector $|\vec{dl}|$, and the cosine of the angle between the two vectors. If now we introduce $\vec{f} = -q\vec{E}$ for the electron, the equation becomes

$$-q\int_{P_1}^{P_2} \vec{E}\cdot \vec{dl} = \frac{1}{2}\,mv_2{}^2 - \frac{1}{2}\,mv_1{}^2 \tag{4.4b}$$

For a static electric field, the negative integral of the electric field between two points is the potential difference $V_2 - V_1$ between the two points. Thus, for static fields,

$$q(V_2 - V_1) = \frac{1}{2}\,m(v_2{}^2 - v_1{}^2) \tag{4.5}$$

For an example to illustrate the use of this expression, assume that an electron initially at rest is accelerated through a potential difference of $V$. Equation (4.5) provides

$$\frac{1}{2}\,mv_2{}^2 = qV \tag{4.6a}$$

$$v_2 = \sqrt{\frac{2q}{m}\,V} \tag{4.6b}$$

Using the values of $q$ and $m$ for the electron, we obtain

$$v_2 = 5.93\cdot 10^5 \sqrt{V} \quad \text{m/s} \tag{4.6c}$$

If $V = 100$ V, $v_2 = 5.93\cdot 10^6$ m/s.

Equation (4.5) is also valid for charges in static magnetic fields, since the magnetic force is perpendicular to charge motion by (4.3) and thus can change direction but not magnitude of velocity. The expression, however, is not generally valid for time-varying fields as we shall see in Chap. 11 when high-frequency vacuum devices are considered.

The energy or velocity of an electron is frequently expressed in *electron volts* (eV). Thus, by (4.1) and (4.6a), 1 eV corresponds to an energy of $1.602 \cdot 10^{-19}$ joules (abbreviated J), and by (4.6c), this produces a velocity of $5.93 \cdot 10^5$ m/s.

## 4.3   the classification and structure of solids

Turning now to charge motion in solids, we recognize that the interaction between charges within the solid will give important contributions to the force law stated in the preceding section. Interactions are present even in electron beams in vacuum, as will be seen when space charge is considered in Chap. 10. The interaction problem is more severe within a solid. For electrons bound to their parent atom, the forces within that atom are dominant, but the effect of neighboring atoms as well as the externally applied forces must be considered. In many problems of importance to us, an outer or valence electron may be removed from the parent atom, by thermal or other forces, and may then wander about the solid. Forces from within the solid again add to the externally applied force to determine the overall behavior of these free electrons. We will be most concerned with the behavior and flow of charged particles in semiconductors, but will consider first the classification of conductivity and the structure of crystals.

**CONDUCTORS OR METALS**   Solids in this group have a very high conductivity, typically of the order of $10^7$ mhos/m. In terms of a particle picture or model the metals have electrons in the valence or outermost orbits of the atoms which are not closely bound to the parent atom. These electrons are free to move about the solid. An applied field produces a net drift in addition to the random, thermal motion of the electrons, and a net current density which is proportional to the electric field through the conductivity $\sigma$:

$$\vec{J} = \sigma \vec{E} \tag{4.7}$$

**INSULATORS OR DIELECTRICS**   These solids have such a low conductivity, of the order of $10^{-12}$ mhos/m, that current flow through the material is negligible for most applications. In terms of the particle model, all of the electrons of the atom are so tightly bound to their nuclei at ordinary temperature that an applied field cannot force them free. However, an applied field can shift the mean position of an electron in an atom with respect to the nucleus. This shift in position is called a polarization of the material and gives rise to the dielectric property of the insulator.

**SEMICONDUCTORS**   The group of solids which have conductivities about mid-way on an order-of-magnitude scale between conductors and insulators, that is, $10^{-3}$ to 10 mhos/m, are called semiconductors. As is brought out shortly, the conductivity of these solids is strongly dependent on temperature, impurity concentration, and incident radiation. Typical semiconductors are germanium (Ge) and silicon (Si).

**CRYSTAL STRUCTURE OF SOLIDS**   Although many amorphous materials, such as glass and plastics, are important in electrical engineering, the solids to be considered in detail are crystalline, i.e., they consist of an orderly space array of atoms. This array, called a *lattice*, has a periodicity and it is convenient to think of a *unit cell*, consisting of several atoms in a particular arrangement, which is repeated in all dimensions.

Several crystal structures are possible, depending on the number of valence electrons of the atom and on whether the solid is composed of one element or is a compound of two or more elements. The most common structures for metals are shown in Fig. 4.2. The structure of Fig. 4.2*a* is

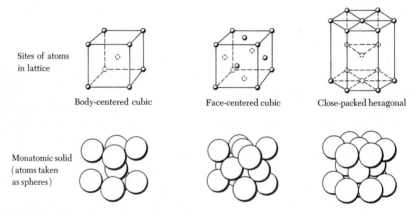

Sites of atoms
in lattice

Body-centered cubic          Face-centered cubic          Close-packed hexagonal

Monatomic solid
(atoms taken
as spheres)

**FIGURE 4.2**   *Crystal structures of metals.*

called the body-centered cubic; that of Fig. 4.2*b*, a face-centered cubic. The structure of Fig. 4.2*c* is the close-packed hexagon and is a property of magnesium (Mg). Semiconductors together with the diamond form of carbon have the crystalline structure shown in Fig. 4.3. Note in this struc-

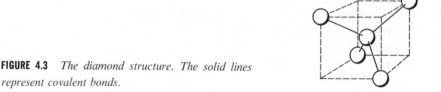

**FIGURE 4.3**   *The diamond structure. The solid lines represent covalent bonds.*

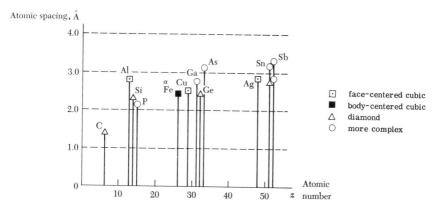

Atomic spacing, Å

face-centered cubic
■ body-centered cubic
△ diamond
○ more complex

Atomic number

**FIGURE 4.4** *Interatomic distances in the crystals and crystal structure of some elements. (Adapted from W. Hume-Rothery and G. V. Raynor, "The Structure of Metals and Alloys," The Institute of Metals, London, 1962.)*

ture that each element has four equidistant neighbors. The structure and the interatomic distances of pure solids are determined by X-ray diffraction. The results for several solids are shown in Fig. 4.4. Note that typical interatomic distances are of the order of angstroms, where 1Å is $10^{-10}$ m.

## 4.4 semiconductor bonds and bands

**COVALENT BONDS**   We now restrict our attention to semiconductors, except for certain comparisons that will be helpful. A pure semiconductor such as Si has four valence electrons, i.e., four electrons in the outermost orbit of an atom. The silicon atom arranges itself in the solid to share valence electrons with four neighboring atoms. Thus, each atom forms four covalent bonds to complete its outer shell or orbit. This arrangement is shown in Fig. 4.3; for convenience it is usually shown schematically in a two-dimensional manner as in Fig. 4.5. Analysis of this arrangement, using quantum-mechanical considerations, shows that this covalent sharing is a minimum energy configuration and is therefore the stable situation for this particular collection of atoms. As indicated in Fig. 4.4, the interatomic distance of Si is approximately 2Å = $2 \cdot 10^{-8}$ cm. The atomic density of Si is approximately $5 \cdot 10^{22}$ atoms/cm³.

The covalent bonds of a semiconductor can be broken if a sufficient energy is imparted to an electron. For an *intrinsic* (ideally pure) semiconductor, the amount of energy which is necessary to break a covalent bond at 300°K is at least 1.1 eV for silicon and 0.7 eV for germanium. This energy can be imparted in several ways, such as by thermal action or electromagnetic radiation, as will be discussed in greater detail later. Here we note that once a bond is broken, an electron is "free" to move about the solid and to participate in current conduction. A second conduction mechanism results from the motion of valence electrons and leads to the special properties of semiconductors. The two mechanisms are discussed in Sec. 4.7.

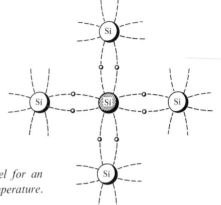

**FIGURE 4.5** *Two-dimensional particle model for an intrinsic semiconductor at very low temperature. (Silicon is used as an example.)*

**ENERGY BANDS**    The bond picture given above is easy to visualize. However, it is not possible to use this scheme to predict the detailed electrical behavior of semiconductors. For an accurate quantitative analysis of electron flow in solids, quantum mechanics is needed. Such an analysis is beyond the scope of this book; therefore, we introduce with only a qualitative argument the principal results from such an approach.[1] As is brought out below, an energy-band representation for the solid is the major item of interest. This we introduce with a single atom.

For a single, isolated atom, the "orbits" of the electrons correspond to certain allowed energy levels and quantum states. At very low temperatures, the electrons are in the lowest possible energy states. This we can represent as a series of energy levels, as at the line $a$ on the right of Fig. 4.6. Only two energy levels are shown for simplicity. (In this figure, the horizontal direction signifies the closeness of atoms in a solid, and the vertical direction represents the energy of the electrons.)

If we now consider that a second identical atom is brought close to the original atom, a splitting of the energy levels occurs because of the interaction between the two atoms. The onset of splitting is shown at line $b$ in Fig. 4.6. This splitting or separating of energy levels is characteristic of the interaction of all dynamic systems when they are closely coupled. For example, electric circuits when coupled together produce a splitting

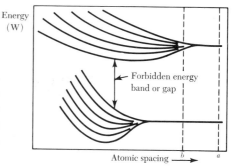

**FIGURE 4.6** *Splitting of energy levels into a band as a function of interatomic distance. (After Shockley, "Electrons and Holes in Semiconductors," D. Van Nostrand Company, Inc., Princeton, N.J., 1950.)*

or spreading of the values of the natural frequencies (resonances) of the individual circuits. In Fig. 4.6 the splitting of energy levels for a system of six atoms is illustrated as the interatomic distance is assumed to decrease. Note that the number of quantum states for each atom is not changed and that the corresponding energy levels can be considered to be grouped into several *bands* of energies. For a solid with a high density of atoms, each energy band has an extremely large number of allowed energy states. For all practical purposes, we can consider the band as if it is a continuum of energy and we can neglect the individual, discrete energy levels. The formation of the bands is significant only for the outermost energy levels of the original atoms.

In general, the outermost energy bands can overlap and cross over each other. This is shown in Fig. 4.7 for the semiconductor, silicon. Silicon (atomic number 12) has 12 electrons in orbit about the nucleus. The inner eight electrons constitute a core corresponding to neon, i.e., each inner orbit is filled. The outer four electrons occur in the third shell, two each in two quantum states known as $3p$ and $3s$. (See Appendix B.) The energy levels for these states are as illustrated in Fig. 4.7. In this figure, we again see the single energy levels on the right for isolated atoms become bands as the interatomic distance is assumed to decrease. In addition, we see

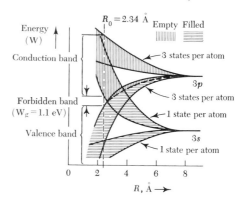

**FIGURE 4.7** *Energy bands versus interatomic distance for a semiconductor such as silicon.*

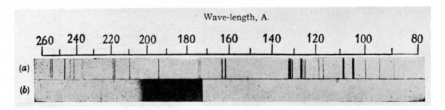

**FIGURE 4.8**  *Emission (X-ray) spectra of aluminum* (a) *from the vapor and* (b) *from the solid.* (*From H. W. B. Skinner, "Reports on Progress: Physics," vol. V, p. 258, Institute of Physics and the Physical Society, 1938.*)

that each original energy level splits into two bands, one of which moves up as the other moves down. For small interatomic distances, the bands cross each other and finally merge. For the actual material, at a given temperature and pressure, the interatomic distance $R_0$ is a fixed distance. For silicon this is approximately $R_0 = 2.34\text{Å}$. This is the distance for which the average energy of the system is a minimum, as mentioned earlier, and a stable configuration results. For the actual material, we can see that the energy levels of the outermost electrons have become two bands separated by an energy gap $W_g = 1.1$ eV for silicon. The lower energy band is called the *valence band*, and the upper is called the *conduction band*. The occupancy of these bands by electrons is discussed shortly.

Experimental evidence to illustrate the splitting of energy levels and the existence of the energy states in the conduction band is illustrated by the emission spectra of the metal, aluminum, in the vapor state and in the solid state. Figure 4.8a shows the emission spectra for the vapor state of aluminum. Well-defined spectral lines are seen. On the other hand, the emission spectra for solid aluminum, as in Fig. 4.8b, shows a large band

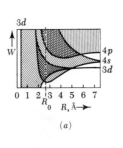

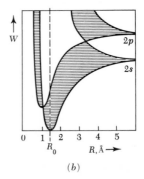

**FIGURE 4.9**  *Energy bands versus interatomic distance* (a) *for a metal* (*copper*) [*after H. M. Krutter, Physical Review, **48**:664 (1935)*] *and* (b) *for an insulator* (*after J. C. Slater, "Quantum Theory of Matter," p. 291, McGraw-Hill Book Company, New York, 1953*).

of radiation in the wavelength range from 170 to 200 Å. This illustrates that the interaction in the vapor state is small, but not in the solid state.

The example above illustrates band splitting and merging in metals. This also occurs in insulators. Metals have partially filled or overlapping bands, or both, as shown in Fig. 4.9a for copper. For the actual interatomic distance of the material, no energy gaps between bands exist. The energy-band diagram of an insulator is illustrated in Fig. 4.9b. The insulator is similar to the semiconductor except that the energy gap between the bands is appreciably larger.

## 4.5 energy distribution of electrons

The energy bands of a solid represent a continuum of *allowed* energy states. However, these bands are not necessarily filled by electrons. The degree of occupancy of the band depends on the energy distribution of the electrons. It is helpful to consider first that the solid is at $0°K$ and is in thermal equilibrium. At zero degrees, all of the orbiting electrons of each atom are at the lowest possible energy state. Of course, this does not mean that all of the electrons have the same lowest energy level. Pauli's exclusion principle[1] demands that no two electrons can be at an energy state with the same quantum number. In Fig. 4.7, a shading of bands is used to illustrate which energy states or bands are filled and which are empty at $0°K$. The lower or *valence band* is filled (i.e., all the available quantum states in this band are occupied), and the upper or

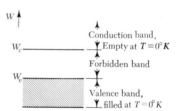

**FIGURE 4.10** *Energy bands for an intrinsic semiconductor at $0°K$.*

*conduction band* is empty. Another representation of these bands for a semiconductor is shown in Fig. 4.10 in which the vertical dimension is again energy. The horizontal dimension in this figure does not have particular meaning here, although we can consider it to be a specific direction in the solid. For a uniform semiconductor, the energy levels do not change with the horizontal dimension on a macroscopic scale.

As the temperature is increased from $0°K$, the electrons gain energy from the thermal, ambient environment. The electrons in the outermost orbits are principally affected and the core of the atoms can be neglected

[1] Feynman et al., *op. cit.*, vol. 3, sec. 4.7.

except for the basic properties of the lattice structure of the material. Not all the valence electrons will assume the same elevated energies; a distribution of electron energies occurs in a manner similar to the distribution of the energies of molecules in a gas, although interactions between particles is much greater in the solid than in the gas. For either case, there is a statistical distribution of energies and a defined probability function $P$ giving the probability of finding a particle in a given energy range. For the solid, E. Fermi and P. Dirac have shown that the probability that electrons occupy a given energy level is[1]

$$P = \frac{1}{1 + e^{(W - W_f)/kT}} \tag{4.8}$$

In (4.8), $W$ is the energy in joules where the reference level is that of the lowest allowed orbit of the electrons; $W_f$ has the dimension of energy and for the temperatures of interest here it may be considered a constant for a given material called the Fermi energy or the *Fermi level*; $k$ is Boltzmann's constant equal to $1.38 \cdot 10^{-23}$ J/°K $= 8.62 \cdot 10^{-5}$ eV/°K; $T$ is the absolute temperature in degrees Kelvin. Note that for $T > 0$, $P = \frac{1}{2}$ at an energy level of $W = W_f$.

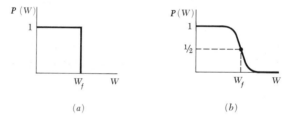

(a)                                   (b)

**FIGURE 4.11**   *Fermi-Dirac probability factor.* (a) $T = 0°K$; (b) $T > 0°K$.

Two plots of $P$ for $T = 0°K$ and for $T > 0°K$ are shown in Fig. 4.11a and Fig. 4.11b, respectively. Of particular interest now is the fact that at $0°K$, we obtain the box-type characteristic of Fig. 4.11a. On the basis of this curve and our earlier reasoning, we can expect the Fermi level $W_f$ to have a value larger than that of the top edge of the valence band, i.e., to lie above the top edge of the valence band in Fig. 4.12a. Note that the *Fermi-Dirac probability function* is plotted vertically in Fig. 4.12b. At $0°K$, all allowed energy states in the valence band are filled and all energy states in the conduction band are empty. The Fermi level lies in the center of the forbidden band or energy gap as shown in Fig. 4.12a and Fig. 4.12b.

At a temperature larger than $0°K$, there exists a finite probability of electrons having energies greater than $W_f$ as shown in Fig. 4.13a and b. However, the distribution of possible energy states is not uniform in energy

[1] Beam, *op. cit.*, pp. 608-622.

and it in fact is proportional to the square root of energy in many cases. The density of *available* energy states is labeled $dS/dW$ and is plotted in Fig. 4.13c. The density of occupied states $dN/dW$ is found by multiplying

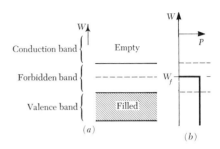

**FIGURE 4.12**  *Semiconductor at $0°K$. (a) Energy-band diagram; (b) Fermi factor.*

the density of allowed states $dS/dW$ by the probability $P$ of occupancy of a given state:

$$\frac{dN}{dW} = P\,\frac{dS}{dW} \qquad (4.9)$$

A plot of (4.9) is shown in Fig. 4.13d and is obtained by multiplying the curves of Fig. 4.13b and c. Clearly, some electrons are present in the conduction band for $T > 0°K$.

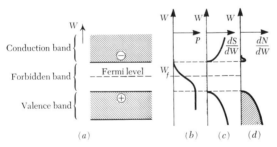

**FIGURE 4.13**  *Semiconductor at $300°K$. (a) Energy-band diagram; (b) Fermi factor; (c) density of available states; (d) density of occupied states.*

Returning to the previous covalent bond picture of the semiconductor, we can think in terms of some electrons gaining sufficient kinetic energy from the thermal energy of the environment to break their bonds with neighboring atoms and to exist "free" to wander about the solid. The energy which must be gained is at least equal to the width of the energy gap $W_g$. Of course, only a small density of electrons becomes free in this manner. This fact is made clear by calculating the probability of occupancy of states at the bottom edge of the conduction band. First, in (4.8), we use $300°K$ ($= 27°C$) as a representative value of temperature. For this temperature, $kT = 4.14 \cdot 10^{-21}$ J $= 0.0259$ eV $\simeq 0.026$ eV. For intrinsic Si at this temperature, the energy gap is 1.1 eV; therefore, the Fermi level, which is in the middle of the forbidden gap, is below the conduction band by half of this value, or 0.55 eV. The probability $P$ is then

$$P = \frac{1}{1 + e^{0.55/0.026}} \simeq e^{-21} \simeq 8 \cdot 10^{-10}$$

Clearly, the relative number of electrons that break their bonds is very, very small at 300°K for silicon.

Because of the magnitude of the energy gap with respect to the value of $kT$, the exponential term in the denominator of (4.8) overshadows the unity term. When considering the free or conduction electrons, we can then approximate $P$ as follows:

$$P \simeq e^{-(W - W_f)/kT} \tag{4.10}$$

This probability function is the *Maxwell-Boltzmann probability function* which describes the energy distribution of classical gases.[1] As mentioned earlier, the interaction of particles in a gas is small and classical theory provides no restriction on the occupancy of a particle at any energy level. For the present case, we can assume that the density of free electrons is so low in the solid that the interaction between them is also negligible. For this reason, we can model these electrons as an "electron gas" existing within the "volume" of the solid and are not surprised to find them obeying classical-gas-law statistics.

The density of free electrons, $n_i$, is found by integrating $dN$ from (4.9) from the bottom edge of the conduction band, $W_c$, to large values of energy (infinity). (In effect, we find the area "beneath" the top curve of Fig. 4.13d.)

$$n_i = \int_{W_c}^{\infty} dN = \int_{W_c}^{\infty} P \frac{dS}{dW} dW \tag{4.11a}$$

The result can be shown to be

$$n_i = A_o T^{3/2} e^{-W_g/2kT} \tag{4.11b}$$

In the final result, the temperature appears both in the exponential term and the $T^{3/2}$ multiplier. As before, $W_g$ is the energy gap of the material and $A_o$ is a constant which is dependent on the material.[2] The dominant temperature term is the exponential term; and the density of free electrons is a strong function of temperature, as we expect from the approximate Boltzmann energy distribution of free electrons.

---

[1] Feynman et al., *op. cit.*, vol. 1, secs. 40.1, 40.2; R. B. Adler, A. C. Smith, and R. L. Longini, "Introduction to Semiconductor Physics," sec. 3.2, John Wiley & Sons, Inc., New York, 1964.
[2] Adler et al., *op. cit.*, p. 128.

For Si, the value of $n_i$ at 300°K is approximately $1.5 \cdot 10^{10}$ electrons/cm³. For Ge, $n_i \simeq 2.5 \cdot 10^{13}$. It is instructive to compare these numbers with the density of the atoms in the solid. The density of silicon atoms is of the order of $5 \cdot 10^{22}$ atoms/cm³. Therefore, only one in $10^{12}$ atoms of Si is ionized at 300°K, whereas for germanium, with an energy gap of 0.7 eV, approximately one in $10^9$ atoms is ionized. These order-of-magnitude estimates are, of course, consistent with our earlier estimate of the very small probability of ionization, i.e., of a valence electron gaining sufficient energy to jump to the conduction band. The difference between the free electron densities for silicon and germanium arises because of the difference in the values of the energy gap, 1.1 eV and 0.7 eV, respectively. At first glance this difference appears slight. However, when these values are included in the exponential term of (4.11b), or (4.10), and a ratio taken with respect to 26 meV, the $10^3$ difference in $n_i$ is understandable.

The flow of the free electrons in the solid is our next major topic of study. However, it is first useful to compare the results of this section for semiconductors with corresponding values for metals and insulators. For the insulator, the major difference is that the energy band gap between the valence and conduction bands is much larger than for the semiconductor. This is illustrated in Fig. 4.14a. Pure carbon, in diamond form,

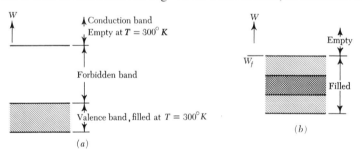

**FIGURE 4.14**   *Energy bands for* (a) *an insulator and* (b) *a metal* (*copper*).

has an energy gap of approximately 5 eV. From our results above, we can expect that the density of free electrons is extremely small. Thus, the conduction of current is almost zero and we have an insulating material. For metals, as has been pointed out, the bands are partially filled or overlap as in Fig. 4.14b.[1] No energy band gap is present. Using a particle viewpoint, we can consider that all the metal atoms are ionized and all the valence electrons are available for conduction of current. For a typical metal, the volume density of allowable states is as illustrated in Fig. 4.15a.

[1] There are two types of metals with respect to the energy band diagram. For one type such as bismuth (Bi) and antimony (Sb), often referred to as semimetals, the conduction bands overlap. For the true metals, such as silver (Ag), the valence band is only partly filled. For both, conduction states are available without a band gap.

The probability of occupancy by conduction electrons at low energies is essentially unity leading to the curve of Fig. 4.15$b$, so the volume density of conduction electrons in a valence 1 metal such as copper is essentially the density of atoms, which is of the order of $8 \cdot 10^{22}/cm^3$.

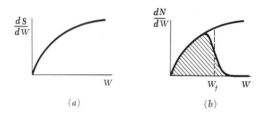

(a)    (b)

**FIGURE 4.15**    *Volume density of* (a) *available energy states at* $T = 0°K$ *and* (b) *occupied energy states at* $T > 0°K$ *for metals.*

## 4.6    effective mass and current conduction in metals

In metals and semiconductors at a temperature greater than $0°K$, free electrons are present within the solid. If an electric field $\vec{E}$ is set up in the solid, we expect that an electron is accelerated by that field. However, the applied electric field is only one of the many forces and interactions within the solid acting on the electron. In fact, the internal fields are usually much stronger than an applied $\vec{E}$ field. Because of all these forces and inter-actions, it may seem that we cannot treat electron flow motion in terms of individual electrons as we did in Sec. 4.2. An average or statistical flow should be considered, using quantum mechanics, rather than individual particles that obey Newtonian mechanics. Fortunately, however, since we are interested primarily in bulk phenomena, it is possible to use Newtonian mechanics and particle flow if we model the free electron in a proper way. In particular, we propose an electron for which the value of the mass is adjusted to simulate the natural bulk phenomena that affect the statistical electron flow in a solid. The value of the *effective mass* includes and in-corporates the interior forces that affect electron flow. Therefore, when external forces are applied to the solid, we can consider that the particle reacts as a classical electron with modified mass, insofar as bulk effects are concerned. Representative values of the effective mass of the electrons in some semiconductors are given inside the covers.

To continue this investigation of electronic motion, we restrict attention for the moment to metals. With an electric field set up in the metal, the free electrons are accelerated and gain kinetic energy. This motion caused by the electric field is superimposed on the thermal random motion of the electrons of the "electron gas" within the solid. This new motion is in the opposite direction to the $\vec{E}$ field but is limited in extent, because the electrons collide[1] with the atoms and ions of the lattice of the solid. On the average, the electrons can move only a distance $l$ along the direction of the $\vec{E}$ field. The average length of time between collisions is called the *mean free time* $t_0$. The electrons, with time, must follow a multicollision course and the path is a succession of straight-line segments having almost random direction. The presence of the $\vec{E}$ field does, however, lead to a net drift motion in a direction opposite to that of the electric field. The net drift velocity $v_d$ is the ratio of $l$ and $t_0$

$$v_d = \frac{l}{t_0} \tag{4.12}$$

The drift velocity can also be simply related to the electric field that produces the net movement. If we use the effective mass $m^*$ for the electrons and neglect the directional aspects of the scattering due to the collisions, the acceleration of the electron between collisions in the direction of the force is

$$\vec{a} = \frac{-q}{m^*}\vec{E} \tag{4.13}$$

The magnitude of the average drift velocity is

$$v_d = \frac{q}{m^*}Et_0 \tag{4.14}$$

where $E$ is the magnitude of the electric field. It might be argued that a factor of $1/2$ should appear in (4.13). However, the result given is correct. Remember that the average time between collisions is proposed. If one studies the statistics of this type of problem, one finds that the collision times shorter than $t_0$ occur more often but make less contribution to the average, because the final acceleration in these short periods is less. In (4.14), we need the average velocity, not the average final velocity. In the same manner, we can show[2] that the average time from the last collision is equal to the average time until the next collision, both of which equal $t_0$.

We see in (4.14) that the mean drift velocity is proportional to the magnitude of the electric field. It is helpful then to propose a normalized drift velocity which is a function only of the material. The normalized drift velocity is called the *mobility* $\mu$. It is common when working with material properties to use *cgs* units rather than *mks* units. The conversion between the units is usually evident.

$$\mu = \frac{v_d}{E} \quad \text{cm}^2/\text{V-s} \tag{4.15}$$

---

[1] A "collision" on the atomic scale means only that the particle is strongly deflected by the close-range forces within the atom.

[2] Feynman et al., *op. cit.*, vol. 1, secs. 43.1 to 43.3.

Typical values of $\mu$ for different materials are given shortly.

Keeping in mind that we are dealing first with metals, we can write an expression for the current density which flows because of the presence of the $\vec{E}$ field and the net drift velocity. If the volume density of free electrons is $n$ and all are moving with the drift velocity, the magnitude of the current density in amperes per unit area is

$$J = qnv_d \tag{4.16}$$

If we use (4.15), we obtain

$$J = qn\mu E = \sigma_m E \tag{4.17}$$

where

$$\sigma_m = qn\mu \tag{4.18}$$

In (4.18), $\sigma_m$ is defined as the electrical conductivity of the metal and has the dimensions of $(\Omega\text{-cm})^{-1}$ or mho/cm. If we use (4.12) and (4.14) in (4.18), we obtain an alternate expression for $\sigma_m$

$$\sigma_m = n\frac{q^2 l}{m^* v_d} \tag{4.19}$$

Typical values of $\sigma_m$—established from direct measurements—are tabulated here for three metals and two alloys at 20°C (293°K):

| Metal | $\sigma_m$ mho/cm |
|---|---|
| Al | $3.5 \cdot 10^5$ |
| Cu | $5.9 \cdot 10^5$ |
| Fe | $1.0 \cdot 10^5$ |
| Stainless Steel (347) | $1.4 \cdot 10^4$ |
| Nichrome alloy | $0.9 \cdot 10^4$ |

From these values, as well as from other experiments, values for $l$, $t_0$, and $\mu$ can be established for a given metal.

Equation (4.17) is, of course, Ohm's law in terms of current density and the magnitude of the electric field. Often the alternate form in terms of the resistivity of the material is used.

$$\rho = \frac{1}{\sigma} \quad \Omega\text{-cm} \tag{4.20}$$

The value of either $\sigma$ or $\rho$ can be used to determine the power which is dissipated in the solid due to the collisions occurring in the conduction process. For a unit cube the power density in the solid is $JE$.

$$JE = \sigma^2 E \quad \text{W/cm}^3 \tag{4.21}$$

As a final point, we should note that in a typical metal the number of conduction electrons does not change with temperature. Because of the lack of an energy gap, all valence electrons are available for $T > 0°K$. However, as temperature increases, the increased thermal energy of the environment is manifested by increased vibrations of the atoms and ions in the lattice. This increases the incidence of electron collision which decreases $\mu$ and the conductivity. The decrease of conductivity or the increase of resistivity is a typical property of a metal. In Fig. 4.16, the resistivity of copper is shown as a function of temperature.

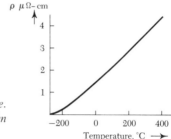

**FIGURE 4.16** *Resistivity of copper versus temperature.* (*From R. L. Sproull, "Modern Physics," 2d ed., John Wiley & Sons, Inc., New York, 1963.*)

## 4.7 electron and hole flow in semiconductors

The mechanism and formulation of current flow in a metal, as in the last section, are not adequate to describe current flow in a pure semiconductor. The reason for this is that a second, independent current conduction mechanism exists in a semiconductor. This mechanism, which was first proposed by A. H. Wilson in 1931, involves the motion of the valence electrons. Wilson showed that this second current mechanism can be modeled by a fictitious particle which is called the *hole*. The hole has an effective mass approximately the same as that of a free electron in the solid and a charge equal to $+q$. Values of the effective mass of the hole for several semiconductors are given inside the covers.

To establish this second current mechanism rigorously, one again needs a quantum-mechanical analysis. In this section, we illustrate the second mechanism in terms of both the band and bond pictures of the semiconductor. Figure 4.17 is a two-dimensional picture representing the covalent bonds between several silicon atoms. At a temperature greater than $0°K$, some covalent bonds are broken because these valence electrons have gained sufficient energy to become conduction or free electrons. These free electrons can move under the influence of an externally applied $\vec{E}$ field in the manner described for metals in the last section. The second current mechanism occurs because nearby valence electrons can easily move into the vacancy caused by the ionization of an atom. We know that the outermost electron orbits of an atom interact and overlap with the orbits of many adjacent atoms. Thus, the vacancies of covalent bonds due to ionization can be considered to move about the solid in a random, brownian-type motion similar to the manner in which free electrons in the conduction band move about the solid. Note that this movement of the vacancies involves electron motion *within* the valence band without recourse to an ionization process. When an electric field is applied, the electron motion in the valence band, i.e., the motion of the vacancies, acquires a net drift velocity similar to that of the free electrons. Note that the vacancy, as illustrated in Fig. 4.17, moves in the direction of the field. From an analysis

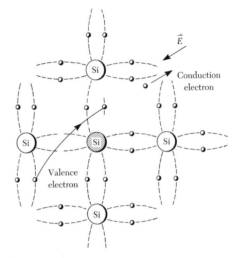

**FIGURE 4.17** *Two-dimensional particle model for a semiconductor at room temperature with a broken covalent bond (silicon assumed), illustrating movement of conduction electron and vacancy of covalent bond.*

of this current mechanism, a particle model, the hole, can be proposed to simulate the charged-particle movement. Because of the positive charge of the hole, the net drift velocity with an applied $\vec{E}$ field is in the direction of the field.

For an intrinsic semiconductor, the density of holes $p_i$ must equal the density of free electrons $n_i$, since a vacancy in the valence band must exist for each ionization that produces a free electron.

$$p_i = n_i \tag{4.22}$$

The conductivity of an intrinsic semiconductor must include both of the charged-particle flows. Following a development similar to that leading to (4.18), we can propose

$$J = q(\mu_e n_i + \mu_h p_i)\, E \tag{4.23a}$$

$$J = \sigma E \tag{4.23b}$$

where

$$\sigma = q(\mu_e n_i + \mu_h p_i) \tag{4.23c}$$

In (4.23), $\mu_e$ is the mobility for electrons and $\mu_h$ is the mobility for holes.

Values of these constants for intrinsic silicon and germanium at 300°K are:

$$\mu_e,\ cm^2/V\text{-}s \qquad \mu_h,\ cm^2/V\text{-}s$$

|    | $\mu_e,\ cm^2/V\text{-}s$ | $\mu_h,\ cm^2/V\text{-}s$ |
|----|------|------|
| Si | 1350 | 480  |
| Ge | 3900 | 1900 |

Values of $\mu_h$ are less than those of $\mu_e$, that is, the holes do not "move" through the lattice as readily as the electrons.[1] Using these results we obtain, for the conductivity of intrinsic silicon and germanium at 300°K, values of $4.4 \cdot 10^{-6}$ $(\Omega\text{-cm})^{-1}$ and 0.02 $(\Omega\text{-cm})^{-1}$, respectively.

The time of existence for a free electron is finite and an average lifetime can be proposed. As the free electron moves about the solid in a sequence of collisions, kinetic energy may be lost or gained. If sufficient energy is lost, i.e., an energy equal to or greater than the value of the energy gap, the electron drops into the valence band and fills a vacancy. The release of energy can take the form of light emission, or thermal energy can be returned to the lattice of the solid. This action or loss of a free electron can be considered to be a *recombination* of a hole-electron pair. Of course, as the thermal energy of the solid is increased due to recombinations, generation of new electron-hole pairs occurs in other locations in the solid. The *rate* of recombination must equal the *rate* of generation in thermal equilibrium. The average lifetime of the free electrons (which is equal to the average hole lifetime for intrinsic material in thermal equilibrium) is not only a function of the basic semiconductor material, but is also strongly dependent on imperfections and impurities in the solid. Experimentally obtained values are always used. Typical values of lifetime are in the order of 1 to 100 $\mu$s for Ge and Si.

## 4.8  impurity doping

As indicated earlier, electrical and physical properties of semiconductors are highly dependent on impurities. Because of unwanted impurities in even small densities, many important aspects of semiconductors were masked for many years. With the ability to make extremely pure semiconductor materials, such as silicon and germanium, controlled impurity doping could be accomplished to obtain desired electronic properties upon which our present semiconductor devices depend.

DONOR DOPING    The impurity materials of greatest interest to us are those which will occupy a normal position in a lattice, i.e., will substitute in the lattice for a semiconductor atom. This substitution is illustrated in Fig.

[1] The proof of this fact must come from the detailed analysis, but it is not surprising in view of the greater number of unoccupied states in the conduction band as compared with the valence band.

4.18. Many elements of valence 3 and valence 5 can serve as these *substitutional impurities*. As we will see, only small amounts of such impurities can make very large differences in the electrical properties of the semiconductor.

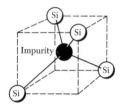

**FIGURE 4.18** *Diamond structure for an extrinsic semiconductor (Si is used as the parent material).*

To understand the change introduced by the addition of certain types of impurity elements, we use first the bond picture of Si, together with phosphorus (P), a valence 5 element, as the impurity. The P atom substitutes for a silicon atom in the lattice as illustrated in Fig. 4.19. Four of the valence electrons of the P atom can be considered to form strong covalent bonds with the neighboring Si atoms. The remaining electron from the P atom is only lightly tied to its parent atom and, at usual temperatures, escapes and becomes a free electron in the solid.

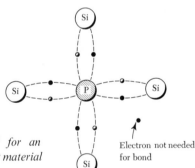

**FIGURE 4.19** *Two-dimensional particle model for an n-type extrinsic semiconductor with Si as parent material and P as the valence 5 impurity.*

Only a minute quantity of impurity can make a great change in the electrical conductivity of a semiconductor. Assume that only one impurity atom in $10^7$ silicon atoms is introduced. If all these impurity atoms are ionized, the density of additional free electrons is $10^{-7} \cdot 10^{22} = 10^{15}$ electrons/cm³. The density of free electrons in intrinsic silicon is $1.5 \cdot 10^{10}$. Therefore, the impurity has drastically increased the density of free electrons and the electrical conductivity of the material. As a point of reference, it may be noted that the purest of the naturally occurring elements is diamond, for which the impurity ratio is approximately $1:10^6$.

A semiconductor in which a controlled *impurity doping* has been introduced is called an *extrinsic* semiconductor. When an extrinsic semiconductor is doped with a valence 5 material, the semiconductor is called *n*-type, because the free electron density is predominant. The impurity atoms are called *donors*. The hole density in an *n*-type semiconductor is not only relatively less than the electron density because of the increase of electrons, but also the actual hole density is less than in an intrinsic semiconductor. This relationship can be visualized as follows. In the doped semiconductor in thermal equilibrium, the rate of generation and the rate of recombination are equal and both rates are almost exactly equal to the values for an intrinsic (pure) semiconductor. Remember that the impurity ratio may be only $1:10^7$; thus, the effect of the impurity atoms is very small on the overall thermal environment. Now if the probability of recombination per electron is the same, the time-average hole density must fall below the intrinsic value, since there are more electrons. This situation is like that found in chemical reactions and is referred to as a *mass-action* relation.[1] For such a relation, the product of the components is a constant. For the present case, the product of the electron density and the hole density is equal to a constant which is the product of the electron density and the hole density for the intrinsic case. For *n*-type material, the electron density is labeled $n_n$ and the hole density is labeled $p_n$. The product of the two is

$$n_n p_n = n_i p_i = n_i^2 \qquad (4.24)$$

It is also instructive to view impurity doping on the basis of the energy band picture, as in Fig. 4.20a. Because of the additional valence electron, a new, available energy level is present just below the conduction band. We show a line for this level and do not show a band because of the usual wide separation of impurity atoms in the semiconductor due to the

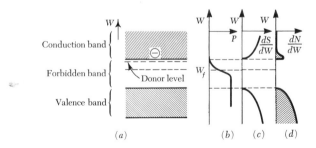

(a)  (b)  (c)  (d)

**FIGURE 4.20** *n-type semiconductor at* $300°K$. (a) *Energy-band diagram;* (b) *Fermi factor;* (c) *density of available states;* (d) *density of occupied states.*

[1]"Handbook of Chemistry and Physics," 46th ed., p. F70, Chemical Rubber Publishing Company, Cleveland, 1965, 1966.

light doping ratio. The new level is close to the edge of the conduction band because of the weak ties of the extra electron to its parent atom. The separation of the new energy states from the edge of the conduction band for several donor materials is shown in Fig. 4.21. Typically, the energy difference is of the order of 0.01 eV.

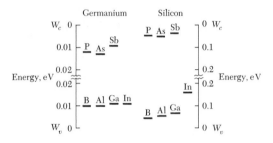

**FIGURE 4.21**    *Location of group III and group V substitutional impurity levels in silicon and germanium. (From L. V. Azaroff and J. J. Brophy, "Electronic Processes in Materials," McGraw-Hill Book Company, New York, 1963.)*

At room temperature, the ionization of the donor atoms is almost complete, the density of the donor atoms, $N_d$, is approximately equal to $n_n$ (see Prob. 4.19).

$$N_d \simeq n_n \qquad (4.25)$$

Returning to Fig. 4.20, we note that the Fermi level for a donor-doped semiconductor moves from the midpoint of the energy gap toward the conduction band. The relative position of the Fermi-Dirac probability function as shown in Fig. 4.20b, the basic shape of the density of allowed energy states as shown in Fig. 4.20c, and the nature of the electron density as shown in Fig. 4.20d are similar to the intrinsic case except that the magnitude of the electron density in the conduction band is greatly increased.

As mentioned earlier, the density of electrons due to donor doping is usually much greater than the density due to the parent material. Approximation (4.25) can be used to estimate the doping density of donors starting with a measurement of the conductivity of a sample of a doped semiconductor. From (4.23c), the conductivity is

$$\sigma = q(\mu_e n_n + \mu_h p_n) \qquad (4.26a)$$

For appreciable donor doping, $n_n >> p_n$ and (4.26a) becomes

$$\sigma \simeq q\mu_e n_n \qquad (4.26b)$$

To check this last point, an example is helpful. Assume that a sample of silicon is doped so that $n_n \simeq 10^{16}$ electrons/cm³. Using the mass-action expression, (4.24), we obtain

$$p_n = \frac{n_i^2}{n_n} \tag{4.27a}$$

$$p_n = \frac{(1.5 \cdot 10^{10})^2}{10^{16}} \simeq 2 \cdot 10^4 \text{ holes/cm}^3 \tag{4.27b}$$

Clearly, in this example, the hole density can be neglected in (4.26a) since $\mu_e$ and $\mu_h$ differ only by a factor of about 2. For an $n$-type material, the electrons are the *majority carriers* of current conduction and the holes the *minority carriers*. Because of the mass-action law, the ratio of majority-carrier density to the minority-carrier density can be large even for modest doping levels. To return to (4.26b), assume that the conductivity of a silicon sample at 300°K is 1 mho/cm. For the moment, we use the intrinsic value for electron mobility, 1350 cm²/V-s. From (4.26b), we obtain

$$n_n \simeq \frac{\sigma}{q\mu_e} = \frac{1}{(1.6 \cdot 10^{-19})(1350)}$$

$$= 0.46 \cdot 10^{16} \text{ electrons/cm}^3 \tag{4.28}$$

This value is not precise since the values of the mobility of electrons and holes in silicon vary with the density of electrons and/or holes. In the first two graphs of Fig. 4.22, data are presented showing the variation of $\mu_e$

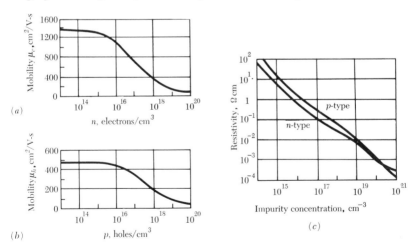

**FIGURE 4.22** *Mobility of majority and minority carriers in silicon at 300°K. (a) $\mu_e$ versus $n_n$; (b) $\mu_h$ versus $p_p$. (From R. B. Adler, A. C. Smith, and R. L. Longini, "Introduction to Semiconductor Physics," John Wiley & Sons, Inc., New York, 1964). (c) Density of majority carriers with resistivity. [From John C. Irvin, "Resistivity of Bulk Silicon and of Diffused Layers in Silicon," Bell Syst. Tech. J., 41:387-410 (1962).]*

and $\mu_h$ for $n$-type and $p$-type silicon. In Fig. 4.22$c$, curves of resistivity versus majority carrier density are presented which include the mobility variation. From this figure, we obtain $n_n \simeq 0.5 \cdot 10^{16}$ electron/cm$^3$. For this density, we see from Fig. 4.22$a$ that $\mu_e$ is 1250 cm$^2$/V-s.

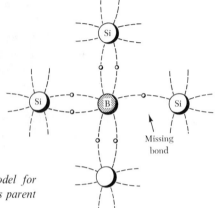

**FIGURE 4.23**  *Two-dimensional particle model for a p-type extrinsic semiconductor with Si as parent material and B as the valence 3 impurity.*

**ACCEPTOR DOPING**    A complementary doping situation is obtained if an intrinsic semiconductor is doped with a valence 3 material such as boron (B) or aluminum (Al). These elements again are substitutional impurities, as illustrated in Fig. 4.23. The three valence electrons of, say, boron form covalent bonds with neighboring silicon atoms. As shown in the figure, one covalent bond cannot be made, i.e., an electron is missing and a vacancy exists in one covalent bond. Therefore, holes exist in this doped material with a density larger than the intrinsic level $p_i$. Because the impurity atom can "accept" electrons from adjacent covalent bonds of the parent material, this type of impurity is called an *acceptor*. The density of acceptor atoms is denoted $N_a$.

The mass-action law for electron and hole densities also holds for an acceptor-doped material. The hole density is labeled $p_p$ and the electron density is labeled $n_p$. Thus

$$p_p n_p = n_i p_i = n_i^2 \tag{4.29}$$

The $p$ subscript is used since the positive carriers (holes) are the *majority carriers* and the material is called $p$-type material. The electrons are the *minority carriers* of $p$-type material. The earlier example of (4.27) can again be used with a change of subscripts to illustrate the density of majority and minority carriers in acceptor-doped silicon. If $p_p = 10^{16}$ holes/cm$^3$

$$n_p = \frac{n_i^2}{p_p} = 2 \cdot 10^4 \text{ electrons/cm}^3 \tag{4.30}$$

In the band picture of $p$-type material, the acceptor atoms introduce a new energy level in relation to intrinsic material which is just above the top edge of the valence band, as shown in Fig. 4.24$a$. A single level is shown rather than a band because the density of impurity atoms is

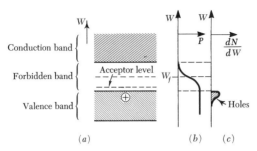

(a)                                  (b)    (c)

**FIGURE 4.24**  *p-type semiconductor at 300°K.* (a) *Energy-band diagram;* (b) *Fermi factor;* (c) *density of holes.*

usually so small—in relation to the density of the silicon atoms—that the interaction between them is negligible. The Fermi level is closer to the valence band for $p$-type material because of the increased density of holes. As implied in Fig. 4.24, the shift in the Fermi-Dirac distribution for $T > 0°$K and the density of available states lead to a density of holes which is the complement of the situation for an $n$-type material, as shown in Fig. 4.20. The density of electrons in the conduction band is not shown in Fig. 4.24$c$ but can be expected to be very small because of (4.29). The separation of the new impurity level from the top edge of the valence band is shown for several impurities in Fig. 4.21 for both silicon and germanium. Values of $\mu_e$ and $\mu_h$ in $p$-type material also vary with doping density. Proper values can be obtained from the curves of Fig. 4.22. In general, the values for $p$-type material are not identical to those for $n$-type material.

For both $n$-type and $p$-type materials, an interesting phenomenon occurs as temperature is increased. Assume we start with an $n$-type material at a very low temperature, say at $-100°$C. As shown in Fig. 4.25, the density of electrons is much larger than the density of holes at this temperature. As temperature is increased, the density of electrons increases slightly

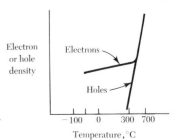

**FIGURE 4.25**  *Electron and hole density of an n-type semiconductor versus temperature.*

due to both an increase in the ionization of the donor atoms and an increase in the ionization of the native atoms. The latter, however, causes a marked increase in hole density, as shown by (4.11$b$). As temperature increases still more, the ratio of electron to hole density decreases rapidly. Finally, a temperature is reached at which the electron and hole densities are equal. The extrinsic material at low temperatures has become intrinsic, except for the presence of the now negligible impurities.

**COMPENSATION AND COMPOUND SEMICONDUCTORS**  A *compensation* of a doped semiconductor is obtained if the material is doped with other types of impurity. For example, an *n*-type semiconductor can be made intrinsic or can be converted to *p*-type by the introduction of acceptor atoms. The compensated material is almost exactly the same as intrinsic material because the density of both dopings is usually sufficiently small. Various compensation techniques are the key to the simple realization of practical semiconductor devices such as transistors. This topic is pursued further in the following chapters.

As a final topic in this section, we consider *compound semiconductors,* which are composed of two or more elements. Examples are the III-V materials, gallium arsenide (GaAs) and indium antimonide (InSb). The process of obtaining a III-V compound semiconductor can be considered to be the limit of the compensation technique wherein only donor and acceptor atoms are used to construct a semiconductor crystal without recourse to a native, valence 4 material. Compound semiconductors can be doped *p*-type or *n*-type with other impurities. These materials are not as simple to produce as elemental semiconductors such as silicon. However, the compound semiconductors have values of the electrical parameters such as mobility and temperature dependence, which are more useful than are silicon and germanium for some purposes. One example of such a use is the direct energy conversion of heat to electrical energy. In this book, we restrict attention to the elemental semiconductors; however, it is important to keep the other possibilities in mind.

It is also possible to obtain compound-semiconductor materials from valence 2 and valence 6 materials. An example of a II-VI semiconductor is cadmium sulfide. Still other valence combinations show semiconductor behavior, such as the IV-VI compounds, lead sulfide, selenide, and telluride.

## 4.9  diffusion current flow

By a variety of methods which are brought out as we progress, the equilibrium densities of electrons and holes as well as the transient densities of electrons and holes can vary with distance in the semiconductor. Because of the density gradient of electrons and holes, a *diffusion flow* of particles occurs that is comparable to the diffusion flow of particles in a true gas, where a density gradient causes particles to diffuse from a dense to a less dense region. This additional current flow over and above the *drift current flow*, caused by applied fields, is very important in semiconductors.

As an illustration, we can assume that a narrow beam of light is incident on *n*-type silicon. We neglect surface effects and assume that the incident radiation causes ionization of silicon atoms in only a particular small volume of the semiconductor. Both the electron and hole densities are changed, but the hole density is changed more since holes are the minority carriers.[1] Because of the relative independence of the electrons and holes during an average lifetime, the electrons and holes are free to move about the solid. In particular, the "excess" holes in the small illuminated region diffuse toward regions of lesser hole density. The diffusion, as in gases, is a result of the fact that particles are in random thermal motion, and so the diffusion produces a net flux across a plane separating a region of high density and one of low density. A sketch of the hole diffusion is shown for one dimension in Fig. 4.26. The illumination occurs in the region near $x = 0$ and increases the density of holes. The holes diffuse in both directions, i.e., to the right and the left. Finally, a definite time-average profile of hole density exists, as shown. As the holes diffuse away from the radiation, recombination with electrons occurs and the excess hole density gradually reduces with distance. The flow of the charged particles constitutes a current flow and the current density of the hole flow at a point $x$ is directly proportional to the gradient of the hole density at the point. This can be written in one dimension as

$$J_h(x) = -qD_h \frac{dp(x)}{dx} \quad \text{A/cm}^2 \tag{4.31a}$$

In (4.31a), $D_h$ is a constant of proportionality called the *diffusion constant* for holes. This constant is a characteristic of the semiconductor material. It is related to the mobility constant as brought out below. The negative sign of (4.31a) is the result of the basic definition of a current flow of positive particles. If $dp/dx$ is positive, the holes flow in the opposite, or negative, direction as does the hole current.

Because of the gradient of electrons in the material as illustrated in Fig. 4.26c, a diffusion of electrons also occurs. The relative change of $n(x)$ is small in relation to $n_n$, the majority-carrier density in thermal equilibrium. Nonetheless, a gradient $dn/dx$ exists (which is equal to $dp/dx$ since charge neutrality holds) and an electron diffusion current flows. The current

---

[1] Regardless of the method of change, the changes of $p$ and $n$ at a given point will be equal. This is a consequence of the requirement of charge neutrality in the semiconductor. If the region is not charge neutral, electric fields are present which always tend by a drift action to bring in the properly charged particle to achieve charge neutrality.

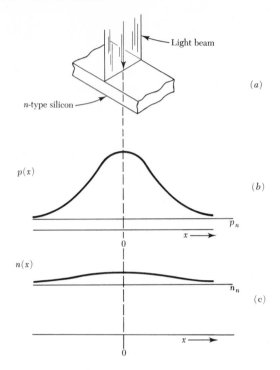

**FIGURE 4.26** *n-type silicon bar.* (a) *Illuminated with a beam of light;* (b) *resulting minority-carrier density with distance from the light beam;* (c) *resulting majority-carrier density, different scale from b.*

density for electrons can be written

$$J_e(x) = qD_e\frac{dn}{dx} \tag{4.31b}$$

$D_e$ is called the diffusion constant for electrons. Note that a positive sign is used in (4.31b) since the electrons have a negative sign.

Values of $D_e$ and $D_h$ at 300°K for very pure materials are given below:

|           | $D_e$, $cm^2/s$ | $D_h$, $cm^2/s$ |
|-----------|-----------------|-----------------|
| Silicon   | 35.0            | 12.5            |
| Germanium | 101.0           | 49.0            |

These values are dependent on the doping of the semiconductor in the same manner as the mobility constants $\mu_e$ and $\mu_h$. However, the ratio of the $\mu$ to $D$ is a constant at a given temperature as first shown by Einstein:

$$\frac{D_e}{\mu_e} = \frac{D_h}{\mu_h} = \frac{kT}{q} \equiv V_T \tag{4.32}$$

Notice that $kT/q$ is labeled $V_T$. At $300°K$, $V_T = 0.0259$ V $\simeq 0.026$ V. Because of (4.32) the mobility curves of Fig. 4.22 can also be used to obtain values of $D_e$ and $D_h$.

The Einstein relation is developed by considering the possibility of both drift and diffusion current flows of the same particle.[1] In the next chapter, we show how an electric field is established in a semiconductor which has a nonuniform doping with distance. For this section, we assume that an $\vec{E}$ field in our one-dimensional situation exists, together with its associated electrostatic potential variation in the $x$ direction $\psi(x)$. If the semiconductor is not connected, i.e., if it is an open circuit, no net current can flow. However, the individual diffusion and drift current components can be present. If a density gradient of holes exists, diffusion current can flow; however, it must be opposed by an equal and opposite drift current. For holes in an $n$-type material, we can express this as follows:

$$J_h = J_{h,\text{diff}} + J_{h,\text{drift}}$$

$$= -qD_h \frac{dp_n(x)}{dx} + q\mu_h p_n(x)E = 0 \tag{4.33a}$$

A rearrangement of this equation, dropping subscripts on $p$, leads to

$$\frac{1}{p}\frac{dp}{dx} = \frac{\mu_h}{D_h} E \tag{4.33b}$$

Now the electric field is the negative gradient of the electrostatic potential which is present in the semiconductor, $E = -d\psi/dx$. If this is used in (4.33b), we obtain

$$d\psi = -\frac{D_h}{\mu_h}\frac{dp}{p} \tag{4.33c}$$

The solution of this differential equation has the form

$$p(x) = Ce^{(D_h/\mu_h)\psi} \tag{4.33d}$$

where $C$ is a constant. Equation (4.33d) has the same form as the Boltzmann factor (4.10), and in fact, it must be a Boltzmann relation. This follows in our situation because the holes (and electrons) have an energy distribution which is Boltzmann. The electrostatic potential in the semiconductor is a potential barrier which impedes the diffusion flow. At a point $x$, then, the density of holes at this point must include only those particles with energy greater than the potential barrier at $x$. The potential energy of the barrier is $W = q\psi$. Therefore, from the Boltzmann relation, we can write directly

$$p(x) = C'e^{-q\psi/kT} \tag{4.33e}$$

[1] Feynman et al., op. cit., vol. 1, secs. 40.1, 40.2, 43.4, 43.5.

where $C'$ is a constant which describes the reference situation for $\psi = 0$, that is, $C' = p_n$. Comparing (4.33$d$) and (4.33$e$), we obtain the Einstein relation from the two exponents

$$\frac{\mu_h}{D_h} = \frac{kT}{q} \qquad (4.33f)$$

A similar development can be used for electrons. The end result, of course, must be the same. As mentioned above, we discuss the origin and nature of the electrostatic potential in nonuniform semiconductors in the next chapter.

## 4.10   hall effect

In the preceding sections, it has been primarily assumed that forces on the particles due to external effects arise because of applied potentials or electric fields. We conclude this chapter with a brief look at the effects in a semiconductor arising from applied magnetic fields. In addition to the inherent importance of forces due to magnetic fields, an experiment due to E. H. Hall can be described which vividly demonstrates the existence of electron and hole currents in a semiconductor.

**ISOLATED ELECTRON MOTION IN A SIMPLE MAGNETIC FIELD**   From Sec. 4.2, we see that the force on an electron in a uniform magnetic field is perpendicular to both the $\vec{B}$ field and the velocity vectors. This is illustrated in Fig. 4.27.

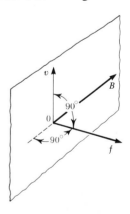

**FIGURE 4.27**   *Force on a moving electron in a B field.*

Of course, the force on the electron modifies its vector direction. If $v$ is a constant, that is, if no electric fields are present, the electron describes a circular path in a plane perpendicular to $\vec{v}$ and $\vec{B}$. This is illustrated in Fig. 4.1$b$. The acceleration of the electron is toward the center of the circle of radius $r$ and can be expressed $v^2/r$. From Newton's second law, and if we choose the $\vec{v}$ and $\vec{B}$ vectors to be perpendicular, the force directed toward the center is found from (4.3). In (4.3), the cross product becomes a simple product since $\vec{v}$ and $\vec{B}$ are perpendicular.

$$f = qvB = m\frac{v^2}{r} \tag{4.34$a$}$$

$$r = \frac{mv}{qB} \tag{4.34$b$}$$

where $f$, $v$, and $B$ denote the magnitudes of the vectors. Note that $f$ increases and $r$ decreases as $B$ increases.

The angular velocity $\omega$ of the electron is

$$\omega = \frac{v}{r} = \frac{qB}{m} \quad \text{rad/s}$$

$\omega$ is independent of $v$ and is called the *cyclotron angular frequency*. The time $\tau$ required for the particle to complete one full circle is found from the relation

$$\omega\tau = 2\pi \tag{4.35$a$}$$

$$\tau = \frac{2\pi}{\omega} = \frac{2\pi m}{qB} \tag{4.35$b$}$$

Using the values of $q$ and $m$ for the electron, we obtain

$$\tau = \frac{3.57 \cdot 10^{-11}}{B} \quad \text{second} \tag{4.35$c$}$$

For a numerical result, if $B = 0.1 \text{ Wb/m}^2$, $\tau = 3.57 \cdot 10^{-10}$ s $= 0.357$ ns.

**HALL VOLTAGE**   In order to think in terms of the motion of individual particles in a solid due to magnetic forces, we continue to use the concepts of effective mass, etc. Assume now that an $n$-type semiconductor is placed in a magnetic field as in Fig. 4.28. The magnetic field is in the positive $z$

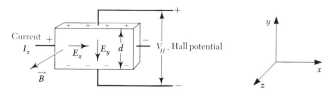

**FIGURE 4.28**   *Hall effect.*

direction. In addition, an electric field, $E_x$ is applied in the positive $x$ direction. The electric field $E_x$ produces a drift motion of the electrons to the left. However, because of the magnetic field, the electrons are deflected down, in the negative $y$ direction. This deflection force $f_{yB}$, from (4.34a), is

$$f_{yB} = -q(E_x\mu_e)\,B \tag{4.36}$$

where $B$ is the magnitude of the magnetic field and $(E_x\mu_e)$ is the magnitude of the drift velocity in the $-x$ direction. The density of the electrons is greater near the bottom of the sample and is smaller near the top of the sample. Consequently, a potential difference must exist within the sample in the $y$ direction and an electric field $E_y$ is present. In equilibrium, the field $E_y$ attains a value which equalizes the force $f_{yB}$ due to the magnetic field.

$$f_{yE} = -qE_y = -f_{yB} \tag{4.37}$$

$f_{yE}$ is directed in the $+y$ direction. From the equality of the forces, we obtain

$$E_y = -E_x\mu_e\,B \tag{4.38}$$

This field produces a potential difference across the sample in the $y$ direction. The potential difference is called the Hall voltage $V_H$. If the depth of the sample is $d$,

$$V_H = -E_y d \tag{4.39}$$

For the case at hand, $V_H$ is positive from top to bottom. Note, however, that if a $p$-type semiconductor is used, the positive particles, holes, move toward the right with the application of the electric field $E_x$ and are deflected down by the $B$ field. The Hall voltage now is negative from top to bottom of the sample. Consequently, a direct measurement of the Hall voltage of a semiconductor indicates by its polarity whether the material is $n$-type or $p$-type.

The measurement of the Hall effect can also be used to determine the value of the mobility of the majority carriers or the density of the majority carriers in conjunction with measurements of the conductivity of the sample. If we define the current in the $x$ direction as $I_x$, we can obtain

$$I_x = AJ_x = A\sigma E_x \tag{4.40a}$$

where $A$ is the cross-sectional area in the $yz$ plane. Equations (4.38) and (4.39) are now used

$$I_x = A\frac{\sigma V_H}{\mu_e Bd} \tag{4.40b}$$

The result is

$$\frac{\mu_e}{\sigma} = \frac{AV_H}{I_x dB} \tag{4.41}$$

The mobility $\mu_e$ can be determined if $\sigma$ is known and if the other constants are measured. Since $\sigma = q\mu_e n_n$, (4.41) is also equal to $1/qn_n$ and the density of carriers can also be obtained from the Hall measurement.

### REFERENCES

G. L. Pearson and W. H. Brattain, "History of Semiconductor Research," *Proc. IRE*, **43**:1794-108 (1955).

R. B. Adler, A. C. Smith, and R. L. Longini, "Introduction to Semiconductor Physics," Semiconductor Electronics Education Committee (SEEC), John Wiley and Sons, Inc., New York, 1964.

R. P. Feynman, R. B. Leighton, and M. Sands, "The Feynman Lectures on Physics," vols. 1 and 3, Addison-Wesley Publishing Company, Inc., Reading Mass., 1963.

W. R. Beam, "Electronics of Solids," McGraw-Hill Book Company, New York, 1965.

R. L. Sproull, "Modern Physics," 2d ed., John Wiley and Sons, Inc., New York, 1963.

### PROBLEMS

**4.1** Electrons moving horizontally with a kinetic energy of 500 eV are injected at point $P$ into a uniform, constant $\vec{E}$ field, as shown. It is required that the electrons leave through point $B$ in an upwards direction 5 ns after entering at $P$.

(a) Find the $\vec{E}$ field.

(b) If the electrons were to travel in the $\vec{E}$ field found under part $a$ but the horizontal distance were doubled, how much must their kinetic energy be for them to pass through the new point $B'$ in the same time?

(c) Assume that the electrons are injected at $P$ but that their velocity vector $v_o$ forms an angle with the $\vec{E}$ vector of 45°. What $\vec{E}$ field is needed for the electrons to leave through point $B$ in the same time? Their kinetic energy at $P$ is 500 eV.

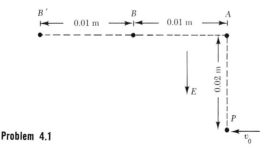

**Problem 4.1**

**4.2**   Electrons are injected into a uniform, constant $\vec{E}$ field of $10^4$ V/m at point $P$, as shown. The kinetic energy of the electrons at $P$ is 100 eV.

(a) Find the time needed for the electrons to arrive at $B$.

(b) What is the distance $AP$?

(c) Calculate the gravitational force on the electron and compare with the force from the $\vec{E}$ field.

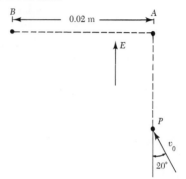

**Problem 4.2**

**4.3**   Compute the mobility of free electrons in silver, atomic weight 108, density 10.5 g/cm$^3$, and resistivity $1.6 \cdot 10^{-6}$ $\Omega$-cm.

**4.4**   Shown is a 5-m long, thin-walled (1 mm) cylindrical pipe of radius 10 cm. The following is known about the pipe: It is metallic; the metal has a valence of 1 and a conductivity of $5 \cdot 10^5$ mho/cm; the electrons in the metal have a mobility of 40 cm$^2$/V-s. A dc voltage has been applied across the pipe, as shown in the figure, causing a current to flow from one end to the other. Assume the drift velocity in the metal to be $8 \cdot 10^{-5}$ cm/s.

(a) What voltage has been applied?

(b) What current is flowing?

(c) What is the resistance of the pipe?

(d) If the voltage were halved and the pipe wall made twice as thick, what would be the change in drift velocity? In mobility?

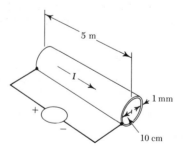

**Problem 4.4**

**4.5**   An ingot of Ge is formed by melting 100 g of Ge and $3.22 \cdot 10^{-6}$ g of antimony. (The density of Ge is 5.35 g/cm$^3$; its atomic weight is

72.60. The atomic weight of antimony is 121.76. One gram atomic weight, e.g., 72.6 g of Ge, contains Avogadro's number of atoms, $6.02 \cdot 10^{23}$.) Calculate the density of antimony atoms if they are uniformly distributed. What is the conductivity of the doped Ge if we assume that all antimony atoms are ionized?

**4.6** A narrow light beam is directed upon a $p$-type semiconductor crystal, as shown. This causes a local increase in the hole density. The light beam was switched on at time $t = 0$. At time $t = 500 \cdot 10^{-6}$ s, the holes are observed at point $B$ by an oscilloscope. Find the value of the hole mobility.

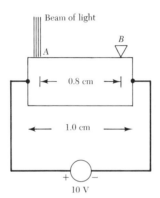

**Problem 4.6**

**4.7** Find the current $I$ flowing through the specimen shown if ($a$) the specimen is pure silicon and ($b$) the specimen is pure silicon to which arsenic has been added in a concentration of one arsenic atom per $10^6$ Si atoms. Neglect any contact effects at the terminals of the specimen, and assume a uniform current flow across the cross section of the sample.

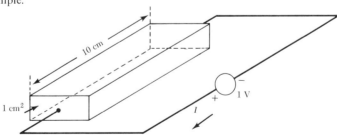

**Problem 4.7**

**4.8** The area under the Boltzmann distribution from $W_c$ to infinity is a measure of the density of conduction electrons in a semiconductor if we assume that the density of available states is a constant. Integrate the Boltzmann factor to obtain an expression for $n_i$ comparable to (4.11$b$). If the energy gap of the material is 1.0 eV, compare the approximate values of $n_i$ at $T = 300°$K and $T = 270°$K using the Boltzmann distribution.

**4.9** A silicon semiconductor has $10^{18}$ acceptor atoms/cm$^3$, all of which are assumed ionized. Using a hole mobility at room temperature of 480 cm$^2$/V-s, (a) calculate the conductivity $\sigma$ at room temperature and (b) calculate the electron density ($n_i = 1.5 \cdot 10^{10}$ cm$^{-3}$).

**4.10** If the effective mass of a free electron in Si is 1.1 times the rest mass of an electron and the mean free time is 8.4 ns, what is the average distance between collisions along the direction of the applied field in a sample of Si 1 mm thick, across which 10 V is applied?

**4.11** A Ge sample with both donor and acceptor impurities has a conduction electron density given by the following expression:

$$n = (N + \sqrt{N^2 + 4n_i^2})$$

where $N$ is the net impurity concentration per unit volume, $N = N_a - N_d$.

(a) Find the value of $N$ if $n = 1.7 \cdot 10^{17}$ electrons/cm$^3$ (since $n > n_i$, the material is $n$-type).

(b) Find the hole density $p_n$.

**4.12** A semiconductor material at room temperature contains a uniform distribution of $N_d = 10^{17}$ donors/cm$^3$ and $N_a = 1.6 \cdot 10^{17}$ acceptors/cm$^3$. At room temperature, $n_i = 10^{13}$ electrons/cm$^3$.

(a) Find $n$, the density of conduction electrons/cm$^3$, and $p$, the hole density/cm$^3$. (Note that two equations are now needed, where the second concerns charge neutrality.)

(b) Is the character of the sample $n$-type or $p$-type?

**4.13** Assume that it is necessary to increase the conductivity of intrinsic silicon by a factor of $10^3$ by adding boron (acceptor) impurities. Find the ratio of boron to silicon atoms required at room temperature.

**4.14** Assume a semiconductor with the following values:

Atomic weight = 60      $\mu_e = 2000$ cm$^2$/V-s

Density = 5.8 g/cm$^3$      $A_1 = 10^{40}$

$n_i^2 = A_1 e^{-W_g/kT}$ cm$^{-6}$      $W_g = 0.75$ eV

(a) Consider an intrinsic semiconductor at room temperature (300°K). By how much does the conductivity of the semiconductor *increase* or *decrease* per degree rise in temperature?

(b) If a donor impurity is added to the extent of one atom per $10^7$ intrinsic semiconductor atoms, what is the conductivity of the extrinsic semiconductor at 300°K? (Assume that the donor impurity contributes one electron per atom and that $N_d >> n_i$.)

**4.15** Find the resistivity of intrinsic silicon at 300°K. If one donor-type impurity atom is added for each $10^8$ Si atoms, find the resistivity of the extrinsic material.

**4.16**   If $A_o$ in (4.11*b*) is $3.86 \cdot 10^{16}$ for Si and $W_g = 1.12$ eV, calculate $n_i$ at $300°$K and at $240°$K. Compare your results with our reference value.

**4.17**   The donor doping of a silicon bar varies linearly with length. At one point, the density is $10^{16}$ atoms/cm$^3$. $10\mu$ away, the density is $10^{17}$ atoms/cm$^3$. What is the magnitude of the diffusion current in this region if the cross section of the bar is 25 by $75\mu$. What value of potential difference across this region is needed to produce an equal but opposite drift current? $1 \mu = 10^{-6}$ m.

**4.18**   Estimate the fraction of covalent bonds which are broken for pure carbon (diamond) at $300°$K. Compare your value with the corresponding value for silicon. For carbon, $W_g = 6$ eV.

**4.19**   Assume that the donor level of an $n$-type semiconductor material is $kT$ below the edge of the conduction band at room temperature. Assume that the total density of available energy states in the conduction band can be considered to be at the bottom edge of the band, with a density of $10^{19}$ states/cm$^3$. In addition, assume that the density of donor atoms is $10^{15}$ atoms/cm$^3$. Find the density of electrons in the conduction band contributed by the donor atoms by combining the probability of occupancy of an energy state with the density of available states in both the conduction band and the donor level. Discuss why this type of calculation illustrates that the donor atoms are essentially all ionized.

**4.20**   If $A_o$ in (4.11*b*) is approximately $2 \cdot 10^{16}$ for Ge and $4 \cdot 10^{16}$ for Si, calculate what change in temperature from $300°$K is needed to double $n_i$ for both materials.

**4.21**   If $n$-type samples of Si and Ge have the same conductivity, which material first becomes "intrinsic" as temperature is increased above $300°$K? What is your estimate of the two temperatures?

**4.22**   At room temperature, a specimen of GaAs has an energy gap of $W_g = 1.35$ eV. The density of available states in the conduction band is $N_c = 4.7 \cdot 10^{17}$/cm$^3$, that of the valence band $N_v = 10^{19}$/cm$^3$.

   (*a*) Find the intrinsic carrier concentration $n_i$ using

$$n_i p_i = N_c N_v e^{-(W_c - W_v)/kT}$$

   (*b*) What is the intrinsic conductivity?

   (*c*) Assume that GaAs has a donor concentration of $N_d = 10^{17}$/cm$^3$ and an acceptor concentration of $N_a = 10^{16}$/cm$^3$. If all the donor and acceptor atoms are ionized, find the concentration of the majority carriers.

   (*d*) Find the extrinsic conductivity for the conditions of part *c*.

**4.23**   An electron is emitted from plane 1, as shown, and is accelerated by potential $V_2$ located in plane 2. Find the time of flight of the electron over the field-free region from plane 2 to plane 3 for (a) $V_2 = 100$ V, (b) $V_2 = 10^6$ V.

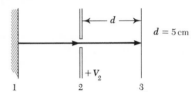

**Problem 4.23**

**4.24**   An electron stream with an initial velocity $v_0$ ($= 10^6$ m/s) is injected at point $a$ into a region in which a horizontal magnetic field $B( = 0.01$ Wb/m$^2$) is present. The angle of injection is $\theta = 30°$, as shown. Sketch and describe the motion of the electrons and give the number of turns of the electron path in traversing the distance $d( = 0.02$ m).

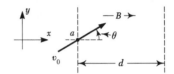

**Problem 4.24**

**4.25**   A bar of intrinsic silicon as in Fig. 4.28 measures 1 mm by 1 mm by 10 cm and has a small amount of donor impurity added.

(a) What is the valence of the elemental impurity atom?

(b) Under an applied electric field of 1 mV/cm applied in the $x$ direction, a current of 1 mA in the $x$ direction is measured. What is the impurity concentration?

(c) The bar is placed in a transverse magnetic field $\vec{B}$, where $B = 1$ Wb/m$^2$ directed along the positive $z$ axis. Sketch the paths of the holes and electrons in the bar.

(d) Indicate the voltage resulting from the current flow in the magnetic field (recall your answer to part $a$).

**4.26**   A specimen of extrinsic silicon as in Fig. 4.28, with $d = 2$ mm and width in the $z$ direction $= 0.2$ mm, has a magnetic field $B = 0.1$ Wb/m$^2$ directed in the $+z$ direction. A current $I = 10$ mA flows through the specimen in the $+x$ direction. Across the terminals shown, a Hall voltage $V_{12}$ is found to be $-2$ mV.

(a) Is this specimen $n$- or $p$-type material?

(b) Determine the impurity concentration $N_d$ or $N_a$.

(c) If the conductivity of the specimen is 1 ($\Omega$-cm)$^{-1}$ at 300°K, determine the mobility of the charge carriers contributing principally to the current flow (assume $n_n \simeq N_d$ and $p_p \simeq N_a$).

chapter **5**

# THE *pn*-JUNCTION DIODE

## 5.1 *pn*-junction devices

By any of several different processing techniques, one of which is described below, single-crystal, semiconductor solids can be obtained in which both *p*-type and *n*-type regions exist with an abrupt change of doping impurity from one region to the other. The sharp transition from a *p* region to an *n* region is called a *pn* junction. Injection and collection of majority and minority carriers from one region of a *pn* junction to the other is possible if the proper external potentials are applied. This control of electron and hole flow leads to important electronic devices such as semiconductor diodes and transistors.[1] In this chapter, the physical behavior of the *pn* junction is investigated. This leads to a first-order description of the current-voltage characteristic of the simplest semiconductor junction device, the *pn* junction diode. In the next chapter, applications of this device are given, together with other descriptions of the diode. In the following three chapters, a similar introduction is made for the junction transistor. With the diode, a nonlinear *IV* characteristic is obtained which is very useful in signal processing. With the transistor, all-important signal power gain can be obtained as is required for amplifiers.

---

[1]At the present, the volume of semiconductor business in the United States is about one billion dollars per year with about $0.5 \cdot 10^9$ individual devices manufactured. Most of these are *pn*-junction devices, but a small fraction are special-purpose devices utilizing bulk effects in a semiconductor.

In order to obtain a usable *pn* junction it is necessary that the transition from *p*-type to *n*-type material be accomplished without a change in the basic lattice structure of the solid. That is, the material should be a single crystal without grain boundaries. If grain boundaries exist, the imperfection in the lattice structure greatly distorts the desired majority-carrier and minority-carrier densities in the solid, as well as the flow of these carriers. Thus, one cannot simply butt together separate *n*-type and *p*-type crystals and expect the behavior to be described below.

A single-crystal *pn* junction is usually obtained by the use of a compensation technique, as mentioned in the last chapter. A common method to achieve *pn* junctions is based on the diffusion of other impurity atoms into an originally doped semiconductor.[1] To illustrate this technique, assume that an original semiconductor wafer is *n*-type silicon (Si) on which is grown a layer of silicon dioxide (SiO$_2$). This is shown in Fig. 5.1*a*. The

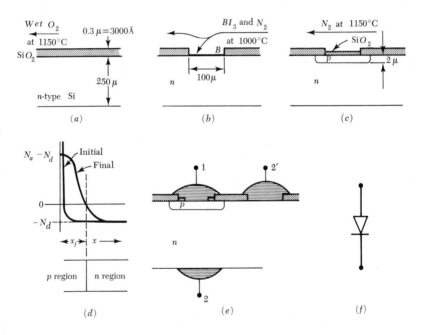

**FIGURE 5.1**   *Construction of a pn diode.* (a) *Thermally grown oxide on n-type* Si, (b) *predeposit of* B *through windows in the oxide;* (c) *drive-in of* B *to obtain p region;* (d) *net acceptor (acceptor − donor) density with distance from the surface;* (e) *window openings in oxide, metallization, and lead attachment;* (f) *pn-diode symbol.*

[1]Other methods include the growing of the *pn* junction during the original crystal formation and an alloying process in which an impurity metal is alloyed into the semiconductor (see Sec. 7.1).

$SiO_2$ layer is grown by placing a highly cleaned and polished Si wafer in an oxygen and water-vapor atmosphere at a temperature around 1150°C. A typical thickness of the Si wafer is 250 $\mu$ ( = 250 · 10$^{-6}$ $m$ = 250 · 10 cm $\simeq$ 0.01 in.). The oxide thickness might be 3000Å = 0.3 $\mu$. A small opening in the oxide layer is made, as shown in Fig. 5.1*b*, using photolithographic techniques. The Si wafer is now placed in a furnace, at say 1000°C, in which is flowing a gas mixture containing boron tri-iodide ($BI_3$) with $N_2$. At this temperature, the $BI_3$ dissociates and boron atoms are deposited on the exposed silicon surface. These boron atoms are taken up in a solid solution by the silicon. The "pre-deposited" wafer is next placed in a furnace, at 1150°C, with only $N_2$ flowing. The solid solution of B in Si near the surface of the wafer redistributes itself by a diffusion process, with the boron atoms migrating to regions of less boron doping. The initial and final distributions of the density of impurity atoms with depth are illustrated in Fig. 5.1*d*. Notice that a net acceptor density is chosen to be positive and that $N_d$ is the magnitude of the background, or original, density of donor atoms in the Si. At a distance $x_j$ from the surface, the net density—acceptors minus donors—is zero. This plane is taken as the location of the *pn* junction, i.e., the metallurgical boundary between the *p* and *n* regions, as illustrated. This boundary can be very flat and uniform if the original surface is parallel to the lattice orientation of the solid. In the redistribution (drive-in) process, wet $O_2$ is usually introduced during a portion of the drive-in to obtain a new $SiO_2$ layer. This step is particularly important since it keeps the surface of the silicon protected. Contacts are made to the *p* and *n* regions as shown in Fig. 5.1*e* to obtain a *pn*-junction diode. Note that a contact to the *n* region can be made at the bottom (2) or from the top surface (2'). The ohmic resistance of this region will be less for the former, although the latter is usually simpler for manufacture. The final element is a diode with two leads which has a highly nonlinear conductance or *IV* characteristic as is brought out below. The circuit element symbol for the diode is shown in Fig. 5.1*f*.

From Fig. 5.1*e*, it is clear that the flow of particles is at least a two-dimensional process and is probably a three-dimensional one if the width of the junction into the paper is also considered. For simplicity, a one-dimensional situation is chosen initially for analysis, and the results are fortunately useful for many three-dimensional devices. In effect, a small filament of the semiconductor is chosen near the center of the *pn* junction. The schematic diagram of the doping in this filament with distance is assumed to be that shown in Fig. 5.1*d*. Only doping and carrier densities with *x* are studied. No variation in doping and majority-carrier densities in the plane parallel to the junction is considered, nor are edge or surface effects included. After the basic electrical properties of this idealized situation are established, one can go back to consider the three-dimensional flow and control of carriers. Fortunately, we can often include the edge effects of the diode by adding to the idealized situation a parallel combination of other diodes which differ only in the constants which characterize their behavior. An actual diode, then, can be considered to be the parallel sum of several one-dimensional diodes and the actual electrical behavior is a composite of the individual characteristics.

## 5.2 the potential barrier of a *pn* junction

An idealized *pn* junction is illustrated in Fig. 5.2. For simplicity, the $p$ region and the $n$ region in Fig. 5.2*a* are assumed to have a constant impurity doping, $N_a$ and $N_d$, respectively. An abrupt change from donor to acceptor doping occurs at $x = 0$ as shown in Fig. 5.2*b*. As mentioned in Sec. 5.1, only one-dimensional phenomena are now considered. At an ordinary ambient temperature (300°K), the densities of holes and electrons well away from the junction are also constant with $x$. The (vertical) scale of particle densities in Fig. 5.2*c* may be considered logarithmic in order to show both majority- and minority-carrier densities. In the vicinity of the junction, a

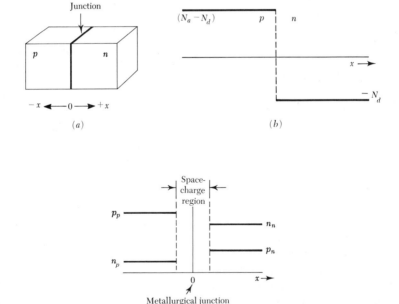

**FIGURE 5.2** *Schematic diagram of a pn diode with abrupt junction. (a) Semiconductor body showing p and n regions and junction; (b) net acceptor density with distance perpendicular to plane of the junction; (c) majority- and minority-carrier densities in bulk regions.*

transition region occurs in which a potential barrier must exist. We now proceed to study this barrier and to develop the relationship between the hole densities and the electron densities on both sides of the junction.

The existence of the barrier can be illustrated in several ways, and we will assume that the *p* region and the *n* region are brought together with a perfect crystal matching. This corresponds to the doping profile of Fig. 5.2*b*. Because of the greater density of holes in the *p* region, *diffusion* of holes toward the *n* region occurs. Similarly, a diffusion of electrons from the *n* region to the *p* region occurs. As holes flow to the right and electrons to the left, the potential of the *n* region must become greater than that of the *p* region, as shown in Fig. 5.3*a*. The potential $\psi$ produces an electric field $\vec{E}$ which is the negative gradient of the potential. For one dimension

$$E_x = -\frac{d\psi}{dx} \tag{5.1}$$

The magnitude of the electric field with distance $x$ is illustrated in Fig. 5.3*b*. The $\vec{E}$ field is directed in the negative $x$ direction and opposes the diffusion of holes and electrons. However, the potential barrier does not completely halt the diffusion flow. Remember that the energy distribution of the electrons and holes is described by the Boltzmann relation $e^{-W/kT}$. Therefore some holes and electrons have very large energies and can flow by diffusion over any barrier of finite height. An equilibrium condition exists, however,

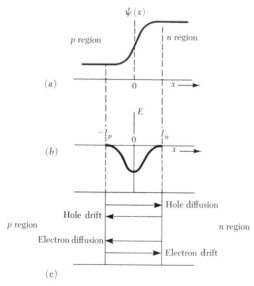

**FIGURE 5.3**  *pn junction in thermal equilibrium.* (a) *Internal electrostatic (built-in) potential with distance from metallurgical boundary;* (b) *electric field with distance;* (c) *electron and hole flow through the junction.*

because the presence of the electric field produces a *drift* of minority carriers from one region to the other, as shown in Fig. 5.3c. For example, the negative electric field of Fig. 5.3b forces to the left holes in the region $-l_p < x < l_n$. In particular, any holes in the *n* region $0 < x < l_n$ (the minority carriers in the *n* region) are swept into the *p* region and any electrons in the region $-l_p < x < 0$ (the minority carriers in the *p* region) are swept into the *n* region. The magnitude of the potential barrier of the junction in thermal equilibrium is the value for which the diffusion flow of the high-energy particles is just equal to the drift flow of minority carriers, as illustrated in Fig. 5.3c.

The description above aids one to visualize the potential barrier as well as the tendencies for equal and opposite diffusion and drift flow of majority and minority carriers. The description is only approximate, however, and must be used with caution. As we will see shortly, the width of the junction, $l_n + l_p$, is very narrow and the peak value of the electric field is very large. Because of the former, the average number of collisions during electron flow through the junction is small and the concept of an average drift velocity is questionable in the junction region. Also, because of the high electric fields, the values of mobility and diffusion constants are very different from the values in a bulk semiconductor in thermal equilibrium.

A conceptual difficulty is that diffusion and drift currents cannot actually flow in the same manner as comparable currents in a bulk semiconductor. If the current densities of these components are calculated using ordinary values of the diffusion and mobility constants, each component is of the order of $10^4$ A/cm$^2$. These large currents cannot exist since the heat produced would destroy the semiconductor. Thus we only model the overall effect of the barrier potential in terms of counteracting diffusion and drift currents. The net current is zero in equilibrium, and we consider this to be the result of two equal and opposite components.[1] It will be helpful later to remember that the two proposed currents are very large and, in fact, are much larger than any net current which we may cause to flow through the junction. As a consequence, it is reasonable to accept the fact that we usually do not upset greatly the conditions of thermal equilibrium when net currents of the usual order of magnitude are allowed to flow.

Other questions arise in conjunction with the flow model above. First, what is the interaction between the diffusing particles and drifting particles? For example, at $x = l_n$, do the holes which have just diffused into the *n* region turn around and drift back? The answer is no. Remember that the

---

[1] The modeling in terms of the diffusion and drift components is analogous to the use of superposition in solving an electric circuit problem. If two independent sources of a circuit are present, and if the circuit is linear, the current in any branch can be considered to be the sum of two components, where each component is the current which is obtained from one source only with the other set equal to zero (see Sec. 3.3).

minority-carrier density is very low. Even for the majority carriers we use an electron gas assumption, i.e., Boltzmann statistics. The energetic holes arriving from the $p$ region and passing through the plane at $l_n$ can be considered to continue to flow toward the right and gradually merge with the existing minority carriers in the $n$ region. The average density of holes near $l_n$ experiences the drift force and flows steadily to the left as will be seen in more detail when we consider the reverse-biased diode. Thus the two processes are independent. There is also the possibility of interaction of electrons and holes. Aside from recombination processes, which will be considered later, this interaction can also be neglected because of the principle of *detailed balancing*. In thermal equilibrium, the flow of electrons (holes) in any direction must equal zero, otherwise net currents can flow which are inconsistent with thermal equilibrium. Therefore, electron and hole processes in the junction can be considered separately. For our model of separate current components, we can then write for the hole flow in the open-circuited junction

$$J_{h,\text{net}} = J_{h,\text{diff}} + J_{h,\text{drift}} = 0 \tag{5.2a}$$

and for the electron flow

$$J_{e,\text{net}} = J_{e,\text{diff}} + J_{e,\text{drift}} = 0 \tag{5.2b}$$

In the next section, we use these ideas and equations to develop expressions for the height of the potential barrier and the relationship between the majority-carrier density and the minority-carrier density on opposite sides of the junction. We end this section by stressing the space-charge region which must exist in the vicinity of the junction as a consequence of the charge redistribution discussed earlier. From another point of view, if an electric field exists, charges must be present to terminate this field. The relationship is given by Gauss' law[1]:

$$\frac{dE_x}{dx} = \frac{\rho}{\varepsilon} \tag{5.3}$$

where $\rho$ is the space-charge density and $\varepsilon$ is the dielectric permittivity of the material. The space-charge region of the junction consists principally of the immobile impurity ions which are exposed near the junction because the charge carriers in the vicinity are swept away by the electric field. For example, the majority-carrier hole density from $-l_p < x < 0$ is decreased below $p_p$ because of diffusion. That is, the mobile holes are swept out, but the impurity ions are immobile and constitute a fixed, unneutralized, negative charge as illustrated by Fig. 5.4c. (Figure 5.4a and b repeats the voltage and field distributions for reference purposes.) The net space-

[1] R. B. Adler et al., "Introduction to Semiconductor Physics," SEEC, vol. 1, p. 146.

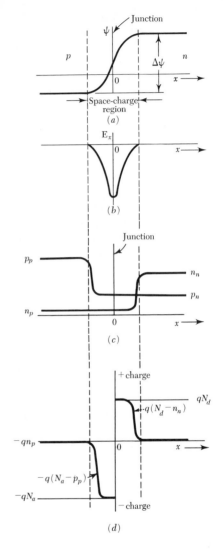

**FIGURE 5.4** *pn junction in thermal equilibrium.* (a) *Electrostatic potential* $\psi$ (x) *versus* x; (b) *electric field* $E_x$ *versus* x; (c) *electron and hole densities with x;* (d) *charge density with x.*

charge density in this region is $-q[N_a - p(x)]$ and varies from zero near $x = -l_p$ to a maximum value at $x = 0$ as illustrated in Fig. 5.4d. Similarly, the net positive space-charge density in the $n$ region is $+q[N_d - n(x)]$. The total exposed charge in the $p$ region must, of course, equal the total exposed charges in the $n$ region since equal and opposite charges are necessary to terminate the electric field. The space-charge region is also called the depletion region of the junction since the majority-carrier densities are depleted in this region.

## 5.3   potential height and the boundary conditions

The relationship between the values of $p_p$ and $p_n$ and the potential difference across the junction can be expected to be related by a Boltzmann factor. This is the result of the energy distribution of holes in the $p$ region, which has the form $e^{-W/kT}$ as shown in Chap. 4. In the $pn$ junction, a potential barrier exists and only a portion of the density $p_p$ has sufficient energy to overcome the barrier and diffuse into the $n$ region. In thermal equilibrium, this portion must equal the density $p_n$ of minority carriers in the $n$ region. The number with sufficient energy to surmount the barrier is given by the integral of the Boltzmann factor from the minimum energy to infinity. Thus

$$p_n = \int_{W_b}^{\infty} C_1 e^{-W/kT} \, dW \tag{5.4a}$$

where $W_b$ represents the height of the barrier and $C_1$ is a constant with respect to energy. If we integrate (5.4a), we obtain an exponential:

$$p_n = C_2 e^{-W_b/kT} \tag{5.4b}$$

It is of particular interest to us to relate $p_n$ to $p_p$. First, we express the potential energy $W_b$ in terms of the potential difference of the barrier, over and above the potential of a uniform $p$-type semiconductor $W_b = q(\Delta\psi + \psi_p)$. If this is used in (5.4b)

$$p_n = C_2 \exp\left[-\frac{q}{kT}(\Delta\psi + \psi_p)\right] = C_3 e^{-q\Delta\psi/kT} \tag{5.5a}$$

The new multiplicative constant $C_3$ must be $p_p$, since $p_n = p_p$ if $\Delta\psi = 0$. For convenience, let us again use the constant $V_T$ equal to the thermal energy expressed in volts:

$$V_T = \frac{kT}{q} \tag{5.5b}$$

Then (5.5a) can be written

$$p_n = p_p e^{-\Delta\psi/V_T} \tag{5.5c}$$

The relationship (5.5c) can also be illustrated by proposing drift and diffusion currents as in (5.2) and by following a development similar to that of Sec. 4.9. The net hole current across the junction is zero in thermal equilibrium. Thus, from (5.2a), we obtain in the junction region $-l_p < x < l_n$

$$0 = -qD_h \frac{dp}{dx} + q\mu_h p E_x \tag{5.6a}$$

The electric field, as given by (5.1), is

$$E_x = -\frac{d\psi}{dx} \tag{5.6b}$$

Using this in (5.6a), we obtain

$$d\psi = -\frac{D_h}{\mu_h}\frac{dp}{p} = -V_T\frac{dp}{p} \tag{5.6c}$$

where Einstein's relation (4.32) has been used. We integrate both sides of this expression from one edge of the space-charge region, $-l_p$, to the other, $l_n$. The corresponding boundary values for the potential are $\psi_p$ and $\psi_n$, respectively, and $p_p$ and $p_n$ for the hole densities. The result is

$$\psi_n - \psi_p = \Delta\psi = +V_T\ln\frac{p_p}{p_n} \tag{5.7a}$$

where $\psi_n - \psi_p$ has been expressed in terms of the potential difference $\Delta\psi$. If (5.7a) is rearranged, we obtain

$$p_n = p_p e^{-\Delta\psi/V_T} \tag{5.7b}$$

Of course, we have obtained the same result as that using the Boltzmann relation directly. (In effect, we have used the Einstein relation in the second development to show that the energy distribution of holes is a Boltzmann distribution.) The same type of development can be used for the electron densities. The result is

$$n_p = n_n e^{-\Delta\psi/V_T} \tag{5.7c}$$

We can also relate the potential to the impurity concentration (doping) of the *pn* junction by solving Gauss' law. Again, we restrict attention to the simple situation of Fig. 5.2 in which constant doping in the *p* and *n* regions is assumed with an abrupt change from one region to the other. At the temperatures of interest, the impurity atoms are all assumed to be ionized. The particle densities are repeated in Fig. 5.5a. In the last section, and in Fig. 5.4, the depletion of mobile carriers is mentioned and the charge density of unneutralized ions is illustrated. For simplicity, we assume complete depletion of mobile carriers in the transition region and obtain a charge-density profile with distance as shown in Fig. 5.5b. This figure should be compared with Fig. 5.4d to visualize the nature of the new assumption. The edges of the space-charge region are now taken to be abrupt. This leads to a very simple mathematical description of $\rho(x)$ and an easy solution of Gauss' equation, (5.3). The solution of (5.3) is obtained by separating the space-charge region into two regions, $-l_p \leqslant x \leqslant 0$ and $0 \leqslant x \leqslant l_n$. The two solutions are similar and are pieced

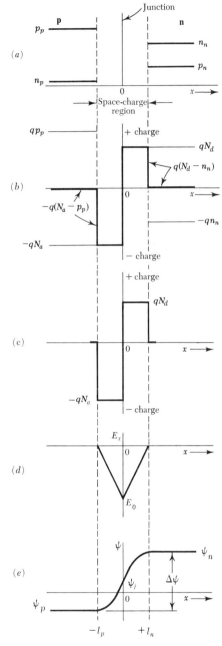

**FIGURE 5.5** *pn junction in thermal equilibrium, depletion assumption.* (a) *Electron and hole densities in bulk regions;* (b) *charge density;* (c) *fixed space-charge density using depletion assumption* (d) $E_x$, (e) $\psi$ (x).

together to obtain a complete solution. In the $n$ portion of the space-charge region, the space-charge density is

$$\rho(x) = q(N_d - n) \simeq qN_d \tag{5.8}$$

where the approximate form on the right is the result of the complete depletion assumption. If (5.8) is used in (5.3), we obtain

$$\frac{dE_x}{dx} = \frac{qN_d}{\varepsilon} \tag{5.9a}$$

or

$$dE_x = \frac{qN_d}{\varepsilon} dx \tag{5.9b}$$

Integrating both sides of this equation, we obtain

$$E_x = \frac{qN_d}{\varepsilon} x + E_0 \tag{5.9c}$$

where $E_0$ is the value of $E_x$ at $x = 0$. $E_0$ and $l_n$ can be related if (5.9c) is solved for $x = l_n$, where $l_n$ is the edge of the space-charge region. Therefore, by definition, $E_x(l_n) = 0$. This leads to

$$E_0 = -\frac{qN_d}{\varepsilon} l_n \tag{5.9d}$$

The shape of the electric field is shown in Fig. 5.5d. The results to this point can now be used in (5.6c) to obtain an expression for the potential with distance

$$d\psi = -E_x \, dx = -\frac{qN_d}{\varepsilon} (x - l_n) \, dx \tag{5.10a}$$

where (5.9d) has been used for $E_0$. Integrating both sides, we obtain

$$\psi(x)\Big|_{0 \leqslant x \leqslant l_n} = -\frac{q}{\varepsilon} N_d \left( \frac{x^2}{2} - l_n x \right) + \psi_j \tag{5.10b}$$

The constant of integration $\psi_j$ is the value of potential at the junction, $\psi(0)$. The form of the potential with distance is shown in Fig. 5.5e.

The same procedure can be used in the $p$ region to obtain

$$E_x = \frac{q}{\varepsilon} N_a x + E_0 \tag{5.11a}$$

$$E_0 = -\frac{q}{\varepsilon} N_a l_p \tag{5.11b}$$

$$\psi(x)\Big|_{-l_p \leqslant x \leqslant 0} = +\frac{q}{\varepsilon} N_a \left( \frac{x^2}{2} + l_p x \right) + \psi_j \tag{5.11c}$$

The electric field and potential plots for $-l_p \leqslant x \leqslant 0$ are also shown in Fig. 5.5. At $x = 0$, the two solutions for the electric field must be equal and the two solutions for the potential must also be equal, hence the use of the same constants. The equality of (5.9d) and (5.11b) leads to

$$l_p N_a = l_n N_d \tag{5.12}$$

This result is equivalent to the statement that the total unneutralized charge in the $p$ region is equal to the total charge in the $n$ region (see Fig. 5.5b).

The solutions for $E(x)$ and $\psi(x)$ are good only in the region of the space charge. The potential difference between the edges of the regions is the height of the potential barrier $\Delta\psi$.

$$\Delta\psi = \psi_n - \psi_p = \frac{q}{2\varepsilon}(N_d l_n^2 + N_a l_p^2) \tag{5.13}$$

If (5.12) is used, one variable can be eliminated. This leads to

$$l_n = \left(\frac{2\varepsilon}{q}\,\Delta\psi\,\frac{N_a}{N_d}\,\frac{1}{N_a + N_d}\right)^{1/2} \tag{5.14a}$$

$$E_0 = -\left(\frac{2q}{\varepsilon}\,\Delta\psi\,\frac{N_a N_d}{N_a + N_d}\right)^{1/2} \tag{5.14b}$$

An expression for $l_p$ is obtained if $N_a$ and $N_d$ are reversed in (5.14a). For a numerical example to illustrate the values of these constants, we choose a silicon $pn$ junction with impurity densities of $N_a = 10^{16}$ atoms/cm$^3$ and $N_d = 10^{14}$ atoms/cm$^3$. The first calculation is for the potential difference $\Delta\psi$, using (5.7a). For these dopings and at a typical temperature (300° K), the density of majority carriers well away from the junction is approximately the density of donor doping.

$$p_p \simeq N_a \qquad n_n \simeq N_d$$
$$n_p \simeq \frac{n_i^2}{N_a} \qquad p_n \simeq \frac{n_i^2}{N_d} \tag{5.15}$$

Using the hole densities in (5.7a), we obtain

$$\Delta\psi = V_T \ln \frac{N_a N_d}{n_i^2} \tag{5.16}$$

At 300° K,

$$n_i \simeq 10^{10} \quad \text{and} \quad V_T = 0.026 \text{ volt}$$

$$\Delta\psi = (0.026)(2.3)(10) \simeq 0.6 \text{ volt} \tag{5.17a}$$

The permittivity $\varepsilon$ can be written $\varepsilon_0 \varepsilon_r$, where $\varepsilon_0$ is the permittivity of free space and is equal to $10^{-9}/36\pi$ F/m $= 1/3.6\pi$ pF/cm. $\varepsilon_r$ is the relative permittivity. For Si, $\varepsilon_r = 12$. These values in (5.14a) lead to

$$l_n = 2.8 \cdot 10^{-4} \text{ cm} \qquad (5.17b)$$

We now use (5.12) to obtain

$$l_p = \frac{N_d}{N_a} l_n = 10^{-2} l_n = 2.8 \cdot 10^{-6} \text{ cm} \qquad (5.17c)$$

As expected, the extent of the depletion (space charge) region into the $p$ region is much less than that into the $n$ region because of the higher doping of the former. Using (5.14b), we obtain

$$E_0 = -4.25 \cdot 10^3 \text{ V/cm} \qquad (5.17d)$$

This is a large value of field strength and it is reasonable to expect that the values of the diffusion and mobility constants in a region of this field strength are considerably different from the values in intrinsic material in thermal equilibrium.

We need to return now to our study of the space-charge region and examine several basic assumptions. First, we look at the assumptions of an abrupt junction and of a complete depletion. Because both of these assumptions do not hold exactly, we will not have the simple space-charge profile of Fig. 5.5b. An actual space-charge profile will be rounded and spread out. This will mean that the peak value of the electric field will be less and that there will be a gradual transition from a space-charge region which is almost depleted to an almost neutral region. Analysis shows that this transition is of the order of $10^{-5}$ cm. This value is less than the estimated width of the depleted region in the $n$ region but is more than the estimated width of that in the $p$ region. Nonetheless, the conclusion concerning the potential barrier, its effect, and the relations of $p_p$ to $p_n$ and of $n_n$ to $n_p$ should be correct in principle and the estimated values of $l_n$, $l_p$, $\Delta\psi$, and $E_0$ provide us with useful numerical guides. In the work to follow, we continue to use these basic assumptions to achieve simple but useful analyses.

### 5.4 the *pn* junction with an external bias

The potential barrier which exists at the junction to inhibit the diffusive flow of majority carriers into the other region is represented in Fig. 5.6 by two hills. This figure illustrates the barrier action in terms of a gravitational analog. One hill is for holes; the other, of the same height, is for electrons. Note that the electrostatic potential is reversed in order for electrons to obtain an "upright hill." It is simple to visualize that these hills can be increased or decreased in height by applying an external voltage to the junction. This application of a dc voltage or current to a device is called applying a bias to the device or simply biasing the device.

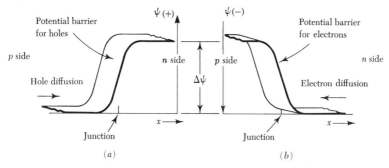

**FIGURE 5.6** *Potential barriers in a pn junction in thermal equilibrium.* (a) *To inhibit hole diffusion and* (b) *to inhibit electron diffusion.*

We neglect for the moment the question of how an external bias is actually applied to a *pn* diode. Assume that a voltage $V$ actually appears across the junction from $-l_p$ to $l_n$ as illustrated in Fig. 5.7a. It is easy to visualize that this voltage modifies the height of the barrier potentials

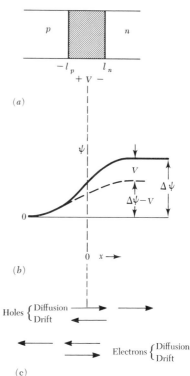

**FIGURE 5.7** *pn junction with applied forward bias.* (a) *Direction of positive applied potential;* (b) *change in* $\psi(x)$; (c) *changes in electron and hole flow.*

or hills of Fig. 5.6 and modifies the diffusion flow across the junction. For the positive polarity shown, a dc voltage appears across the junction which is positive on the $p$ side of the junction and negative on the $n$ side. This is the opposite polarity of "built-in" potential $\Delta\psi$. Therefore, the net barrier to diffusive flow is decreased to $(\Delta\psi - V)$ as illustrated in Fig. 5.7b. This decrease in the barrier permits an exponential increase in the diffusion components of hole current flow and electron current flow across the junction as shown in Fig. 5.7c. The exponential increase is, of course, a result of the Boltzmann energy distribution of majority carriers. The drift components change little since these components are limited by the density of minority carriers in thermal equilibrium near the junction. There is, then, a net exponential increase in the carrier flow across the junction. Both the hole flow from the $p$ region and the electron flow from the $n$ region are increased by the same ratio. Because of the negative charge of the electrons, both increases of carrier flow correspond to a net current flow through the junction from the left to the right. If we increase the applied potential, i.e., if we increase the *forward bias* of the junction, we get a further increase of current as shown in Fig. 5.8. If $V$ is decreased, an exponential decrease of current through the junction is obtained.

If $V$ becomes negative, the potential barrier of the junction is increased in relation to $\Delta\psi$, the value in thermal equilibrium. The diffusion components of flow now become smaller than the drift components. With sufficient *negative bias*, the diffusion components of current are negligible and only the drift components remain. The latter are constant in the ideal and will be discussed in Sec. 5.7. Again a (small) net current flows through the junction, this time from the $n$ region to the $p$ region. This is defined as the negative direction for current, and a current is plotted in the third quadrant as shown in Fig. 5.8.

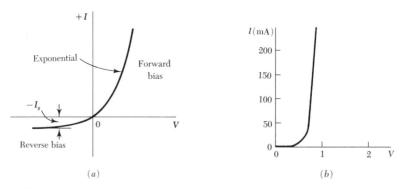

**FIGURE 5.8** *Ideal IV characteristic of pn-junction diode.* (a) *For small values of current and voltage and* (b) *for normal values of current and voltage.*

The form of the $IV$ characteristic of a biased $pn$ junction is substantiated in the next section. First, we need to investigate how a potential is applied to a diode. An *ohmic* contact to a semiconductor is typically made by heavily doping the immediate region of the proposed contact. Aluminum is then deposited and is alloyed into the doped region. A gold wire is then bonded to the aluminum. This type of contact has a very low resistance and its $IV$ characteristic is linear and independent of the polarity of an applied potential. The contact acts like a pure "ohmic" material. There is a contact potential from the metal wire to the semiconductor body; however, another contact potential of opposite sign must be present from the other semiconductor region to its wire connection. Such contact potentials will be discussed again in Chap. 10. It is sufficient to note here that the net contact potential for two ohmic contacts plus the potential barrier of the junction is zero since in thermal equilibrium no net voltage can appear around a closed loop consisting of the wire and the $pn$ diode. For our purposes, we can assume that the wire, the ohmic contacts, and the semiconductor body all act as a linear resistor.

If an external dc voltage source is applied to the ohmic contacts of a diode, say to forward bias the junction, a net current flows through the diode from the plus terminal to the minus terminal. This current produces voltage drops across the bulk semiconductor regions (not including the transition and space-charge regions). These voltage drops are usually very small in relation to the drop across the junction itself. It is usual to neglect these potential drops and the electric fields associated with the majority-carrier drift flow in the bulk semiconductors. The potential applied across the diode can be considered to be the external potential that appears across the actual junction. In practice, this assumption is first made to establish approximate current flow. The voltage drops in the bulk semiconductor are then calculated using this value of the current. If the voltage drops are not negligible, a correction is made and a new value of current is established. It should be clear that for a reverse bias, the externally applied voltage is very close to the actual junction voltage because the reverse current is small.

## 5.5 junction with forward bias

If a forward bias is applied to a junction, an increased density of minority carriers is produced on both sides of the junction by the increased diffusion of majority carriers from the other region. This increase at the edges of the space-charge (depletion) region is shown in Fig. 5.9. In this figure and in the analysis to follow, we use a new coordinate with shifted references, $x' = x - l_n$. Thus $x = l_n$ becomes $x' = 0$. Of major interest now is the region outside the space-charge (junction) region, $x' > 0$. A new

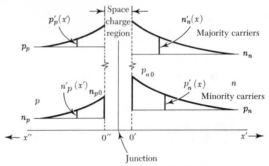

**FIGURE 5.9**   *Carrier densities with x under forward bias (linear scale).*

variable, $x'' = -(x + l_p)$, is defined in a similar manner for the $p$ region so that $x'' = 0$ corresponds to $x = -l_p$. Note that $x''$ is positive to the left. Because of the similarity of the two regions, only one analysis— that of the $n$ region—is made. To obtain solutions for the $p$ region, only the constants need be changed in the solution for the $n$ region. In the following, we denote $0'$ as the zero for $x'$, and $0''$ as the zero for $x''$.

A value for the hole density in the $n$ region at the edge of the junction, $p_n(0') = p_{n0}$, is simply obtained from a modification of the Boltzmann relation for the junction in thermal equilibrium, (5.7b). In Sec. 5.2, it is pointed out that the diffusion and drift currents, if thought of as separate components, are extremely large. Thus, if a bias change is made to obtain a net current which is orders of magnitude less than the separate parts, it is reasonable to assume that the junction is still practically in equilibrium. Boltzmann statistics should then continue to hold. Continuing this argument, we need only modify (5.7b) in order to relate the edge densities of holes to the modified potential barrier $(\Delta\psi - V)$. The result is

$$p_{n0} = p'_p e^{-(\Delta\psi - V)/V_T} \qquad (5.18a)$$

Note that a constant $p'_p$ is used. The value of $p'_p$ is greater than the value of $p_p$ because an excess of minority carriers at $x' = 0$ also leads to an increase (excess) of majority carriers over the thermal equilibrium value. Outside of the junction, we must have charge-neutral regions since we do not have a mechanism to support a nonneutral space charge. As minority carriers are injected into the $n$ region, a majority-carrier flow occurs to maintain this region charge neutral. Note, however, that $\Delta p$ must equal $\Delta n$. Therefore, even though the percentage increase in minority carriers is large, the percentage increase in the majority carriers is extremely low since $n_n >> p_n$. Thus $p'_p$ can be replaced by $p_p$ in (5.18a). Using (5.7b), we obtain

$$p_{n0} = p_n e^{V/V_T} \qquad (5.18b)$$

On the $p$ side of the junction

$$n_{p0} = n_p e^{V/V_T} \qquad (5.18c)$$

The excess of holes over $p_n$ at the edge of the junction $x' = 0$ leads to a diffusion flow of holes away from the junction since a density gradient exists. As these holes flow toward the right, the holes gradually recombine with electrons. We can define an average lifetime of holes before recombination, $\tau_h$. At a far enough distance from the junction, the recombination of excess minority carriers is complete and the hole density is $p_n$, as shown in Fig. 5.9. Because of charge neutrality, the density of excess electrons also decreases with increasing $x'$. The diffusion flow of electrons due to $dn/dx$ is considered shortly.

We have assumed the doping of the two regions to be uniform (although not necessarily equal in the $n$ and $p$ regions) and the injected level of minority carriers small compared to the density of majority carriers. For this situation we can determine the hole current diffusing through the plane $x' = 0$ toward the right. Because of our earlier assumptions, the hole current is a pure diffusion current. From (4.31a),

$$J_h(0') = -qD_h \frac{dp}{dx'}\bigg|_{x' = 0} \qquad (5.19a)$$

The excess density $p_{ne}(0') = p_{no} - p_n$ is the important quantity since we expect that $J_h(0')$ should be zero when the excess density is zero. As we will see in the last part of this section, $p_{ne}(x')$ has an exponential decrease with distance into the $n$ region because of recombination of holes with the majority carriers (electrons). The form is

$$p_{ne}(x') = p_{ne}(0')e^{-x'/L_h} = p_n(e^{V/V_T} - 1)\,e^{-x'/L_h} \qquad (5.19b)$$

The length $L_h$ is a characteristic distance called the *diffusion length of holes* in the $n$ region. Using (5.19a), we obtain

$$J_h(0') = \frac{qD_h p_n}{L_h}(e^{V/V_T} - 1) \qquad (5.19c)$$

Equation (5.19c) has the form we expect from the physical reasoning of Sec. 5.4.

We now switch to the $p$ region. If a similar line of reasoning is followed, we obtain

$$n_{p0} = n_p e^{V/V_T} \qquad (5.20a)$$

$$n_{pe}(0'') = n_{p0} - n_p = n_p(e^{V/V_T} - 1) \qquad (5.20b)$$

The electron current flowing to the right (because of electrons flowing to the left) due to diffusion through the plane $x'' = 0$ is, from (4.31b),

$$J_e(0'') = -qD_e\frac{dn}{dx''}\bigg|_{x''\,=\,0} \tag{5.21a}$$

This is a current which flows in the negative $x''$ direction, which is the positive $x'$ direction (to the right). The diffusing current density, by analogy with (5.19c), is

$$J_e(0'') = \frac{qD_e n_p}{L_e}(e^{V/V_T} - 1) \tag{5.21b}$$

where $L_e$ is the diffusion length for electrons in the $p$ region. Because the width of the space-charge region of the junction is so narrow, it is reasonable to assume that little recombination occurs as the two diffusing currents flow through this region. This assumption leads us easily to an expression for the total current flow through a plane such as $x' = 0$. If recombination is small, the value of the current density from (5.21b) is approximately equal to the value of the current density which supports this flow at the plane $x' = 0$, and in fact for all planes between $0'$ and $0''$.

$$J_e(0') \simeq J_e(0'') = J_e(0) \tag{5.22a}$$

Similarly, $J_h$ may be considered constant through the space-charge region. The total minority-carrier current at $x = 0$, summed from (5.22a) and (5.19c), is then

$$J(0) = J_h(0) + J_e(0)$$
$$= q\left(\frac{D_h p_n}{L_h} + \frac{D_e n_p}{L_e}\right)(e^{V/V_T} - 1) \tag{5.22b}$$

If the area of the junction is introduced to obtain a total current instead of the current density, the result may be written

$$I = I_s(e^{V/V_T} - 1) \tag{5.22c}$$

where $I_s$ is a constant equal to

$$I_s = Aq\left(\frac{D_h p_n}{L_h} + \frac{D_e n_p}{L_e}\right) \tag{5.22d}$$

Equation (5.22c) has exactly the form we expect on the basis of our earlier physical reasoning. This equation has been derived on the basis of a forward-bias situation. The final result, however, is also valid for reverse bias as is brought out shortly.

**SOLUTION OF THE CONTINUITY EQUATION FOR MINORITY CARRIERS**   It is instructive at this point to derive the exponential nature of the minority-carrier flow (diffusion) with distance in the $n$ and $p$ regions stated in (5.19b). From Fig. 5.9, we expect that this flow in the $n$ region decreases due to recombination of majority and minority carriers. A mathematical description of this is obtained from a solution of a continuity equation for minority carriers in the bulk regions of the diode. In this section, only the $n$ region is considered. The results for the $p$ region can then be obtained by inspection.

In the $n$ regions, the continuity equation for holes in an infinitesimal volume at point $x$ has the form (see Appendix C)

$$\frac{\partial p}{\partial t} = -r - \frac{1}{q}\nabla \cdot \vec{J}_h \tag{5.23a}$$

where $\nabla \cdot \vec{J}_h$ is the divergence of current density $\vec{J}_h$. In one dimension

$$\nabla \cdot \vec{J}_h = \frac{\partial J_h}{\partial x} \tag{5.23b}$$

Equation (5.23a) states that the (positive) time rate of change of holes in the volume is equal to the negative of the net recombination of holes in the volume plus the negative of the net flow of holes (hole current) out of the volume. This follows directly from the conservation of charge (or Kirchhoff's current law). Because of the assumed charge neutrality in the bulk regions, we do not include explicitly the presence of charge arising from majority carriers.

The hole current at $x$ is in general the sum of a diffusion component and a drift component.

$$J_h = q\left(-D_h\frac{dp}{dx} + p\mu_h E_x\right) \tag{5.23c}$$

In the bulk region outside the space-charge region, we continue to assume that any electric fields are very small and that the hole current is due principally to diffusion flow ($E_x \simeq 0$). Next, we assume that recombination of holes in the $n$ region occurs with a characteristic time $\tau_h$. Thus the excess hole density in the volume, $p_{ne}(x')$, decreases at a rate given by

$$r = \frac{p_{ne}(x')}{\tau_h} \tag{5.23d}$$

Finally, note that $p_{ne}(x')$ rather than $p_n(x')$ can be used wherever a partial or total derivative is taken. The continuity equation becomes

$$\frac{\partial p_{ne}(x')}{\partial t} = -\frac{p_{ne}(x')}{\tau_h} + D_h\frac{\partial^2 p_{ne}(x')}{\partial x'^2} \tag{5.23e}$$

We are interested here in the dc or static situation only for which $\partial[p_{ne}(x')]/\partial t = 0$. The derivative with $x'$ may then be written as a total derivative. After division by $D_h$, we obtain

$$\frac{d^2 p_{ne}(x')}{dx^2} = \frac{1}{L_h^2} p_{ne}(x') \tag{5.23$f$}$$

where the constant $L_h$ is defined as

$$L_h = (D_h \tau_h)^{1/2} \tag{5.24}$$

The solution of this second-order differential equation provides a description of the change of the excess minority-carrier density with distance from the edge of the space-charge region.

$$p_{ne}(x') = C_1 e^{-x'/L_h} + C_2 e^{+x'/L_h} \tag{5.25$a$}$$

In this solution, $C_1$ and $C_2$ are constants which are related to the boundary values of $p_{ne}(x')$. One boundary value is obtained from (5.18$b$)

$$p_{ne}(0') = p_n(e^{V/V_T} - 1) \tag{5.25$b$}$$

The second boundary value is obtained from an inspection of Fig. 5.9. At large values of $x$, $p_{ne}(x')$ drops to zero because of recombination, that is,

$$p_{ne}(\infty) = 0 \tag{5.25$c$}$$

The second boundary condition, (5.25$c$), requires $C_2 = 0$, and (5.25$b$) then yields

$$C_1 = p_n(e^{V/V_T} - 1) \tag{5.25$d$}$$

The final expression is

$$p_{ne}(x') = p_n(e^{V/V_T} - 1)e^{-x'/L_h} \tag{5.25$e$}$$

The plot of Fig. 5.9 is a plot of the exponential function of (5.25$e$). This equation also provides a physical interpretation of $L_h$. At $x' = L_h$, the excess density of holes has dropped to $1/e$ of its value at the edge of the space-charge region. $L_h$ is thus a characteristic length of the combined diffusion and recombination processes called the diffusion length of holes in the $n$ region, as stated earlier. A typical value of $L_h$ lies in the range $10^{-2}$ to 1 mm depending on doping levels and on the density of unwanted impurities.

The hole current can now be obtained, using (4.31$a$):

$$J_h(x') = q\frac{p_n D_h}{L_h}(e^{V/V_T} - 1)e^{-x'/L_h} \tag{5.25$f$}$$

A similar analysis of minority-carrier continuity in the $p$ region leads to

$$n_{pe}(x'') = n_p(e^{V/V_T} - 1)e^{-x''/L_e} \tag{5.26$a$}$$

The electron current, defined positive to the right, is

$$J_e(x'') = q \frac{n_p D_e}{L_e}(e^{V/V_T} - 1)e^{-x''/L_e} \tag{5.26b}$$

## 5.6 total current flow in the *pn* diode in forward bias

An external bias on the *pn* junction enables us to control the concentration of majority and minority carriers at the edges of the space-charge region. In particular, we know that a forward bias produces an injection of minority carriers into both bulk regions. We now need to investigate not only the minority-carrier currents but also the majority-carrier currents that flow in the bulk region because of this injection phenomenon. Again, we restrict our attention to the total current flow in the *n* region and obtain results for the *p* region by inspection.

For the one-dimensional situation, it is certainly necessary that the total current through every plane parallel to the junction be constant, as illustrated in Fig. 5.10*a*, since there can be no loss of total current. This total current, however, is made up of several components and the magnitudes of these components change with distance even though the total value remains constant. Looking first at Fig. 5.10*b*, we have assumed that the hole current is constant through the space-charge region and can be calculated from (5.19*c*). From (5.25*f*), we obtain its exponential form as

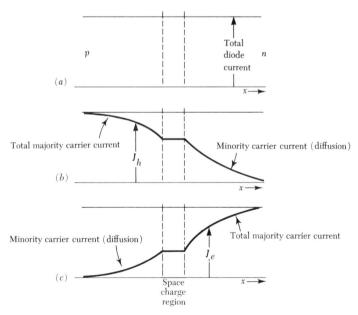

**FIGURE 5.10** *Current flow in a pn-junction diode with x.* (a) *Total diode current;* (b) *hole current;* (c) *electron current.*

it diffuses and recombines in the $n$ region. Thus, to maintain total current constant with distance, the electron or majority-carrier current must be the difference between total current and the hole diffusion current, as shown in Fig. 5.10$c$. Similarly, we know the electron current in the junction from (5.21$b$) and its exponential diffusion and recombination form in the $p$ region from (5.26$b$). These quantities are shown in the left portion of Fig. 5.10$c$. The hole current in that region is the difference between total current and this electron diffusion current, as shown at the left in Fig. 5.10$b$.

The majority current flow ($J_h$ in the $p$ region and $J_e$ in the $n$ region) can be visualized in a general way since there must be some flow of the majority carriers to replace those eliminated by recombination. The process is actually fairly complicated and will next be considered in more detail.

**DETAILED DISCUSSION OF CURRENT COMPONENTS**   One way to separate the current into components is illustrated in Fig. 5.11. In Fig. 5.11$a$, the diffusion hole current is shown. Note that we return to the unprimed coordinate $x$. This component as discussed in the last section decreases with $x$ because of recombination. To supply the majority carriers for this recombination, we expect an electron flow from the right to the left which is a positive current

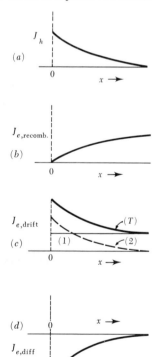

**FIGURE 5.11**   *Electron and hole current density components in the n region.* (a) *Total hole current;* (b) *recombination electron current;* (c) *drift electron current;* (d) *diffusion electron current.*

flow (to the right) as in Fig. 5.11*b*. This current increases with $x$ as shown. At a distance far from the junction, the hole current is zero and the electron component to supply the recombination is constant.

Another electron component is necessary to supply the electrons which are injected into the *p* regions. This component can be shown as a constant with distance as (1) in Fig. 5.11*c*. A third electron current component arises because of diffusion. Remember that the electron density near the junction is increased as in Fig. 5.9 in order to maintain charge neutrality. The gradient of electron density leads to a diffusion of electrons to the right, which constitutes a negative current. This current can be expressed

$$J_e(x)\Big|_{\text{diff}} = qD_e\frac{dn}{dx} \tag{5.27a}$$

But to maintain neutrality $dn/dx = dp/dx$, so

$$J_e(x)\Big|_{\text{diff}} = -\frac{D_e}{D_h}J_h \tag{5.27b}$$

As shown in (5.27*b*) and as illustrated in Fig. 5.11*d*, this current is directly related to the hole current by a constant equal to the ratio of the diffusion constants. This current is larger in magnitude than the hole current because $D_e > D_h$. However, a net current flow equal to the injected components across the junction must flow. This implies that a drift component must exist to counter the diffusion flow of electrons. In effect, the gradient of majority carriers also establishes an electric field to produce a drift component which in turn nullifies the diffusion of majority carriers. (Of course, this point of view is only valid if the density of minority carriers is so small that the electric field is small. If the electric field is large, the hole current is also affected and we must go back and solve for the current components on a simultaneous basis rather than a sequential basis.) The value of the necessary electric field is found from the basic drift-current expression in an *n* region

$$J_{e,\text{drift}} = q\mu_e n_n E_x \tag{5.28a}$$

This component must equal total current minus the diffusion components

$$J_{e,\text{drift}} = J - J_{h,\text{diff}} - J_{e,\text{diff}} = J - J_h\left(1 - \frac{D_e}{D_h}\right) \tag{5.28b}$$

This leads to

$$E_x = \frac{J_{e,\text{drift}}}{q\mu_e n_n} = \frac{J - J_h(1 - D_e/D_h)}{q\mu_e n_n} \tag{5.28c}$$

The electron drift component to nullify the electron diffusion is shown by the dashed curve of Fig. 5.11c. The total of the two electron drift currents is shown by curve $T$. The electric field to support this total current must of course be larger than the value proposed above to nullify the diffusion alone. From Sec. 5.4, it should be remembered that the additional electric field, to support net majority-carrier flow through the bulk regions, is assumed small. In (5.28c), it is noted that $n_n$ is in the denominator. If the currents in the bulk region are not too large, the large value of $n_n$ leads to very small values of the total electric field. If the value of $E_x$ is sufficiently small such that the hole drift current is very much smaller than the hole diffusion current, we are justified in our initial assumption of an almost neutral bulk region outside of the space-charge region.

If all of the components are summed, we obtain the minority and majority currents in the *pn* diode as was shown in Fig. 5.10. Recall that in the space-charge region of the junction, the current components are shown flat to represent the assumption that little recombination occurs there. The space-charge region is normally very small with respect to the diffusion length of the minority carriers in the bulk regions, so for clarity it is exaggerated in the figure. The assumption of negligible recombination in the space-charge region is well justified for germanium, but not for silicon. Nonetheless, the major features of current flow are correct even for the silicon diode. At low currents, the constant of the current-voltage relation must be modified, however, as discussed in Sec. 5.8.

We are now in a position to investigate a *pn* diode in which the bulk regions are not doped uniformly with distance. As a simple example, we choose the doping profile shown in Fig. 5.12a. The acceptor doping is again taken to be flat with distance; however, the donor doping $N_d$ decreases with distance from the abrupt junction. The corresponding density profiles of majority carriers are shown in Fig. 5.12b. Of particular

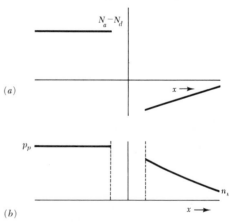

**FIGURE 5.12**   *pn diode with nonuniform doping.* (a) *Net acceptor doping;* (b) *majority-carrier densities.*

interest is the profile of electron density in the $n$ region. This profile is similar to that of Fig. 5.9. Following the reasoning above, we expect that a small electric field must be present in the $n$ region to nullify a diffusion flow of electrons. If the density of electrons is much larger than the density of holes, this electric field can be neglected. Therefore, our earlier results for the simpler case of uniform doping can be used directly.

## 5.7 reverse bias

Our developments of the last two sections stress forward bias. However, the basic equations also apply to reverse bias as is pointed out in the discussion after (5.22). In this section, this aspect is investigated in greater detail. In addition, we consider the effect on the space-charge region as the potential barrier is increased in reverse bias.

For convenience, the external voltage which is applied across the internal junction is relabeled in Fig. 5.13a as $-V_r$, where $V_r$ is a positive

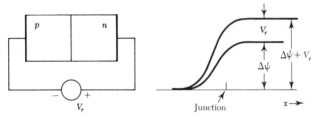

**FIGURE 5.13** *pn-junction diode with applied reverse bias.* (a) *Voltage polarity for reverse bias;* (b) *potential barrier.*

number and is the magnitude of the reverse bias. The potential barrier, as shown in Fig. 5.13b, becomes $(\Delta\psi + V_r)$, and the Boltzmann relations between the density of carriers on either side of the junction become

$$p_{n0} = p_n e^{-V_r/V_T} \tag{5.29a}$$

$$n_{p0} = n_p e^{-V_r/V_T} \tag{5.29b}$$

At the edge of the space-charge region, there now is no excess density of minority carriers in relation to the density in thermal equilibrium. In fact, for values of $V_r \gg V_T$, the edge density of minority carriers is approximately zero with respect to $p_n$ or $n_p$, as shown in Fig. 5.14. Note that a slope exists at the edges of the space-charge region. Considering the $n$ region, we see that the gradient toward the junction produces a diffusion flow of holes toward the junction. Once these holes approach the edge, they fall through the potential barrier (that is, are accelerated by the potential barrier) as a drift current. Since the slope or gradient of minority carriers does not change for a change of $V_r$, if $V_r \gg V_T$, this drift current

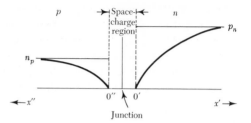

**FIGURE 5.14** *Carrier densities with x under reverse bias.*

is not affected. These two drift components, one from each side of the junction, constitute the *saturation current* $I_s$ of (5.22*d*).

In forward bias, the external junction voltage has a value of the order of the potential barrier in thermal equilibrium, $\Delta\psi$. Certainly, the external voltage cannot exceed $\Delta\psi$. In reverse bias no such restriction is present. However, the reverse-bias voltage cannot be increased without limit. At large voltages, a *breakdown* of the junction occurs due either to an ionizing collision process or to a field-emission effect.

*Avalanche breakdown* occurs when the electrons or holes flowing in the junction are accelerated to large velocities. If the energy gained between collisions is sufficient, ionization of atoms occurs in the collision process. This ionization produces a hole-zero pair which in turn can be accelerated to produce further ionization. Hence, the name avalanche breakdown. The *IV* characteristic including breakdown is shown in Fig. 5.15. The value of

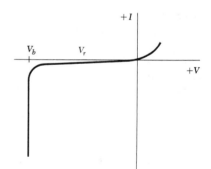

**FIGURE 5.15** *IV characteristic showing diode breakdown.*

the reverse bias to produce breakdown is labeled $V_b$. The value of $V_b$ is a function of the impurity concentration at the edges of the junction. As the concentration of the least-doped side is increased, $V_b$ decreases. From (5.14*b*) and for $N_a \gg N_d$, as $N_d$ increases, $E_0$ increases and the necessary value of external voltage for breakdown decreases.

When the impurity doping on both sides of a junction is increased, the breakdown phenomenon changes from the avalanche process to a field-emission process. As the doping is increased, we can see from (5.14*b*) that the maximum electric field in the junction increases. If this value is sufficiently large the field can produce ionization directly. This breakdown is referred to as *Zener breakdown*. For silicon diodes, the transition between the two types of breakdown occurs in the range $4\ \text{V} < V_b < 6\ \text{V}$. For voltages less than 4 to 6 V, Zener breakdown occurs.

As a final topic in this section we investigate the width of the space-charge region under a bias condition. The equation of interest is (5.14*a*). In the equation for $l_n$, and in a similar one for $l_p$, the value for the magnitude of the potential barrier is replaced by ($\Delta\psi - V$), where $V$ is positive for forward bias. The width of the junction can be written emphasizing only the variation with the barrier.

$$l_n + l_p = H(\Delta\psi - V)^{1/2} \qquad (5.30)$$

where $H$ is a constant. We see that the width of the junction decreases for forward bias and increases for reverse bias. For the latter, the penetration of the space-charge region is increased to uncover more ions on which the increased electric field terminates. Small changes of the width occur for forward bias. However, the *voltage modulation* of the space-charge region can be large for large reverse bias and is an important effect, as will be seen in later chapters.

## 5.8   actual diode *IV* characteristics

In this chapter, we have for simplicity dealt almost exclusively with idealized *pn*-junction performance. The idealizations have permitted us to understand most easily the basic nature of particle flow and current flow in the diode. We close this chapter with a brief look at an actual diode characteristic as shown in Fig. 5.16. An ideal characteristic is shown in this figure by the dashed line. The deviations of the actual characteristic are considered at four values of voltage. At point *a*, voltage breakdown occurs as mentioned in the preceding section. The slope of the characteristics in the voltage-breakdown region is not infinite, principally because of the finite conductivity of the bulk regions of the diode. At point *b*, the slope of the characteristic is not zero as expected if $I_s$ is a constant,

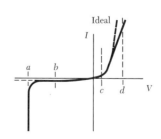

**FIGURE 5.16**   *IV characteristic of actual pn-junction diode.*

because of surface leakage at the *pn* junction. Thus the reverse current contains both a bulk or interior component and a surface component which is approximately ohmic.

The bulk component of reverse diode current is a rapid function of temperature. Remember that $I_s$ is proportional to $p_n$ and $n_p$. These, in turn, are proportional to $n_i^2$ which increases exponentially with temperature [see (4.11$b$)]. For either Ge or Si diodes, $I_s$ approximately doubles for every increase of 10°C.

At low values of current in the forward direction, as at point $c$ of Fig. 5.16, recombination in the space-charge region causes a deviation from ideal performance. This deviation is illustrated by the curve in Fig. 5.17. At very low current, the exponent of the Boltzmann factor is divided by 2 to become $e^{V/2V_T}$. For large forward currents, the recombination effect vanishes and two other effects become dominant. One arises from voltage drops due to the ohmic resistance of the bulk regions. These voltage drops have the effect of making the $IV$ characteristic linear, as shown in Fig. 5.16 at point $d$. In this region there occurs a second phenomenon, called *high-level injection*, which also produces a component of electric field in the bulk regions. This last effect can be considered to be incorporated in the ohmic effect of the $IV$ characteristic since an electric field is involved.

For an actual diode, heating due to the $IV$ power loss in both the junction and the bulk regions is a major limiting process. At first glance, the power loss may seem small enough to be neglected. However, if we consider that the actual semiconductor of the diode has an extremely

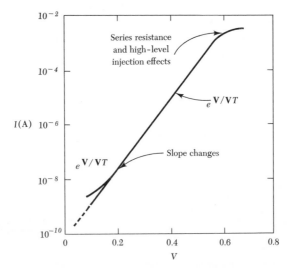

**FIGURE 5.17** *IV characteristic of actual pn-junction diode for forward bias.* [*After Sah, Noyce, and Shockley, Proc. IRE, **45**:1228-43, (1957).*]

small volume, then it is clear that the power per unit volume can be very large. For very small diodes, currents of the order of milliamperes and voltages of only a few volts may produce sufficient heating so that there is permanent damage to the semiconductor crystal.

## REFERENCES

P. E. Gray, D. DeWitt, A. R. Boothroyd, and J. F. Gibbons, "Physical Electronics and Circuit Models of Transistors," SEEC, vol. 2, chaps. 1-4, John Wiley & Sons, Inc., New York, 1964.

## PROBLEMS

**5.1** (*a*) In the space-charge region of an isolated *pn*-junction diode in thermal equilibrium, the drift and diffusion component currents must be equal and cancel each other out. Explain why.

(*b*) If ohmic contacts are made to the diode and a bias voltage applied in the forward direction, why is the expected *IV* characteristic of the diode exponential? Explain.

**5.2** Consider an isolated (or unbiased) *pn*-junction diode in thermal equilibrium.

(*a*) Explain the presence of an electric field in the space-charge region.

(*b*) Associated with this electric field is an electrostatic potential. Can this potential be measured with a conventional voltmeter (requiring current flow)? Explain.

**5.3** In an abrupt silicon *pn* junction, both the *n* and *p* sides have an impurity density of one impurity atom per $10^7$ silicon atoms. Calculate the contact potential $\Delta\psi$ at room temperature and at $-30°F$.

**5.4** Calculate for the *pn* junction of Prob. 5.3 the average hole-diffusion current density if no drift current opposes it. To determine the gradient, use carrier densities as in Fig. 5.2*c* at the space-charge edges. Assume room temperature. Estimate the hole density at the junction for the opposing hole drift current.

**5.5** An abrupt silicon *pn* junction has the following impurity concentrations:

$$n_i = 1.5 \cdot 10^{10} \text{ electrons/cm}^3$$

$$N_a = 10^{16} \text{ donor atoms/cm}^3 \text{ in one region}$$

$$N_d = 10^{16} \text{ donor atoms/cm}^3 \text{ in the other region}$$

(*a*) Calculate the contact potential $\Delta\psi$ at $T = 300°K$.

(*b*) Calculate the peak electric field in the space-charge region and the width of the region for bias voltages $V = 0$ and $V = -20$ V. Assume full depletion of the space-charge region.

(*c*) Would you expect the concepts of drift mobility and diffusion constant to be applicable in this space-charge region?

**5.6**  The germanium *pn* junction shown has a resistivity in the *p* region of $10^{-3}$ Ω-cm and in the *n* region of 0.1 Ω-cm.

(*a*)  Calculate the built-in barrier potential of the junction.

(*b*)  Calculate the width of the space-charge region.

(*c*)  What are the values of the body resistances?

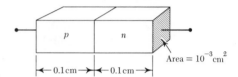

**Problem 5.6**    $\leftarrow$ 0.1 cm $\rightarrow$ $\leftarrow$ 0.1 cm $\rightarrow$    Area = $10^{-3}$ cm$^2$

**5.7**  Consider the germanium diode shown, where

$$n_p = 1.9 \cdot 10^8 \text{ cm}^{-3} \qquad L_h = 2.10 \cdot 10^{-2} \text{ cm}$$

$$p_n = 3.9 \cdot 10^{11} \text{ cm}^{-3} \qquad L_e = 3.05 \cdot 10^{-2} \text{ cm}$$

For a forward bias of 150 mV, and at room temperature ($T = 300°$K),

(*a*)  Evaluate the excess-hole density (minority carriers) at $x' = 0$ and the excess-electron density (minority carriers) at $x'' = 0$.

(*b*)  Find an expression for the excess-hole density in the *n* material as a function of $x'$.

(*c*)  Find an expression for the excess-electron density in the *p* material as a function of $x''$.

(*d*)  Find the electron current in the *p* material at $x'' = 0$.

(*e*)  Find the hole current in the *n* material at $x' = 0$.

(*f*)  Find the total current flowing through the diode.

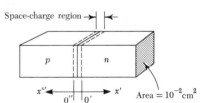

Space-charge region $\rightarrow$ $\mid$ $\leftarrow$

$x'' \leftarrow$  $0'' \mid 0'$  $\rightarrow x'$   Area = $10^{-2}$ cm$^2$

**Problem 5.7**

**5.8**  Consider a *pn* junction with space charge width $w_j = l_n + l_p$, as shown. The potential distribution within the space charge region is assumed to be

$$\psi(x) = \frac{Hq}{24\varepsilon}(3w_j^2 x - 4x^3)$$

where *H* is an unknown constant and $\psi(x)$ is constant outside the space-charge region.

(*a*)  What is the electric field at the metallurgical junction?

(b) What is the electric field at either edge of the region, that is, at $x = \pm w_j/2$?

(c) What is the charge distribution within the space-charge region? Sketch it.

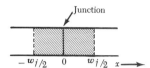

**Problem 5.8**

$-w_j/2 \qquad 0 \qquad w_j/2 \quad x \longrightarrow$

**5.9**  For the junction of Prob. 5.8,

(a) What is the potential $\psi(w_j/2)$?

(b) What is the potential $\psi(-w_j/2)$?

(c) What is the height of the potential barrier?

**5.10**  For the junction of Prob. 5.8,

(a) Show that the total charge in the portion of the region from $x = 0$ to $x = -w_j/2$ is $Q = Hqw_j^2 A/8$, where $A$ is the cross-sectional area of the junction.

(b) What is the total charge in the region $x = 0$ to $x = w_j/2$?

**5.11**  Consider an abrupt-junction diode with a hole-diffusion length $L_h = 1$ mm and a hole current (at the diode junction) of 1 mA.

(a) What is the hole current at a distance of 0.5 mm from the space-charge region (in the $n$ region)?

(b) For an area $A = 10$ mm$^2$, what is the charge density at the distance as under (a) if the material is Si?

(c) If the forward bias of the diode is doubled, show that the change of electron current in the $p$ region at a distance $0.5\,L_e$ from the space-charge region is 682 percent. What is the percent change at $3L_e$?

**5.12**  Given an abrupt silicon junction diode with $N_a = 10^{18}/\text{cm}^3$ in one region and $N_d = 10^{16}/\text{cm}^3$ in the other, determine the width of the space-charge region as a function of the applied external bias voltage. For bias voltages of $+0.2$, $+0.1$, $0.0$, $-0.1$, $-0.4$, $-1.0$, $-5.0$, and $-20.0$ V, calculate the width of the space-charge region. (Assume that no voltage breakdown occurs.)

**5.13**  Repeat Prob. 5.12 for Ge.

**5.14**  For the circuit shown, the source is a dc voltage $V_s$. It is necessary to find the current $I$ flowing in the circuit. Use a graphical method to find the solution. Two different methods are applicable as follows:

*Method 1:* From the $IV$ characteristic of the resistor $R$ (shown in figure $b$) and that of the diode (shown in figure $c$) an overall $IV$ characteristic is established by adding the two voltages for a given current value. The solution for the current for a specified value of $V_s$ is then found.

*Method 2:* Use the load-line method of Prob. 3.13, as illustrated there in figure *b*. The *I* intercept of the load line is at $V = 0$ and $I = V_s/R$. For both methods, assume an ideal diode $I = I_s(e^{V/V_T} - 1)$, where $I_s = 10 \ \mu A$, and a series resistor $R = 1 \ k\Omega$ connected to a dc source of 3 V.

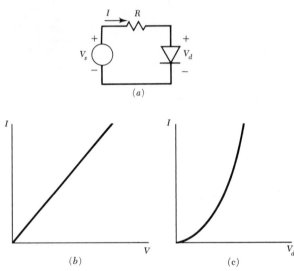

**Problem 5.14**

**5.15**  The *IV* characteristic of a *pn* diode is a function of temperature. Figure *a* shows the *IV* curves of a particular *pn* diode for five different temperatures, $T_A$ through $T_E$.

(*a*) Which temperature is higher, $T_A$ or $T_E$? Briefly explain why.

(*b*) If this diode is placed in series with a 100 Ω resistor and a battery, as shown in figure *b*, what voltage will appear across the diode at temperature $T_D$ if a current of 2 mA flows in the circuit at temperature $T_A$?

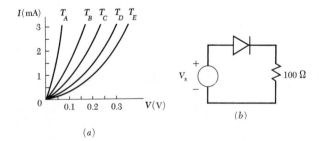

**Problem 5.15**

**5.16** A *pn*-junction diode, as shown, has a reverse saturation current of 20 μA, negligible ohmic resistance, and a breakdown voltage of 75 V. A 2-kΩ resistor is connected in series with this diode, and a 20-V battery is connected across terminals 1 and 2. Find the current (*a*) if the diode is forward biased and (*b*) if the battery is inserted into the circuit with reverse polarity. Repeat parts *a* and *b*, using a breakdown voltage of 5 V.

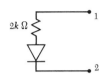

**Problem 5.16**

**5.17** For a semiconductor diode,

(*a*) Calculate and plot the *IV* characteristic of an ideal germanium diode at room temperature over the range $-0.2\ V \leqslant V \leqslant 0.2\ V$. The reverse saturation current is 1 μA.

(*b*) Repeat part *a* for a silicon diode over the range $-0.4\ V \leqslant V \leqslant 0.4\ V$. The reverse saturation current for the Si diode is 1 nA.

(*c*) Explain why the voltage drop across the silicon diode is larger than for the germanium diode at a forward current of 20 mA. [*Note*: On many applications at normal values of the forward current, these characteristics might be approximated by the dashed straight line at a voltage which we might call the "on voltage" (see figure *a*).]

(*d*) A 1-V battery and a 50-Ω resistor are connected in series with an ideal silicon diode, as in figure *b*. Draw the load line on the *IV* characteristic of the silicon diode of part *b*. Find the operating point, i.e., the current flowing through the diode and the voltage across the diode.

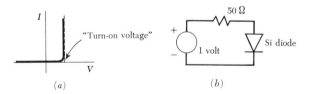

(*a*)            (*b*)

**Problem 5.17**

**5.18** The circuit in figure *a* contains a nonlinear resistor and a diode. The characteristics of the nonlinear resistor and diode are given in figure *b* and *c*, respectively.

(*a*) Find the value of *V* and *I* graphically for a source voltage of $V_s = 3.5\ V$, where *V* is the voltage across *R*.

(*b*) Assume that the nonlinear resistor is replaced by a linear resistor *R*. What should the value of *R* be to provide $V = 0.15\ V$?

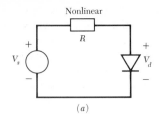

(a)

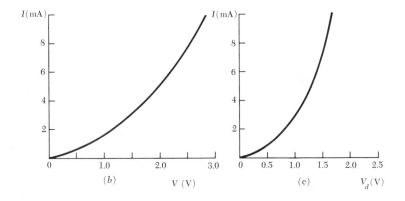

(b)                    (c)

V (V)                    $V_d$(V)

**Problem 5.18**

**5.19**  A circuit with two diodes $D_1$ and $D_2$ in series is shown in figure *a*. The diode characteristics are given in figure *b*. Find $V_2$ graphically when $V_1 = 0.7$ V. (*Hint:* Assume that diode $D_1$ is the load of diode $D_2$.)

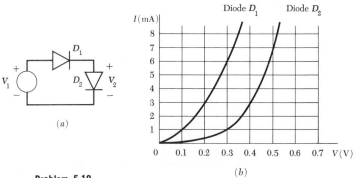

(a)

(b)

**Problem 5.19**

**5.20**  Two diodes are connected in series.

(*a*) Diodes $D_1$ and $D_2$ in figure *a* have saturation currents of 10 μa and 15 μa, respectively. Find the current flowing in the circuit.

Assume that the magnitude of the breakdown voltage of each diode is larger than 5 V.

(b) The diodes $D_1$ and $D_2$ are now connected in opposing series, as indicated in figure b. A 4-V voltage source is impressed upon this arrangement. Find the voltage across each junction. Assume that the diodes have the same reverse saturation current instead of the values given in part a.

(c) Diodes $D_1$ and $D_2$ are next connected as shown in figure c. The reverse saturation current of both diodes is now taken to be 5 $\mu$A. The magnitude of the breakdown voltage of the diodes is 2 V. What is the current flowing in the circuit?

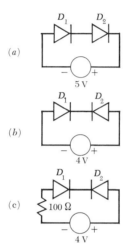

**Problem 5.20**

**5.21** Consider the circuit shown. The $IV$ characteristics of diodes $D_1$ and $D_2$ can be approximated by straight lines, as shown. Find the current flowing in the circuit.

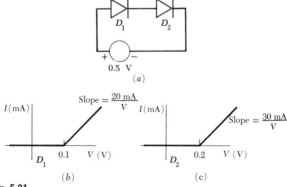

**Problem 5.21**

**5.22**    Assume two diodes in a circuit, as shown in figure *a*.

(*a*) The *IV* characteristics of two diodes $D_1$ and $D_2$ are shown in figure *b*. Find the *IV* characteristic for the two diodes in parallel.

(*b*) A resistor and a battery are connected between terminals 1 and 2, as shown below in figure *c*. Find the current flowing in the circuit and the voltage across each diode; make use of the result of part *a*. Show the graphical construction.

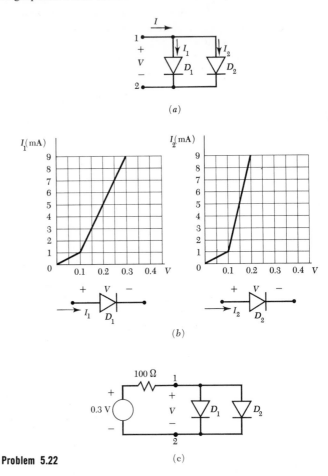

(*a*)

(*b*)

**Problem 5.22**                    (c)

**5.23**    Given the *IV* characteristic of an actual diode shown, compare it with that of an ideal diode. Choose some operating point and compare the slope at that point with that you would obtain on an ideal diode for the same value of current. Try to fit the characteristic of the actual diode by using an ideal diode with a combination of series and shunt resistances. Figures *a* and *b* represent different ranges for *I* and *V*.

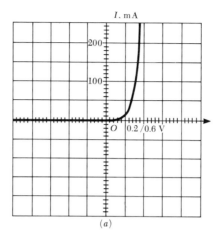

(a)

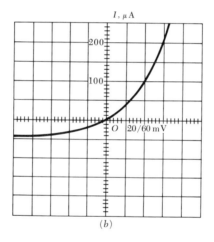

(b)

**Problem 5.23** (*From Gray, et al., SEEC, vol. 2, p. 45.*)

# chapter 6

# APPLICATIONS AND MODELS OF THE
# *pn*-JUNCTION DIODE

## 6.1 mathematical device model

Having discussed the physical operation of the *pn*-junction diode in the previous chapter we now consider the junction diode as a device which is connected to other circuit elements. In particular, we are interested in its behavior and performance when connected in a complete circuit, as well as in the various applications that emphasize and utilize different properties of the *pn*-junction diode. For example, the diode may be used for its strongly nonlinear behavior under forward or reverse bias. Alternatively, we may concentrate on perturbations around an operating point to bring out other effects of the diode, such as the capacitance effect. The particular model of the diode that is used in a specific instance to analyze the performance of the diode depends on which aspect of its behavior we wish to study.

In the last chapter, a *mathematical model* of the *pn* diode is proposed:

$$I = I_s(e^{V/V_T} - 1) \tag{6.1}$$

where $V_T = kT/q$ and $I_s$ is a constant. Because simplifying assumptions are made in developing this equation, it cannot describe the behavior of the *pn* junction exactly. As an illustration, remember that the charge-carrier generation or recombination in the space-charge region has been neglected in deriving (6.1), and there are other idealizations as discussed in Chap. 5. However, the correspondence of (6.1) with the current-voltage characteristic of an actual diode is surprisingly good. Although (6.1) is only a model, it is not merely a crude approximation; in a sense, (6.1) describes an ideal diode.

## 6.2 diode applications

Diodes are used principally because of their nonlinear $IV$ characteristic. Therefore, we begin our study of the diode by considering applications that illustrate its nonlinear behavior. For these examples, it is convenient to approximate initially the actual or mathematical model of the $IV$ characteristic by an idealized broken-line characteristic, as shown in Fig. 6.1a.

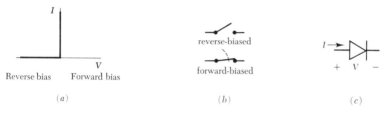

FIGURE 6.1 *Idealized pn diode.* (a) *IV characteristic;* (b) *switch analog;* (c) *diode symbol.*

In forward bias, we assume that no voltage drop exists across the diode, and in reverse bias no current flows through the diode. This can be likened to the behavior of a perfect switch with its contacts either closed or open as illustrated in Fig. 6.1b. The closed contact corresponds to the forward-bias condition of the idealized diode; the open contact corresponds to the reverse-bias condition.

When using diodes in circuits, it is convenient to use the diode symbol which is shown in Fig. 6.1c. The arrow points in the direction of positive current flow under the forward-bias condition (when the bias voltage is positive at the $p$ side). This current direction is called the "easy flow" direction.

The diode applications that are presented below are those for modifying the waveforms of signal waves, i.e., for wave shaping. Depending on the specific action of the diodes on the waveform, we call the circuits clippers, slicers, or clamps. We also include in these applications the rectifier, which is a specialized form of a clipper.

**THE RECTIFIERS** The diode-resistor circuit of Fig. 6.2a is called a *halfwave rectifier*. Let us assume that a signal source is present which produces the sinusoidal voltage $v_s$, as shown in Fig. 6.2b. The output of the circuit is taken as the voltage developed across $R$. We now recognize that the diode can conduct only when the input voltage $v_s$ is in the positive half cycle, which means that a clipping action cuts out the negative half cycle of the

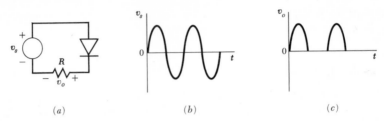

**FIGURE 6.2**  *Halfwave rectifier. (a) Circuit diagram; (b) input voltage waveform; (c) output voltage waveform with negative half-cycle clipped.*

signal, as shown in Fig. 6.2c. The output voltage is thus a pulsating voltage consisting of a series of positive, half sine waves if the diode has the idealized *IV* characteristic of Fig. 6.1a. Hence the name halfwave rectifier. It is clear that the output voltage waveform $v_o(t)$, has an average (dc) component in its Fourier-series representation. If a filter is introduced at $R$, the fundamental and higher harmonics of the waveform of $v_o(t)$ can be prohibited from developing any output voltage. The output is, then, a dc voltage which is proportional to the height of the input sinusoid. The rectifier is an *ac-to-dc converter.*

More efficient conversion can be obtained if two halfwave rectifiers are combined. A simple arrangement is shown in Fig. 6.3a. The two voltage

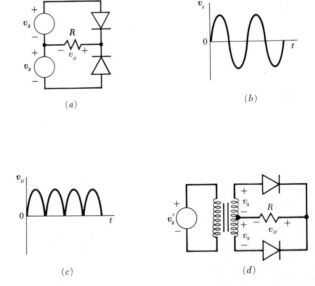

**FIGURE 6.3**  *Fullwave rectifier. (a) Circuit; (b) input-voltage waveform; (c) output-voltage waveform; (d) circuit using transformer.*

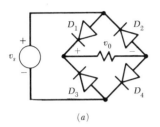
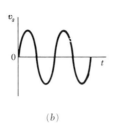
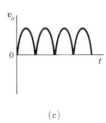

(a)                               (b)                               (c)

**FIGURE 6.4** *Diode bridge rectifier.* (a) *Circuit;* (b) *input-voltage waveform;* (c) *output-voltage waveform.*

inputs are assumed to be identical as in Fig. 6.3*b*. Because of the "phasing" of the two sources, first one side of the circuit conducts current and produces an output, and then the other side does. The total output waveform is shown in Fig. 6.3*c*. This circuit is called a *fullwave rectifier.* The average component of $v_o(t)$ in Fig. 6.3*c* is larger than that of Fig. 6.2*c*. The requirement of two $v_s$ sources is met in practice by the use of transformers with a center tap on the secondary winding, as shown in Fig. 6.3*d*. Voltage $v_s$ appears on both sides of the center tap with the proper phase.

Four diodes can also be used to obtain fullwave rectification without requiring two $v_s$ sources. The circuit, for which *pn*-junction diodes are particularly suitable, is shown in Fig. 6.4*a* and is called a diode bridge circuit. The input again is a sinusoid as in Fig. 6.4*b*. When $v_s$ is in the positive half cycle, diodes $D_1$ and $D_4$ are forward biased. The current then flows from the source to the load resistance $R$ through these two diodes. When $v_s$ is in the negative half cycle, diodes $D_3$ and $D_2$ are forward biased. However, the current flows through $R$ in the same direction as before. The output voltage across $R$ is shown in Fig. 6.4*c*.

The Fourier analysis of Chap. 2 shows that the average value for the halfwave and fullwave rectified sine waves are, respectively,

Half wave:
$$V_{av} = \frac{V_m}{\pi} \tag{6.2a}$$

Full wave:
$$V_{av} = \frac{2V_m}{\pi} \tag{6.2b}$$

where $V_m$ is the maximum value of the sine-wave voltage $v_s$.

**CLIPPERS** We turn now to the general application of diodes as signal waveform clippers. To illustrate this, consider a signal source $v_s$ which produces a triangular waveform, as in Fig. 6.5*a*. This signal is now used as the input to a circuit consisting of a diode and a dc bias voltage source $V$ as in Fig. 6.5*b*. Note that a battery symbol is used in this figure in place

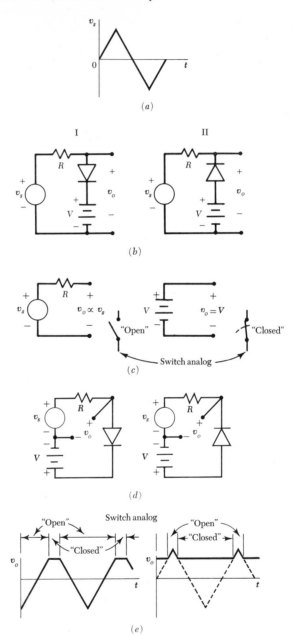

**FIGURE 6.5** *Diode shunt clippers, I—positive peak clipping, II—negative peak clipping. (a) Input-voltage waveform; (b) clipper circuits; (c) output-voltage under different bias conditions, left: reverse bias, right: forward bias; (d) bias state of diode; (e) output-voltage waveforms.*

of the ideal dc voltage source symbol of Sec. 3.2. In the remainder of the book, the battery symbol is used in electronic circuits to conform with usual practice. A resistance $R$ is inserted to limit the current flow through the diode (remember that the diode is assumed to have a resistance of zero ohms under forward bias). Two such circuits (I and II) are shown in Fig. 6.5$b$. The two differ only in the forward direction of current for the diode. The waveshape of the output voltage $v_o$ is found by following the input signal through a complete cycle.

For the diode, the idealized characteristic of Fig. 6.1$a$ is used. Using the switch analogy, we investigate what happens at the output when the switch is "open" (reverse-biased diode) and when it is "closed" (forward-biased diode). Figure 6.5$c$ shows the output voltage $v_o$ that would appear for these two switch positions. The problem, of course, is to find the state of bias of the diode under the combined action of the signal voltage $v_s$ and the dc bias voltage $V$. Figure 6.5$d$ (a redrawn version of 6.5$b$) shows that the voltages $v_s$ and $V$ oppose each other. For circuit example I, the diode is reverse biased as long as $v_s$ is in the negative half cycle and even during the positive half cycle when $v_s < V$. When $v_s > V$, however, the bias condition is changed to forward bias (switch closed). For the latter case, the output voltage is the constant value $V$ as can be seen from Fig. 6.5$c$. Figure 6.5$e$ shows the waveform of the output voltage $v_o(t)$. Note that circuits I and II both clip the waveform of the input signal $v_s$. Circuit I clips the top of the waveform, circuit II the bottom.

In Fig. 6.6, two other clipping circuits are shown. In these circuits, the diode is placed in series with the signal source. (For the circuits shown in

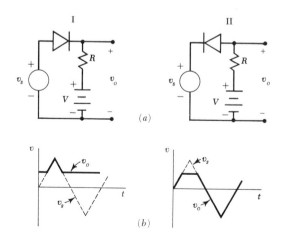

**FIGURE 6.6**  *Diode series clippers, I—negative peak clipping, II—positive peak clipping,* (a) *Circuit diagrams;* (b) *input- and output-voltage waveforms.*

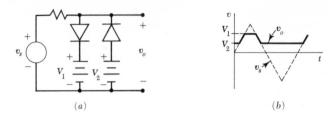

(a)                                                 (b)

**FIGURE 6.7** *Diode slicer circuit.* (a) *Circuit diagram with* $V_1 > V_2$; (b) *input- and output-voltage waveforms.*

Fig. 6.5 the diode is effectively in parallel with the output.) Again there are two possible circuits, I and II, as shown in Fig. 6.6, and the two circuits differ only in the forward direction for the diodes. The input waveform and the output waveform are shown for both circuits in Fig. 6.6*b*. The clipping action of the two circuits is complementary.

**SLICERS**    If two clipping diodes are used in one circuit, each with an individual dc bias voltage, a *slicer* is obtained. Such a circuit is shown in Fig. 6.7*a*. The two dc bias voltages are labeled $V_1$ and $V_2$, and we assume that $V_1 > V_2$. On the basis of the results of Fig. 6.5*e*, for each diode sep-

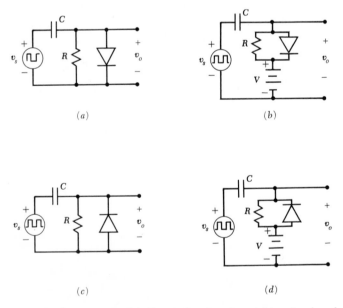

(a)                                                 (b)

(c)                                                 (d)

**FIGURE 6.8** *Diode clamp circuits.* (a) *Circuit for clamping positive signal peak to zero;* (b) *circuit for clamping positive signal peak to* $+V$; (c) *circuit for clamping negative signal peaks to zero;* (d) *circuit for clamping negative signal peak to* $+V$.

parately, we can readily understand that an output waveform as in Fig. 6.7*b* results. Note that a slice is cut from the $v_s$ wave.

**CLAMPS** Sometimes it is necessary to "clamp" the positive or negative peak of an input waveform to a certain constant voltage level. This can be achieved by using *clamp circuits*. Four different types are shown in Fig. 6.8. An explanation of the circuit performance is given below.

The circuit of Fig. 6.8*a* clamps the positive peaks of $v_s$ to a zero-voltage level at the output. Note that the circuit does not have a dc source. Figure 6.8*b* represents the same circuit, but with a dc voltage source. In this circuit, the positive peaks are clamped to the dc level of the source voltage $V$. Figure 6.8*c* shows a circuit which is identical to that of Fig. 6.8*a* except that the forward direction of the diode is reversed. This circuit will clamp the negative peaks to zero at the output. Figure 6.8*d* is a circuit as in Fig. 6.8*b*, but with the forward direction of the diode reversed. This arrangement results in clamping the negative peaks to a given dc voltage level at the output.

Because of the similarity of the circuits, we study only one, that of

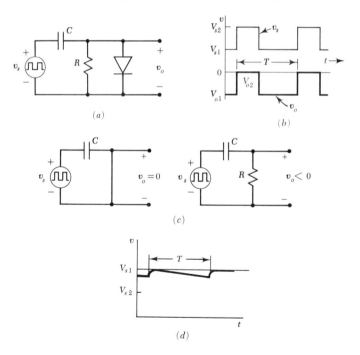

(a)

(b)

(c)

(d)

**FIGURE 6.9** *Piecewise analysis of the diode clamp circuit.* (a) *Circuit diagram;* (b) *input- and output-voltage waveforms;* (c) *circuit with diode forward biased (on left) and reverse biased (on right);* (d) *voltage across C.*

Fig. 6.8*a*, which is redrawn in Fig. 6.9*a*. The assumed input waveform for $v_s$, as shown in Fig. 6.9*b*, is an asymmetrical rectangular wave. Using an idealized-diode characteristic, as in Fig. 6.1*a*, we now visualize the circuit performance under the two possible bias conditions. Figure 6.9*c* shows the circuit conditions for both forward and reverse bias of the diode. Note that the diode shorts the resistor $R$ for forward bias. Therefore, the output voltage $v_o$ is clamped to a zero-voltage level when the diode is forward biased. Under reverse bias of the diode, however, we have an $RC$ circuit and the output voltage $v_o$ is the voltage developed across $R$. That is, we obtain the response of the $RC$ circuit due to the excitation by the signal voltage $v_s$. From Chap. 3, it should be remembered that the voltage which builds up across the capacitor due to the sudden application of a constant voltage to a series $RC$ combination is

$$v_C = V(1 - e^{-t/\tau}) \tag{6.3a}$$

where $\tau$ is the time constant of the response:

$$\tau = RC \tag{6.3b}$$

This type of rise of the voltage $v_C$ versus time is shown in Fig. 6.10.

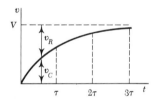

**FIGURE 6.10** *Voltage versus time in a series RC circuit with an applied step voltage V; $v_C$ is voltage across C, $v_R$ is voltage across R.*

We now consider the circuit response for a complete input cycle. If the input wave has been applied for some time at its lowest level, a certain output voltage $V_{o1}$ is present which corresponds to the value of the input voltage $V_{s1}$ (see Fig. 6.9*b*). When the input voltage rises suddenly to the value $V_{s2}$, the voltage across the diode increases as well and the diode becomes forward biased. Because of the near-short circuit supplied by the diode, the capacitance can charge very quickly to the maximum value $V_{s2}$, and the output voltage $V_{o2}$ is clamped to the zero-voltage level by the diode. Now when the input voltage drops to the lower level $V_{s1}$, the diode becomes reverse biased, because of the combined voltages of the source and the capacitor. The voltage across the diode drops by $(V_{s1} - V_{s2})$ to $V_{o1}$. The output then appears as in Fig. 6.9*b*. In Fig. 6.9*d*, the voltage across $C$ is shown. Notice that the capacitor charges very rapidly when the diode is forward biased. When the diode is reverse biased, the discharge of the capacitance must be slow in order to hold the output at $V_{o1}$. Consequently, the value of the time constant $RC$ must be large in relation to the period $T$.

Diode clamps have many important applications. For example, when asymmetrical signals are amplified by ac-coupled amplifiers, which do not pass the dc component of a signal, one uses "dc restoration" circuits. These are clamp circuits which enable us to clamp a signal to a certain dc level. In television receivers, one must use such dc restoration to maintain the black level at the cutoff point of the picture tube.

**LOGIC CIRCUITS**  Circuits which can perform logical operations, usually on the basis of binary signals, are called *logic circuits*. Two examples of diode logic circuits are shown in Fig. 6.11. These circuits are basic building blocks for some electronic digital computers. The circuit shown in Fig. 6.11a is used to obtain the logical OR operation and that of Fig. 6.11b is used to obtain the logical AND operation.

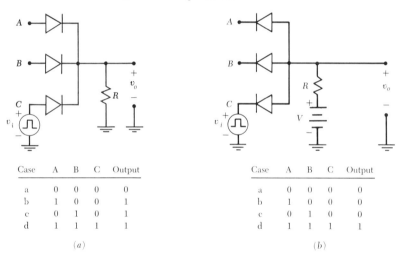

| Case | A | B | C | Output |
|------|---|---|---|--------|
| a | 0 | 0 | 0 | 0 |
| b | 1 | 0 | 0 | 1 |
| c | 0 | 1 | 0 | 1 |
| d | 1 | 1 | 1 | 1 |

(a)

| Case | A | B | C | Output |
|------|---|---|---|--------|
| a | 0 | 0 | 0 | 0 |
| b | 1 | 0 | 0 | 0 |
| c | 0 | 1 | 0 | 0 |
| d | 1 | 1 | 1 | 1 |

(b)

**FIGURE 6.11**  *Diode logic circuits.* (a) OR *circuit;* (b) AND *circuit.* (*Only one input pulse signal $v_i$ is shown for simplicity.*)

The logic OR circuit of Fig. 6.11a provides a voltage $v_o$ across $R$ whenever a positive pulse $v_i$ is applied to any one of the input terminals $A$, $B$, or $C$. The name OR is derived from the fact that a positive pulse to A *or* B *or* C will produce an output pulse. (If negative pulses are to be used, the diodes have to be connected in the reverse direction of that shown.)

The table below the circuit, called a *truth table*, lists the outputs for different inputs. Instead of using certain voltage values, we simply use statements of "0" or "1" which correspond to the "binary notation" system. Each of these represents a certain voltage level. A 1, for example, may signify the presence of an input or the presence of an output, and 0 the absence of input or output. Alternatively, the two may represent any two discrete voltage levels. For case *a* of the table, we have no input, i.e., a zero input, on all of the terminals *A*, *B*, or *C*. The output is then also zero. If an input is present, marked by 1, an ↝output will be present too. The table shows several possible input situations with the corresponding outputs.

For the logic AND circuit of Fig. 6.11*b*, no output is obtained unless all the inputs are present. Inputs *A and B and C* must be present. In the absence of any adequate signal, all three diodes are forward biased and the output is clamped to ground, the 0 state. However, if we apply a pulse of magnitude $v_i > V$ to each terminal *A*, *B*, and *C*, all the diodes are reversed biased and an output voltage equal to $v_i$ is obtained as long as *A*, *B*, and *C* are present simultaneously. Thus a 1 input corresponds to an input signal $v_i$, which exceeds the value of the dc source *V*. The table below the circuit in Fig. 6.11*b* shows several possible input situations with the corresponding outputs.

It is possible to modify the output from an OR circuit by using an inverter in cascade with the OR circuit. The combination is called a NOR circuit and is shown in Fig. 6.12. The inverter action is presented in detail in

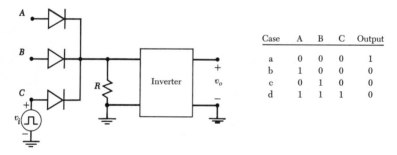

| Case | A | B | C | Output |
|------|---|---|---|--------|
| a | 0 | 0 | 0 | 1 |
| b | 1 | 0 | 0 | 0 |
| c | 0 | 1 | 0 | 0 |
| d | 1 | 1 | 1 | 0 |

**FIGURE 6.12**   NOR *circuit (with only one input pulse signal shown).*

Chapter 9 on transistor applications.[1] For here, we consider case *a* of the table in Fig. 6.11*a*, where the output is 0. If we connect an inverter to the output circuit, we obtain the inverse of 0, which is a 1. On the other hand, if the output from the OR circuit is 1, as for case *c* of Fig. 6.11*a*, the output from an inverter is 0. A comparison of the NOR table of Fig. 6.12 with that of the OR table of Fig. 6.11*a* illustrates the modified performance

---

[1] In Chap. 9, it is also pointed out that an inverter not only changes a 0 into a 1, and vice versa, but also provides amplification of the actual voltage and current levels. Amplification is necessary to make up for any losses incurred in the resistances of the circuits and also to compensate for the voltage drops across forward-biased diodes (of the order of a few tenths of a volt).

which is obtained with the inverter. For the NOR circuit we obtain an output of 1 only when neither $A$ nor $B$ nor $C$ has an input of 1.

When we use an inverter in connection with the AND circuit, we obtain a NAND circuit, as shown in Fig. 6.13. Whenever the AND circuit has an

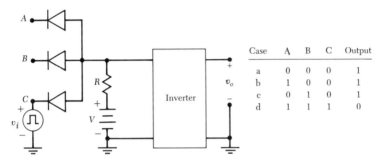

| Case | A | B | C | Output |
|------|---|---|---|--------|
| a | 0 | 0 | 0 | 1 |
| b | 1 | 0 | 0 | 1 |
| c | 0 | 1 | 0 | 1 |
| d | 1 | 1 | 1 | 0 |

**FIGURE 6.13**    NAND *circuit (with only one input pulse signal shown).*

output of 0, the inverter provides an output of 1, and vice versa. An inverter output of 0 results now only when all of the inputs are applied. A 1 is obtained in the output when any one of the inputs do not have a pulse. The table of Fig. 6.13 shows the basic possibilities and should be compared with Fig. 6.11$b$.

Basic logic NOR and NAND circuits such as those above are actually used as the building blocks for the arithmetic and control units of modern digital computers. For proper application of these circuits it is necessary, of course, to design the circuits on the basis of actual characteristics and properties of typical diodes rather than the idealized characteristic of Fig. 6.1$a$.

## 6.3    circuit-model parameters

The dc or low-frequency performance of typical diode circuits can be established from actual $IV$ characteristics of actual or typical $pn$-junction diodes. "Load-line constructions," which have been introduced in several problems in Chaps. 3 and 5 and which are also used in Chap. 7, provide an easy method of obtaining initial and final values of the dc voltages and current in a circuit. For the transient response, or high-frequency performance, of the circuit, the $IV$ characteristics are not sufficient since they do not provide any information on the time rate of charge flow into and out of the diode due to changes of the external excitation of the diode. If large-signal excursions are present, as is typical in the diode circuits of the last section, the analysis problem can be severe. This difficulty is due to the nonlinear nature of the charge flow and charge storage in the diode. On the other hand, if we are interested primarily in an output response over only a limited voltage or current range, we can model the *pn* diode with a "small-signal" circuit model. Even when the large-signal case is of interest, the results for the small-signal case provide us with insight into the performance of the circuit for signals which vary with time.

A small-signal circuit model of the diode consists of resistances and capacitances. The resistances (or conductances) model the relation of changes of voltage $\Delta V$ to changes in current $\Delta I$ about a fixed bias point in certain regions of the diode. The capacitances relate the changes of stored charge $\Delta Q$ in various regions to changes in the diode or junction voltage $\Delta V$, again with respect to the conditions which exist at a fixed bias point. In this section, we return to the basic mechanisms of the *pn*-junction diode and propose resistance or capacitance elements to model these mechanisms. In the next section, the separate circuit elements are combined to obtain a small-signal circuit model for the diode.

If we refer to Chap. 5, the need for at least two resistance elements is immediately obvious. The bulk resistance of the semiconductor regions is labeled $r_x$. The leakage resistance of the *pn* junction is labeled $r_l$. A third resistance or conductance is also needed to represent or model the incremental *iv* characteristic of the junction itself about the bias point. In addition to these resistances, capacitances are needed to model the storages of charge in the diode. Two types of charge storage can be considered. In the transition or depletion region of the junction, we have the fixed, immobile charge of the impurity ions. For a small perturbation about the bias point, equal and opposite charges must flow in the diode terminals to supply or absorb the change in charge resulting from the change in width of the depletion region. There is also a stored charge of minority and majority carriers in the bulk regions of the semiconductor when the diode is biased in the forward direction. This is a mobile charge; nonetheless, at a given time, a storage of charge is present. For a perturbation about the bias point, a new distribution of mobile charge is established and a corresponding charge $\Delta Q$ flows in the diode terminals. Capacitances may be used to model both of these changes of charge with a change in voltage.

We now consider these elements, one by one, in greater detail.

**INCREMENTAL JUNCTION CONDUCTANCE**    From the last chapter, it is clear that if a bias voltage is applied to a junction, a net current flows. If the bias voltage is changed, the current also changes. Looking at the graphical characteristic of an ideal junction, as in Fig. 6.14a, we assume a certain operating point $A$ which has a forward-bias voltage $V_A$ and a forward current $I_A$. We now introduce a signal voltage, which causes variations about the operating point $A$ as shown in Fig. 6.14b. The signal voltage may be considered to be

$dV$ which causes a change in current $dI$. The *incremental conductance* $g_d$ is therefore the slope of the characteristic at this point, as shown.

$$g_d = \frac{dI}{dV} \simeq \frac{\Delta I}{\Delta V} \tag{6.4}$$

Note that the conductance is defined in terms of differential changes, i.e., in terms of the tangent to the $IV$ curve at point $A$ of the figure. However,

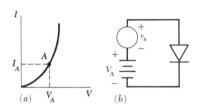

**FIGURE 6.14**  *Diode with dc operating point.*
(a) *Operating (bias) point on characteristic;*
(b) *small signal* $v_s$ *added to produce variations about the bias point.*

$g_d$ can be used for finite changes if $\Delta V$ is not too large. In addition, notice that the voltage change is taken as the independent variable and the current change is the dependent variable. An expression for $g_d$ can be found from the mathematical model (6.1) of the diode. Differentiating (6.1) with respect to $V$, we obtain

$$g_d = \frac{dI}{dV} = \frac{1}{V_T} I_s e^{V/V_T} = \frac{1}{V_T}(I + I_s) \tag{6.5a}$$

For a forward-bias condition, we often have the inequality $V \gg V_T = 26$ mV at 300° K. Therefore, the unit term of (6.1) can be neglected, and we can obtain an approximate value

$$g_d \simeq \frac{I}{V_T} = \frac{I \,(\text{mA})}{26} \qquad \text{mho} \tag{6.5b}$$

Note that a denominator of 26 can be used when $I$ is given in milliamperes.
For a numerical example, let us assume that $I = 5.2$ mA and $I_s = 1 \, \mu$A. Using (6.5a), we obtain

$$g_d = \frac{1}{0.026}(5.2 \cdot 10^{-3} + 1 \cdot 10^{-6}) = 0.2 \text{ mho} \tag{6.5c}$$

It is clear that the second term in the parentheses can be neglected with respect to the first term. The approximation of (6.5b), namely, $g_d \simeq I/V_T = 5.2/26 = 0.2$ mho is clearly valid. The incremental resistance $r_d$, the reciprocal of $g_d$, is $1/0.2 = 5$ ohms. For reverse bias, $V < 0$ and usually $|V| \gg V_T$, the diode current approaches $-I_s$ and the incremental conductance is very small. (That is, the incremental resistance for large reverse bias is very high.)

**SPACE-CHARGE CAPACITANCE**   We know that in the space-charge region the fixed charges of the donor and acceptor ions face each other across the metallurgical junction. We will use here the same approximations as in the previous chapter, namely, that all mobile charges are removed from the space-charge region. In addition, we continue to assume that the space-charge region has abrupt boundaries at the edges, as shown in Fig. 6.15. The charge on the $p$ side of the space-charge region, which has the chosen positive sense for external applied potentials, is the negative of charge on the $n$ side:

$$Q = -qAl_pN_a = -qAl_nN_d \tag{6.6a}$$

where $A$ is the area. This can be rewritten using (5.12), (5.14a), and (5.30):

$$Q = -A\left(2\varepsilon q\frac{\Delta\psi - V}{1/N_a + 1/N_d}\right)^{1/2} \tag{6.6b}$$

If we change the applied bias voltage by an amount $dV$, then $Q$ will change by an amount $dQ$. We define now a space-charge capacitance of the junction as follows:

$$C_j = \frac{dQ}{dV} = \frac{K}{(\Delta\psi - V)^{1/2}} \tag{6.7a}$$

where $K$ is a constant for a given $pn$-junction diode. The form on the right is obtained from (6.6b) by a differentiation with respect to $V$.

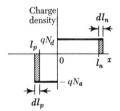

**FIGURE 6.15** *Changes in space-charge region within increase of applied voltage.*

In Fig. 6.15, the change of charge $dQ$ resulting from a change of applied voltage $dV$ is found at the edge of the space-charge region. Consequently, the space-charge capacitance $C_j$ can be considered to be that of a parallel-plate capacitor having an area $A$ and a spacing $l_p + l_n = w_j$:

$$C_j = \frac{\varepsilon A}{w_j} \tag{6.7b}$$

where $\varepsilon$ is the dielectric permittivity. This equation is easily verified by including in (6.7a) the fact that $w_j = l_p + l_n$ and that $w_j$ is a function of $(\Delta\psi - V)^{1/2}$ from (6.6a) and (6.6b).

From (6.7a), we can see that $C_j$ increases with a forward-bias voltage

$V$ since the barrier potential $(\Delta\psi - V)$ decreases for forward bias; and conversely, when reverse bias is applied, that capacitance $C_j$ becomes small and decreases further as $V$ becomes more negative.

**EXAMPLE OF SPACE-CHARGE CAPACITANCE**   For a numerical example of the space-charge capacitance, we assume a silicon $pn$-junction diode with dimensions as shown in Fig. 6.16. The resistivity on the $p$ side is $\rho_p = 0.001$ $\Omega$-cm,

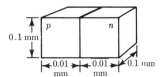

**FIGURE 6.16** *Geometry and dimensions of an idealized diode.*

and that on the $n$ side as $\rho_n = 1.0$ $\Omega$-cm. From these values, we obtain the following concentrations of the charge carriers in each region:

$$N_a \simeq p_p \simeq \frac{1}{q\rho_p\mu_h} = \frac{1}{(1.6\cdot10^{-19})(10^{-3})(0.48\cdot10^3)} = 1.3\cdot10^{19} \text{ holes/cm}^3$$

$$N_d \simeq n_n \simeq \frac{1}{q\rho_n\mu_e} = \frac{1}{(1.6\cdot10^{-19})(1)(1.35\cdot10^3)} = 4.6\cdot10^{15} \text{ electrons/cm}^3$$

From these values, we obtain

$$p_n = \frac{n_i^2}{n_n} = \frac{2.25\cdot10^{20}}{4.6\cdot10^{15}} = 4.9\cdot10^4 \text{ holes/cm}^3$$

From (5.7a), the built-in potential $\Delta\psi$ in thermal equilibrium is

$$\Delta\psi = V_T \ln\frac{p_p}{p_n} = 0.026 \ln\frac{1.3\cdot10^{19}}{4.9\cdot10^4} = 0.86 \text{ volt}$$

We now calculate the width of the space-charge region for zero (applied) bias. Because $N_d << N_a$, we can neglect $l_p$ because it is much smaller than $l_n$ [see (6.6a)]. Therefore $w_j = l_n$. From (5.14a),

$$l_n \simeq \left(\frac{2\varepsilon\Delta\psi}{qN_d}\right)^{1/2} = \left[\frac{2\cdot12\cdot8.85\cdot10^{-14}}{(1.6\cdot10^{-19})(4.6\cdot10^{15})}0.86\right]^{1/2}$$
$$= 5\cdot10^{-5} \text{ cm}$$

We calculate $l_p$ only to verify that it is negligible compared with $l_n$. From (6.6a) we obtain

$$l_p = \frac{N_d}{N_a}l_n = \frac{4.6\cdot10^{15}}{1.3\cdot10^{19}}(5\cdot10^{-5}) = 1.77\cdot10^{-8} \text{ cm}$$

For no applied external bias, the space-charge capacitance from (6.7*b*) is

$$C_j(0) = \frac{\varepsilon A}{w_j} = \frac{(12 \cdot 8.85 \cdot 10^{-14})(10^{-4})}{5 \cdot 10^{-5}} = 2.1 \text{ pF}$$

We next assume that an external, forward-bias voltage $V$ is applied to the diode and that a forward current $I = 5$ mA flows. We wish to find the space-charge capacitance $C_j$ for this forward-bias condition. First we need a value of the reverse saturation current $I_s$. A typical value is $10^{-8}$ A for a silicon diode of the dimensions of Fig. 6.16. We find now the forward-bias voltage which produces the forward current of 5 mA. Assuming room temperature at $T = 300°$K and using (6.1), we obtain

$$V = V_T \ln\left(\frac{I}{I_s} + 1\right) = 0.026 \ln\left(\frac{5 \cdot 10^{-3}}{10^{-8}} + 1\right) = 0.34 \text{ volt}$$

We now obtain $l_n$ for this bias condition from (6.6) by taking the following ratio:

$$\frac{l_n(0.34)}{l_n(0)} = \left(\frac{\Delta\psi - V}{\Delta\psi}\right)^{1/2} = \left(\frac{0.86 - 0.34}{0.86}\right)^{1/2} = 0.78$$

The space-charge capacitance, taking $l_n(0.34) \simeq w_j$ and using ratios, becomes

$$C_j(0.34) = \frac{l_n(0)}{l_n(0.34)} C_j(0) = \frac{2.1}{0.78} \text{ pF} = 2.7 \text{ pF}$$

We now consider a reverse-bias condition, $V = -4$ V. We obtain

$$\frac{l_n(-4)}{l_n(0)} = \left(\frac{\Delta\psi + 4}{\Delta\psi}\right)^{1/2} = \left(\frac{4.86}{0.86}\right)^{1/2} = 2.38$$

The corresponding space-charge capacitance is obtained using ratios

$$C_j(-4) = \frac{l_n(0)}{l_n(-4)} C_j(0) = \frac{2.1}{2.38} \text{ pF} = 0.9 \text{ pF}$$

The variation of $C_j$ with bias is illustrated in Fig. 6.17.

**DIFFUSION CAPACITANCE**  When the *pn* junction is forward biased, minority-charge carriers are injected into the bulk regions (holes into the *n* side and electrons into the *p* side). These carriers diffuse and recombine with the majority carriers. Figure 6.18*a* shows the excess-minority-carrier profile in both "neutral" regions outside of the space-charge region of the junction. As mentioned earlier, we have a time-average *stored charge of minority carriers* on both sides of the junction for a given bias condition. Furthermore, we also have a time-average stored charge of excess majority carriers in these regions. Thus, we have equal and opposite charges as in an actual capacitor.

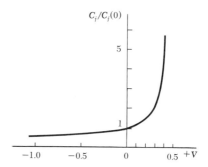

**FIGURE 6.17**   *Space-charge capacitance versus bias voltage.*

When we change the applied forward-bias voltage by an increment $dV$, we also change the stored charge. The increment $dQ$ caused by an increment

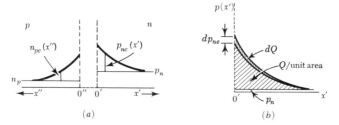

(a)                    (b)

**FIGURE 6.18**   *Minority-charge density outside of space-charge region under forward bias.* (a) *Minority-carrier density;* (b) *change in carrier density with incremental bias change (n region only).*

$dV$ is illustrated in Fig. 6.18$b$. We define now an excess carrier storage capacitance for the $n$ region.

$$C_d = \frac{dQ}{dV} \tag{6.8}$$

This capacitance is often called a *diffusion capacitance* because of the diffusion of minority carriers away from the junction. An expression for $C_d$ in terms of the parameters and biasing point can be obtained by establishing the total excess-minority-carrier charge for a given bias condition. For a *long-base diode* in which the bulk regions are sufficiently long that the excess-minority-carrier density has fallen to zero with distance away from the junction and in which the flow of minority carriers is primarily due to diffusion, we have already established the density of excess minority carriers, $p_{ne}(x)$, in (5.25e). For the one-dimensional situation, the total excess-minority-carrier charge in the $n$ region, using an unprimed coordinate, is

$$Q = qA \int_0^\infty p_{ne}(x)dx \qquad (6.9a)$$

where $A$ is the cross-sectional area of the diode. Here $p_{ne}(x)$ is the excess density of minority carriers in the $n$ region (5.25e)

$$p_{ne}(x) = p_n(e^{V/V_T} - 1)e^{-x/L_h} \qquad (6.9b)$$

where $x$ is the distance from the boundary of the space-charge region and $L_h$ is the diffusion length for holes in the $n$ region. Substitution in (6.9a) gives

$$Q = qAp_n(e^{V/V_T} - 1)\left[ -L_h e^{-x/L_h} \right]_0^\infty = qAp_n L_h(e^{V/V_T} - 1) \qquad (6.9c)$$

A similar charge of minority carriers can be calculated for the $p$ region, and together with a corresponding charge of excess majority carriers, the stored charge in each region can be represented with a capacitance by (6.8).

Instead of completing this approach we analyze an alternate situation, the *short-base diode*. The results for the short-base diode are directly applicable to our investigation of the junction transistor in the later chapters.

A short-base diode has metallic contacts a short distance from the edges of the space-charge region. For convenience we consider only the $n$ region

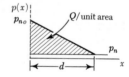

**FIGURE 6.19**  *Idealized minority-carrier density for short-base diode in n region.*

in Fig. 6.19. At an ohmic contact, any excess minority carriers immediately recombine with the majority carriers of the metal. In other words, no excess minority carriers exist at the metallic contact. The ohmic contact is a nonrectifying junction which behaves as an infinite recombination surface and has a linear *IV* characteristic.[1]

We consider first the $n$ side of the diode. As a result of the ohmic contact we have at the edge of the metal only the thermal-equilibrium value $p_n$ of the minority carriers as shown in Fig. 6.19. At the edge of the space-charge region (on the left side of the figure) we have, for a forward bias, a hole concentration $p_{n0}$. For convenience, we further assume that recombination is negligible because of the small linear dimension $d$. This is the short-base approximation. Because the recombination is almost negligible, the hole

[1]Gray et al., SEEC, vol. 2, sec. 4.6.

current $I_h$ must be almost constant. If no $\vec{E}$ fields are present, the hole current is the diffusion current. For a cross-sectional area $A$, this current is

$$I_h = -AqD_h\frac{dp}{dx} \tag{6.10}$$

Since $I_h$ is almost constant, $dp/dx$ must be constant, and the slope of $p(x)$ must be that of a straight line, as shown in Fig. 6.19.

Because of the triangular shape in Fig. 6.19, we can now easily find the excess stored charge of holes in the $n$ side.

$$Q = qA(p_{n0} - p_n)\frac{d}{2} \tag{6.11}$$

$$I_h = +AqD_h\frac{p_{n0} - p_n}{d} \tag{6.12}$$

The plus sign appears because $dp/dx$ is negative. Using (6.12), we rewrite (6.11)

$$Q = I_h\frac{d^2}{2D_h} \tag{6.13}$$

A diffusion capacitance can now be proposed to model the storage of excess majority and minority carriers in the $n$ side. However, it is simpler to introduce first the usual approximation that the doping of the $p$ region is much larger than that of the $n$ region. For this case the minority carrier storage in the $p$ region is negligible compared with that in the $n$ region and $I \simeq I_h$.

$$C_d = \frac{dQ}{dV} = \frac{dQ}{dI}\frac{dI}{dV} \tag{6.14a}$$

From (6.5b),

$$\frac{dI}{dV} = g_d \simeq \frac{I}{V_T} \tag{6.14b}$$

where $g_d$ is the incremental conductance of the diode at the given forward bias. Equation (6.13) yields

$$\frac{dQ}{dI} = \frac{d^2}{2D_h} \tag{6.14c}$$

Using this expression in (6.14a), we obtain

$$C_d = \frac{I}{V_T}\frac{d^2}{2D_h} \tag{6.15}$$

We should now recall that stored minority-carrier charge is actually the charge that is in transit from the junction to the ohmic contact, thus constituting the average current $I$. This charge in transit $Q$ must be equal to the average current $I$ times an *average transit time* $\tau_t$.

$$Q = I\tau_t \qquad (6.16a)$$

Consequently, we recognize that the $dQ/dI$ at the operating point is equal to $\tau_t$. Therefore, (6.14a) can be rewritten to include the average transit time of the short-base diode.

$$C_d = g_d\tau_t \qquad (6.16b)$$

A value of the transit time for the dimensions of the diode shown in Fig. 6.16 is 40 ns. Using a value of $g_d = 0.2$ mho, we obtain $C_d = 8000$ pF. This value is considerably larger than that of the space-charge capacitance $C_j$ which we have obtained for a similar value of forward bias. Generally, one finds, for forward bias, $C_d > C_j$. For reverse bias, the opposite is true of course, since the excess-minority-carrier storage is zero.

The dependence of $C_d$ on $I$ (or $g_d$) and on $\tau_t$ (or the electrical parameters and dimensions of the diode) which has been derived for the idealized short-base diode is also valid for more general situations. For the long-base diode discussed earlier, an additional factor of $\frac{1}{2}$ would be found if the analysis were carried out. Properly, the storage and change of storage of excess minority carriers is a distributed phenomenon and any "lumped" or quantized approximation introduces some error. In any case, we seldom start from the electrical properties and dimensions of a diode and calculate the diffusion capacitance. Instead, we start with an expression like (6.16b) and make measurements with an actual diode to establish an effective value for $\tau_t$. A value for $g_d$ is calculated from (6.5b), that is, $dI/dV \simeq I/V_T$.

The development above has been restricted to the $n$ region. Thus we need to consider the $p$ region. In the $p$ region a change of excess-minority-carrier storage also occurs for a change of bias. A second diffusion capacitance can be proposed to model this change. The two diffusion capacitances are effectively in parallel since the charging currents must flow in parallel to produce the change of stored excess-minority-carrier and excess-majority-carrier charges. Because of the relative independence of flow of majority and minority carriers, the two capacitances can be considered independently. As mentioned earlier only the lightly doped side of the junction need be considered since the minority-carrier density of the heavily doped side is so small.

**LEAKAGE RESISTANCE**    As mentioned in the last chapter, one finds in measuring the reverse (saturation) current of an actual diode that the reverse current increases with negative bias. This increase is usually the result of surface leakage. We can model this parameter in terms of a leakage resistance across the junction. The nature of the surface leakage is complicated and it is usually necessary to establish the value of the leakage resistance $r_l$ from measurement or from the slope of the $IV$ characteristic in reverse bias. A typical value for silicon diodes is 10 MΩ, or more.

**BODY RESISTANCE** The length of the semiconductor material in actual diodes may be great enough that its resistance cannot be neglected. This is the body resistance of the bulk material. The resistance value depends on the impurity concentrations on both sides of the junction. For an example, we take the $n$ side of the silicon $pn$-junction diode of Fig. 6.16. The resistivity is $\rho_n = 1$ Ω-cm. The distance from the junction to the ohmic contact is 0.001 cm. The body resistance of this region is then

$$r_x = \rho_n \frac{d}{A} = 1 \frac{1 \cdot 10^{-3}\,\text{cm}}{1 \cdot 10^{-4}\,\text{cm}^2} = 10\ \Omega \tag{6.17}$$

The $p$ side of the diode has a much lower resistivity; therefore, the body resistance of the $p$ side can be neglected and the overall body resistance is only that of the $n$ side.

## 6.4 circuit models

In the preceding section, we have considered the most important circuit parameters which must be included in a circuit model of the $pn$-junction diode. For the diode such as that of Fig. 6.16, a model is constructed starting from the terminal on the $p$ side moving toward the other terminal. First, we consider the body resistance of the $p$ material. Because we have assumed a high impurity concentration for this region, its body resistance is negligible. Across the junction from the $p$ region to the $n$ region we include a conductance $g_d$. This parameter is shown in Fig. 6.20$a$, as a resistance $r_d$, the

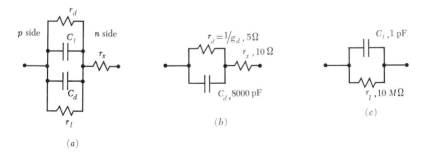

**FIGURE 6.20** *Small-signal circuit model of pn-junction diode.* (a) *General model;* (b) *model for forward bias (values are from text);* (c) *model for reverse bias (4V).*

reciprocal of conductance. The space-charge capacitance $C_j$ and the diffusion capacitance $C_d$ are also shown in Fig. 6.20*a*. The last parameter that is needed across the junction is the leakage resistance $r_l$. Continuing now into the *n* side of the diode, we next include its body resistance $r_x$, as is also shown in Fig. 6.20*a*. This complete circuit model can now be simplified when we are primarily interested in either a forward-bias or a reverse-bias situation.

**CIRCUIT MODEL FOR FORWARD BIAS**    In the preceding section we found that for forward bias the diffusion capacitance is considerably larger than the space-charge capacitance. Thus, in forward bias we can often neglect the latter and the circuit model is then as shown in Fig. 6.20*b*. (Of course, even if $C_j$ is not negligible, it can be combined with $C_d$ to obtain a single capacitor.) To compare the resistance elements, we consider typical values. Assume that a silicon diode is operated with a forward current of $I = 5$ mA at room temperature. For this value, $g_d = 0.2$ mho from (6.5). The corresponding resistance is $r_d = 1/g_d = 5$ ohms. This value is certainly much smaller than our estimated value of $r_l$. Thus the latter may be ignored. The reduced circuit is shown in Fig. 6.20*b*.

It is important to keep in mind how the values of the circuit parameters change as we change the forward current of the diode. The body resistance $r_x$ is independent of the operating point (at least to a first-order approximation), and therefore, its value is constant. From (6.5) we note that the conductance $g_d$ is directly proportional to the forward current. The corresponding resistance $r_d = 1/g_d$ is therefore inversely proportional to the forward current. Finally, the diffusion capacitance $C_d$ is directly proportional to the forward current.

To illustrate these changes, we establish numerical values for the element values and then change the forward current. For the conditions above, $C_d = 8000$ pF if $\tau_t$ is 40 ns. The parameter values for the diode forward current of 5 mV are shown in Fig. 6.20*b*. We now change the forward current to $I = 10$ mA. Resistance $r_d$ is reduced to $^5/_2$ ohms. $C_d$ increases to twice its former value, or 16,000 pF, and $r_x$ remains constant. We now can use the circuit model with modified element values for this new operating point.

**CIRCUIT MODEL FOR REVERSE BIAS**    When the reverse bias is several times larger than $V_T$, we have $g_d = dI/dV \simeq 0$, and the corresponding resistance $r_d = 1/g_d$ is very large. By comparison the surface leakage resistance $r_l$ is much smaller, and we can omit $r_d$. The diffusion capacitance $C_d$ is also zero for reverse bias, because there are no stored excess minority carriers. Finally, we can neglect the body resistance $r_x$. It is much smaller than the impedance of $r_l$ in parallel with $C_j$ for useful frequencies. The circuit model for reverse bias is shown in Fig. 6.20c. The values shown are for the numerical example of the last section and for a reverse bias of 4 V.

**SUMMARY**   It is important to remember that these circuit models are directly useful when we deal with small variations around a given dc operating point. That is, the circuit models are appropriate for *small-signal analysis.* When large-signal variations are to be considered, a different approach has to be used. In the case of switching circuits, such as those presented earlier in this chapter, where our interest is primarily in low-frequency variations, we propose that the *IV* characteristic be modeled with broken straight lines and that a piecewise linear analysis be made. For situations where charge-storage effects must be included, a piecewise linear analysis can also be used in which piecewise linear circuit elements including capacitances are used in the circuit model of the diode.

   As a final point, it should be remembered that we have assumed a very simple geometrical shape for our ideal model, and we cannot expect to obtain this simple elementary form in an actual device. However, as pointed out earlier, an actual diode can be considered to be a parallel combination of many elementary diodes. The elements of the circuit model of each can be combined to obtain a composite circuit model. For each model, the parameters we develop are natural ones and are applicable to actual devices. Therefore, measurements with actual diodes can be made and from these measurements, values of the coefficients of the mathematical model and of the parameters of the circuit model can be obtained. Because of the natural description, we can confidently estimate the nature of the change of the values of these parameters as a new bias point is chosen.

## 6.5 examples of circuit models

For the diode, the exact details of a small-signal model are usually not of major importance because of its primary use in large-signal applications.

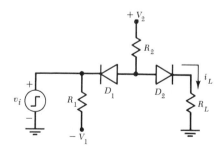

**FIGURE 6.21**   *A simple diode* AND-OR *circuit.*

To illustrate the effects of charge storage in the diode and the use of a circuit model in actual diode circuits, two examples are considered. For the first, the turn-off performance of the simple diode AND-OR circuit shown in Fig. 6.21 is studied. This circuit constitutes an AND-OR circuit with only one input and one output. In this circuit the bias sources $V_1$ and $V_2$ are not shown explicitly. It is understood, for example, that a dc source $V_2$ is connected between the $+V_2$ node and ground. Before the application of the positive input pulse, diode $D_1$ is forward biased. If $R_1$ and $R_2$ are chosen correctly with respect to $V_1$ and $V_2$, diode $D_2$ can be reverse biased. With the application of a positive step of input voltage of sufficient magnitude, $D_1$ is reverse biased, $D_2$ is forward biased, and an output current of approximately $V_2/(R_2 + R_L)$ flows into the load. This change in output current cannot occur instantly, however, because of the time delay required to remove the stored minority carriers in diode $D_1$, as well as to establish the minority carriers in $D_2$. Here we consider only the former and use the simpler circuit shown in Fig. 6.22*a* to bring out the salient features. Before $t = 0$, we assume that the switch is in position 1 and that the forward current is $V_1/(R_1 + R_L)$ as shown in Fig. 6.22*b*. This current corresponds to a certain minority-carrier distribution in the bulk regions of the diode such as illustrated by the top line in Fig. 6.22*c*.

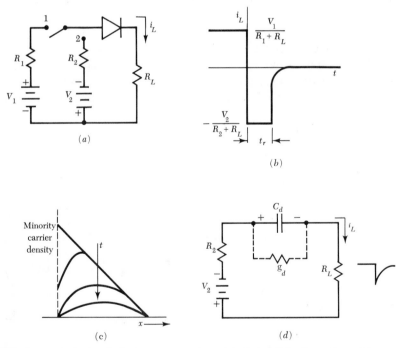

**FIGURE 6.22** *Analysis of diode recovery time. (a) Switch circuit analog; (b) output current waveform; (c) variation of minority-carrier density; (d) $C_d$ circuit model.*

When the switch is thrown to position 2, the current cannot drop immediately to the reverse-bias saturation current $I_s$ because of the stored minority carriers which must flow out of the diode. At the time of switching, the junction voltage decreases to zero, the injection of minority carriers into the bulk regions ceases, and the stored minority carriers start to collapse, as illustrated in Fig. 6.22c. Note, in particular, that the gradient of minority carriers near the junction is very steep. If the external load resistance of the diode is almost zero, a very large diffusion-limited current could be present in a negative direction. However, the negative or reverse current is usually limited by the external resistance and by the voltage, so that $i_L = -V_2/(R_2 + R_L)$, as shown in Fig. 6.22b. After a recovery period, when the gradient of the minority carrier is small enough, the diffusion flow of carriers becomes dominant, the current increases to near zero, and the diode becomes reverse biased, that is, $-V_2$ becomes the bias of the diode.

As an alternative to the above approach, it is possible to propose the circuit model of Fig. 6.22d in order to think about the recovery in terms of a conventional circuit problem. In the model, the capacitor $C_d$ represents the diode and includes both the diffusion and junction capacitances of the forward-biased diode. Note that the diode conductance $g_d$ is not included since the injection phenomenon is assumed to be absent after the switch is changed at $t = 0$. $C_d$ has an initial charge as shown in the figure. From the moment of switching, a negative input current flows due to both the voltage source $V_2$ and the initial charge of the capacitor. The final circuit is a simple $RC$-series circuit comparable to those studied in Chap. 3. The output current is described by a single time constant $T = (R_2 + R_L)C_d$, and in about five time constants the current is approximately zero. The difference between the actual and estimated output current waveforms is the result of the assumed linear circuit model ($C_d$) for the diode.

For the second example, we consider the diode detector circuit shown in Fig. 6.23a. This circuit is often utilized in high-frequency voltmeters. In operation, an input ac signal is rectified and the value of the output dc signal is a measure of the input signal strength. The resistor $R_i$ is used to provide an approximately constant input resistance. The capacitor $C_L$ is the filter element to bypass the unwanted fundamental and harmonics of the input signal, permitting only the average component of the clipped input signal to develop an output across $R_L$. Clearly, the nonlinear aspect of the circuit is the most important from the viewpoint of signal processing and transmission to the load. On the other hand, the entire detector circuit constitutes a load for the signal source.

Because the input signal level is often small, the study of the loading of the circuit on the source can be considered to be a small-signal problem. Consequently, we can use a small-signal circuit model of the diode to investigate the input characteristic of the detector. As an example, we

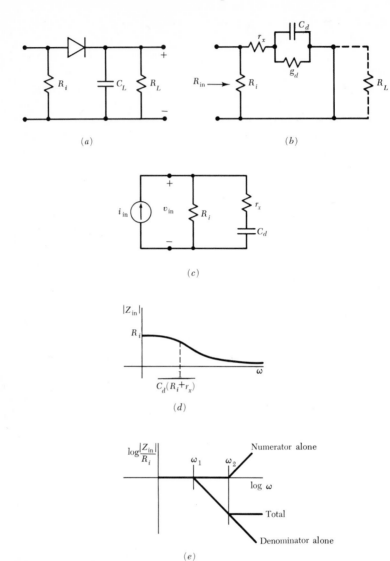

**FIGURE 6.23** *A diode rf detector circuit. (a) Circuit diagram; (b) small-signal circuit model; (c) simplified input circuit; (d) magnitude of* $|Z_{in}|$ *versus* $\omega$; *(e) Bode plot of* $|Z_{in}|$.

choose as our task the estimation of the frequency interval over which the input impedance of the detector is "flat."

The diode is operated near zero bias; therefore, the diode capacitance is principally the junction capacitance. The diode conductance $g_d$, shown in

Fig. 6.23*b*, is small and can be neglected. In addition, we also assume that $C_L$ is a short circuit for the frequencies of interest, as mentioned above. The circuit then is that shown in Fig. 6.23*c*. The input impedance is found by assuming a sinusoidal input voltage (or current) and by forming the ratio of phasor input voltage to phasor input current. The result is

$$Z_{in} = \frac{V_{in}}{I_{in}} = \frac{1}{\dfrac{1}{R_i} + \dfrac{1}{r_x + 1/j\omega C_d}} \qquad (6.18a)$$

$$Z_{in} = R_i \frac{1 + j\omega C_d r_x}{1 + j\omega C_d(r_x + R_i)} \qquad (6.18b)$$

The shape of $|Z_{in}|$—the magnitude of $Z_{in}$ with frequency—is shown in Fig. 6.23*d*. For the problem at hand it is more instructive to use a "Bode plot," i.e., a plot of $\log |Z_{in}|/R_i$ versus $\log \omega$, as shown in Fig. 6.23*e*. From the curves and from (6.18*b*), we estimate that for frequencies below $\omega_1 = 1/C_d(r_x + R_i)$ the magnitude of the input impedance is almost flat and equal to $R_i$. Since $r_x < (r_x + R_i)$, $\omega_2 = 1/C_d r_x > \omega_1$. Therefore, the change of the denominator of (6.18*b*) with frequency becomes important before the change of the numerator.

It is probably clear that there are few applications when the details of the circuit model of the diode need be considered. The material of the last two sections is used in Chap. 8, where circuit models for the junction transistor are proposed.

### REFERENCES

P. E. Gray, D. DeWitt, A. R. Boothroyd, and J. F. Gibbons, "Physical Electronics and Circuit Models of Transistors," SEEC, vol. 2, chaps. 1-6, John Wiley & Sons, Inc., New York, 1964.

J. Millman and H. Taub, "Pulse, Digital, and Switching Waveforms," chap. 9, McGraw-Hill Book Company, New York, 1965.

### PROBLEMS

**6.1** Consider the circuits shown in figures *a* and *b*. Assume, in each, identical diodes having the idealized characteristic shown at the right in the figure.

    (*a*) Using figure *a*, plot $v_R$ as a function of time.

    (*b*) Using figure *b*, plot $v_R$ as a function of time.

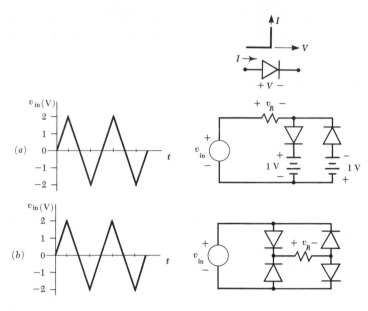

**Problem 6.1**

**6.2** Given a diode in a circuit as in figure *a*. The idealized diode has a characteristic as in figure *b*. Find $V_d$ and $I_d$ for the following values of $I$: (*a*) $I = 9$ A; (*b*) $I = -1.5$ A; (*c*) $I = -5$ A. (*Hint*: Reduce the circuit to the left of *a-b* to a simpler equivalent circuit.)

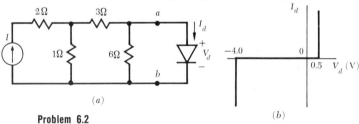

**Problem 6.2**

**6.3** In figure *a*, an *IV* characteristic of an idealized voltage-breakdown diode with breakdown voltage $V_b$ is shown. The diode is series connected with a resistor $R$ and a voltage source (sinusoid) is applied to the circuit as shown in figure *b*. Sketch the waveform of the voltage across $R$, (*a*) when $V_1 < V_b$ and (*b*) when $V_1 > V_b$.

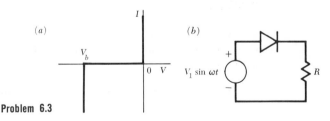

**Problem 6.3**

**6.4** The diode shown in figure $a$ has the characteristic curve shown in figure $b$. This curve can be approximated by the piecewise linear curve shown in figure $c$. Draw a circuit model of the diode, using resistors and dc voltage sources in the four states indicated. If the diode is connected in series with a 10-$\Omega$ resistor $R$ and a voltage source $v_i$, as shown in figure $d$, plot the current through the diode if the input voltage has the waveform shown in figure $e$.

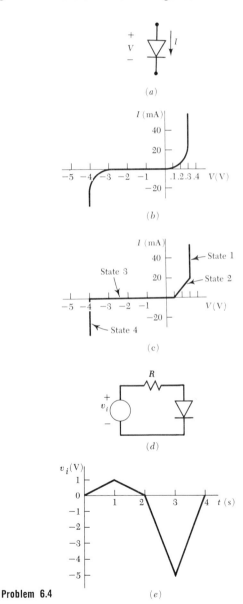

**Problem 6.4**

**6.5** Using ideal diodes, as shown in figure *a*:

(*a*) For the circuit in figure *b* and for thē input waveform given, find the output waveform.

(*b*) For the circuit shown in figure *c* and for the input waveform given, find the output waveform.

(*c*) For the input shown in figure *d*, where would you add a voltage source in the circuit to obtain the output voltage $v_{\text{out}_3}$ shown in that figure? What value of the dc voltage source is needed? Draw the required circuit.

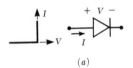

(*a*)

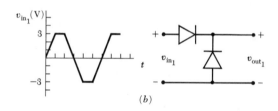

(*b*)

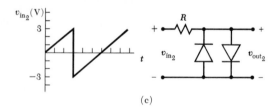

(*c*)

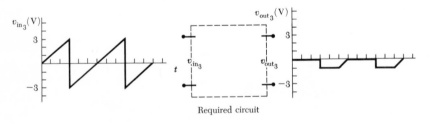

Required circuit

(*d*)

**Problem 6.5**

**6.6** In the circuit shown in figure *a*, the diodes have the idealized diode characteristic shown in figure *b*. The circuit must be in one of three states, depending on the value (sign and magnitude) of $v$:

> State 1: Both diodes "off"
> State 2: Diode $D_1$ "on," diode $D_2$ "off"
> State 3: Both diodes "on"

(*a*) Draw an equivalent circuit for this network in state 1.

(*b*) Draw an equivalent circuit for this network in state 2.

(*c*) Draw an equivalent circuit for this network in state 3.

(*d*) What is the state of the circuit at $v = 0$?

(*e*) At what value of $v$ (sign and magnitude) will diode $D_1$ go "on," i.e., will the circuit pass from state 1 to state 2?

(*f*) At what value of $v$ (sign and magnitude) will diode $D_2$ go "on," i. e., will the circuit pass from state 2 to state 3?

(*g*) If $v$ has the waveform shown in figure *c*, sketch the waveform of the current $i$ flowing from the source $v$ into the circuit.

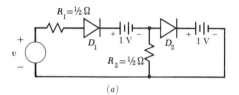

(*a*)

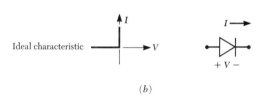

Ideal characteristic

(*b*)

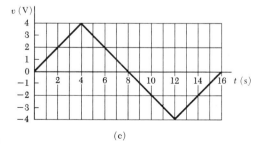

(*c*)

**Problem 6.6**

**6.7**   For the circuit shown, plot $v_o$ versus $v_i$, assuming idealized diode characteristics. Let $v_i$ assume negative and positive values.

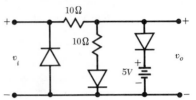

**Problem 6.7**

**6.8**   The "black box" of figure *a* contains a circuit which has, at most, two ideal diodes, three resistors, and two batteries. The measured *IV* characteristic is given in figure *b*. Find a circuit with all its element values.

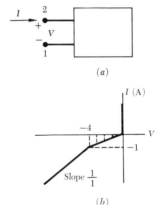

(*a*)

**Problem 6.8**                          (*b*)

**6.9**   The clamp circuit shown contains an idealized diode. A voltage source $v_s = kt$, where $k$ is a constant, is applied to the circuit at $t = 0$. Suppose that at $t = 0$ the capacitor $C$ was charged to a voltage $V_{CO}$ with the polarity as indicated.

   (*a*) Find the time $t$ at which the diode starts to conduct.
   (*b*) What is the capacitor voltage at that time?
   (*c*) Express the capacitor voltage as a function of time.

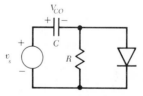

**Problem 6.9**

**6.10**   In some applications, diode breakdown may be undesirable. The peak reverse voltage ($V_b$) that can be applied without causing breakdown must then be specified.

(a) For the circuit shown in figure a, sketch $v_s$, $v_d$, and $v_C$ as a function of time, assuming $v_s$ to be a sinusoid.

(b) What reverse voltage rating is required for the diode so that breakdown does not occur under normal operation?

(c) Sketch $v_s$ and $v_C$ if the breakdown voltage of the diode $v_d$ is less than the peak value of $v_s$.

(d) For the circuit of figure b, how much is $v_C$ when the capacitor is fully charged?

(e) For the circuit shown in figure c, find the voltage $v_{C1} + v_{C2}$ when the capacitors are fully charged.

(f) What reverse voltage rating is required for the diodes, when used in the circuits of figures b and c, to prevent breakdown under normal operation?

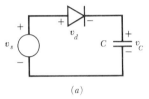

(a)

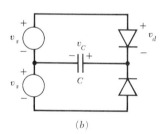

(b)

**Problem 6.10**

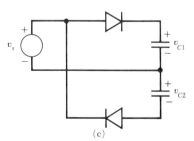

(c)

**6.11** Using diode AND and OR circuits and inverters, design a binary logic circuit having four input terminals A, B, C, and D. The circuit must produce an output 1 when the input terminal A is 1 and B is 0, or when C is 1 and D is 0.

**6.12**   A *pn*-junction diode described by $i = I_s(e^{v/V_T} - 1)$ is connected to a voltage source, $v = V_0 + \Delta V \sin \omega t$, as shown in figure *a*. Assume $\Delta V << V_T << V_0$. As shown in figure *b*, an operating point is established by $V_0$ and a sinusoidal perturbation is made about this operating point. Find, in terms of $V_0$, $\Delta V$, $I_s$, $V_T$,

(*a*)   The dc component of $i(t)$.

(*b*)   The amplitude of the fundamental frequency of $i(t)$. [*Hint*: Make a Taylor series expansion of $i(t)$, in terms of $v$, about the point $V_0$ and use appropriate approximations.]

(*c*)   The amplitude of the second harmonic component of $i(t)$.

(*d*)   The amplitude of the third harmonic component of $i(t)$.

Would it be possible to use this circuit for frequency doubling or tripling? Explain.

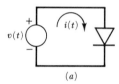

(*a*)

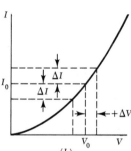

**Problem 6.12**

(*b*)

**6.13**   For the *pn*-junction diode shown,

(*a*)   Calculate and plot the volt-ampere characteristic for the *pn*-junction diode at room temperature, neglecting the ohmic resistances. The reverse saturation current is 5 μA. Assume input voltages in the range from $-0.2$ to $0.2$ V. Find the diode resistance for a 0.2-V bias in the forward and reverse directions.

(*b*)   A series resistance of 25 Ω is now included. Plot the new volt-ampere characteristic, taking the ohmic drop into account. Use the same graph sheet and the same voltage range as above.

Resistance
due to the junction

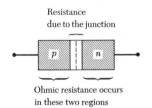

**Problem 6.13**

Ohmic resistance occurs
in these two regions

**6.14** The circuit model for a *pn*-junction diode is shown. The following data about the model are available: At a forward current of 204 mA the slope of the *IV* characteristic is $2 \cdot 10^2$ mA/V. At zero applied bias the slope of the *IV* characteristic is 1 $\mu$A/V. At zero dc bias, a 20 MHz signal is applied to the diode. The peak magnitude of the signal voltage across the diode is 2 $\mu$V, and the resulting peak current through the diode is $8 \cdot 10^{-9}$ A. Assume room temperature.

   (a) What is the reverse saturation current $I_s$?

   (b) What is the ohmic resistance of the diode?

   (c) What is the diode resistance $r_d$ at zero dc bias?

   (d) What is the total capacitance $(C_d + C_j)$ of the diode at zero dc bias?

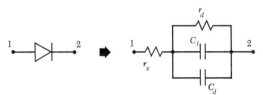

**Problem 6.14**

**6.15** For a silicon *pn* diode of cross-sectional area $10^{-3}$ cm$^2$ and lengths of 0.1 cm for both *p* and *n* regions, a set of measurements on the diode (at room temperature) yield the following information: The ohmic resistance of the *p*-type region $= 10^{-2}$ $\Omega$; the ohmic resistance of the *n*-type region $= 10$ $\Omega$; the slope of the *IV* characteristic at 4 V reverse bias is 3.2 $\mu$A/V; the breakdown voltage is much greater than 4 V; and the space-charge capacitance at zero applied bias is 200 pF.

   (a) Find the impurity concentration on the *n* and *p* sides of the junction, assuming that $N_d$ and $N_a >> n_i$.

   (b) Find the reverse saturation current.

   (c) Find the width of the depletion layer at zero applied bias. (*Hint*: Use the idea of a capacitance between two parallel plates).

**6.16** Assume that the waveform shown in figure *a* is applied at terminals 1 and 2 of the circuit shown in figure *b*. Sketch the waveform of the current flowing in the circuit as a function of time, and explain your sketch briefly. (*Hint*: Consider the variation in minority-carrier density after application of the signal).

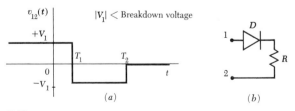

**Problem 6.16**

**6.17**  Prove that the average values of the output of a halfwave rectifier are given by (6.2*a*); of a fullwave rectifier by (6.2*b*).

**6.18**  The input voltage of the shunt-diode clipper circuit shown is $v(t) = 10 \sin t$. For a diode with an idealized $IV$ characteristic, as in Prob. 6.1, and with $V = 5$ V, sketch the output waveform $v_o(t)$. What is the Fourier spectrum of the output voltage?

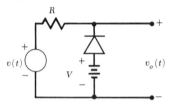

**Problem 6.18**

**6.19**  For the diode dimensions of Fig. 6.16, determine the small-signal circuit model for a Ge diode at a forward bias of 10 mA and at a reverse bias of 10 V. The conductivity of the *n* side is 1 $(\Omega\text{-cm})^{-1}$ and of the *p* side is 100 $(\Omega\text{-cm})^{-1}$. The value of the reverse saturation current is 1 $\mu$A, and the diffusion length of holes in the *n* region is 0.01 cm.

**6.20**  Establish an expression for the diffusion capacitance of a long-base diode if $p_p \gg n_n$. A long-base diode is one in which dimensions are much greater than the diffusion length of minority carriers. Use (6.9*c*) and (6.8). Compare your result with the expressions for a short-base diode. Can an expression comparable to (6.16*b*) be developed?

**6.21**  In a Ge diode of the cross-sectional area of Fig. 6.16, but with much longer *p* and *n* regions, the lifetime of holes in the *n* region is 100 $\mu$s and the lifetime of electrons in the *p* region is 1 $\mu$s. Determine (*a*) the diffusion length of minority carriers in both regions, (*b*) the value of $I_s$, and (*c*) the value of $C_j$ at zero bias. Use the results of Prob. 6.20 to determine a value for $C_d$ at a forward bias of 5 mA.

**6.22**  For the Ge diode of Prob. 6.19, estimate the value of the average transit time of minority carriers in the *n* region. What is the magnitude of the stored minority-carrier charge at a forward bias of 10 mA?

**6.23**  What is the space-charge capacitance $C_j$ for the diode of Prob. 5.8?

**6.24**  For the silicon diode of Prob. 5.12, calculate and plot $C_j$ per unit area.

chapter 7

# TRANSISTOR ELECTRONICS

### 7.1 transistor concept

A junction transistor is an arrangement of two *pn*-junction diodes back to back in one crystal, as shown conceptually in Fig. 7.1*a*. Of particular importance is the fact that minority carriers can flow between the two junctions. This provision for minority-carrier flow between the two junctions leads to a very different situation than the series connection of two diodes through external connections, as shown in Fig. 7.1*b*.

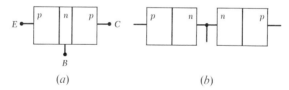

(*a*)                     (*b*)

**FIGURE 7.1** *Successive pn regions or connections.* (a) *The pnp transistor;* (b) *two pn diodes connected in series.*

For historical reasons, we call the region sandwiched between the two junctions the *base*. The region to the left of it is the *emitter*, and the third region, to the right, is the *collector*. The left-hand *pn* junction between emitter and base regions is called the *emitter junction*. The other *pn* junction is the *collector junction*. If we forward bias the emitter junction, we obtain an emission of minority carriers into the base region. As in a *pn*-junction diode, these injected minority carriers diffuse away from the emitter junction toward the collector junction. If

219

the collector junction is reverse biased, the diffusing minority carriers in the base region are "collected" by the accelerating potential of the collector junction and are swept into the collector region. We will see shortly that because of this emission, flow, and collection process, a large voltage and power can be developed in an external resistance and thus we can obtain power gain.

In contrast to the above situation, two separate pn-junction diodes which are series connected, as in Fig. 7.1b, do not provide transistor action. For the series connection of pn-junction diodes, there is only majority-carrier coupling because the ohmic contacts of diodes convert the minority carriers into majority carriers. The all-important flow of minority carriers between a forward-biased junction and a reverse-biased junction is absent.

In 1948, John Bardeen and Walter Brattain at the Bell Telephone Laboratories invented the point-contact transistor. As the name implies, the pn junctions were realized by contacts of metal points to the semiconductor surface. In 1949, William Shockley developed the theory of the junction transistor. Following Shockley's theory, Sparks and Teal at the Bell Telephone Laboratories realized the first junction transistor in 1951. This first junction transistor was a grown-type transistor. In a grown-junction transistor, the sequence of pnp regions, or npn regions, is achieved by introducing appropriate impurities into the semiconductor as the semiconductor crystal is grown. Another early method of fabrication was an alloying technique. The first alloyed junction transistor was produced by the RCA Research Laboratory in 1953. A typical alloy transistor is shown

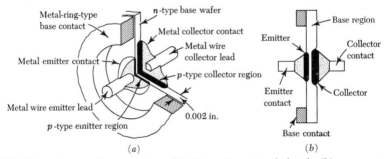

**FIGURE 7.2**   *The pnp alloy transistor.* (a) *Three-dimensional sketch;* (b) *cross section.* (*From Gray et al., SEEC, vol. 2.*)

in a three-dimensional sketch in Fig. 7.2a and in cross section in Fig. 7.2b. In the alloy transistor, the base region is the original semiconductor wafer (in our example of n-type material). Small dots of a suitable acceptor material such as indium for a pnp transistor are alloyed into both sides of the wafer. During the alloying process, the acceptor materials diffuse into the semiconductor material forming appropriately doped semiconductor regions. We thus obtain the *pnp* sequence of regions. Metal contacts to the acceptor dots produce the emitter and collector connections, while a ring-type contact is used to make the base connection. Germanium is the principal semiconductor which is used for this type of transistor.

The silicon transistor was introduced by the Texas Instruments Company in 1954. Again the first units were grown-junction transistors. Silicon is very important as a material for transistors. Its advantage can be appreciated if we recall from Chaps. 4 and 5 that the energy gap of silicon is larger than that of germanium. In terms of *pn*-junction diode properties, the reverse saturation current for silicon is much smaller than that of germanium (nanoamperes for silicon as compared with microamperes for germanium). This property is very important for operation of the transistor with low currents or for the operation of the transistor at high temperatures. This aspect is brought out in Chap. 9.

A diffusion process of achieving doped semiconductor regions, such as described in Sec. 5.1, was developed by the Bell Telephone Laboratories in 1955. This led first to the high-frequency germanium mesa transistor.[1] The Fairchild Semiconductor Division adapted the technique to produce

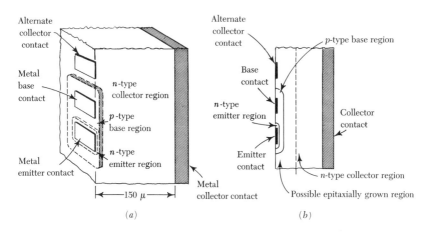

**FIGURE 7.3** *The npn planar diffused transistor.* (a) *Three-dimensional sketch;* (b) *cross section.* (*After Gray et al., SEEC, vol. 2.*)

diffused silicon transistors in 1958. Shortly thereafter, Fairchild also introduced the silicon planar transistor, which is the most important transistor presently available. This type is shown in Fig. 7.3. The process is similar

---

[1] The initial fabrication of the mesa transistor is similar to that described in Sec. 5.1. However, for Ge, a germanium oxide cannot be used to "mask" different regions of the surface. An acid etching is used as a final step to leave exposed flat-top hills or mesas, the tops of which have been protected from etching by wax.

to that described in Sec. 5.1, except that a second, sequential diffusion is added to obtain the desired *npn* layers.[1]

In Fig. 7.1*a*, an *n*-type material is shown for the base and a *p*-type material for the emitter and collector regions. We call this a *pnp* transistor. On the other hand, if a *p*-type material is sandwiched between *n*-type regions, an *npn* transistor is produced. Schematic symbols for these two different arrangements are shown in Fig. 7.4. We make a distinction in the symbols

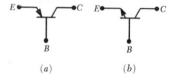

**FIGURE 7.4** *Transistor symbols.* (a) *pnp transistor;*
(b) *npn transistor.*

*(a)*      *(b)*

because the polarities of the necessary biases to obtain the desired electronic action depend on the type of transistor. For the *pnp* transistor, we use the symbol of Fig. 7.4*a*, where an arrow on the emitter side is into the transistor. For the *npn* transistor, we use the symbol of Fig. 7.4*b*, where the arrow is away from the transistor. In this chapter, we use both types of transistors in our discussions and in the examples. Initially, however, we use the *pnp* configuration.

## 7.2 transistor operation

In this section, we consider only the *normal active mode* of transistor operation which is used to achieve amplification of signals. In the active mode, the emitter junction is forward biased and the collector junction is reverse biased, as shown in Fig. 7.5 for a *pnp* transistor. From the previous

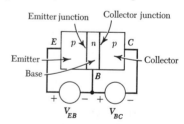

**FIGURE 7.5** *p and n regions in a pnp tran-*
*sistor and bias voltages for operation in the*
*normal active mode.*

chapters concerning the *pn*-junction diode, forward bias is obtained if the applied voltage is plus on the *p* side and minus on the *n* side. The opposite holds for reverse bias. (Of course, we are at liberty to bias each

---

[1] If the original semiconductor material, which forms the collector region, is *n*-type, the first diffusion process as described in Sec. 5.1 involves a boron-compound gas. The second diffusion process which follows will usually involve a phosphorus-compound gas. When done properly, an *npn* layer arrangement is obtained in depth. Both the upper *n* region and the interior *p* regions have a graded doping with depth.

junction either forward or reverse. Different biasing schemes lead to other modes of operation, which are brought in later in this chapter.) As shown in Fig. 7.5 we label the contact to the emitter region $E$, the contact to the base $B$, and the collector contact $C$.

For the *pnp* transistor, it is convenient to assume that the emitter region has a high concentration of impurity atoms in relation to the base region. If forward bias is applied to the emitter junction, we have hole injection into the base and electron injection from the base to the emitter. However, because of the assumption just made, the injection or emission is much greater from the emitter into the base, i.e., from the region with the heavier impurity concentration. This follows from the results of Chap. 5. Therefore, we can neglect for now the electron flow from the base into the emitter. The emitter current is then approximately equal to the hole current flowing across the emitter junction into the base. As mentioned earlier, these minority carriers diffuse (and drift) away from the junction to the right in the figure, just as in a diode. It is desirable that as large a hole current as possible arrive at the collector. Therefore, we want to minimize the recombination in the base region. This makes a narrow basewidth mandatory and the performance in the base is then similar to that of the short-base diode discussed in Sec. 6.3. If the width of the base is labeled $w$, the narrow-base constraint is $w \ll L_b$, where $L_b$ is the diffusion length of minority

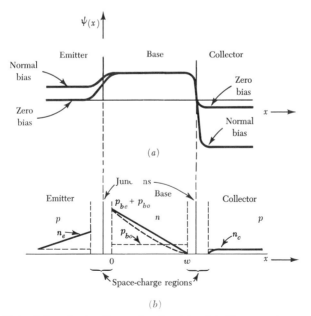

**FIGURE 7.6**  *Potential and minority-carrier densities.* (a) *Electrostatic potential plots for zero and normal bias;* (b) *minority-carrier density profiles (scales exaggerated).*

carriers in the base (holes in our *pnp* example). The collector junction has a reverse bias and presents a steep, accelerating hill for holes. The potential barriers of the emitter and collector junctions are shown in Fig. 7.6a for thermal equilibrium and with a forward-biased emitter and a reverse-biased collector. For zero bias, the potential of the collector region may not be the same as that of the emitter region because of different dopings. The difference of potential is taken up by the contact potentials (see p. 159). The useful gain of the transistor is obtained by allowing the collector current to flow through a properly selected load resistance, as will be seen.

**MINORITY CARRIER FLOW IN THE BASE REGION**    It is helpful at this time to look at the profiles of excess-minority-carrier density in all three regions of the transistor in the normal active mode, similar to the profiles that have been presented for *pn*-junction diodes in Chap. 5. Figure 7.6b shows these excess concentrations where we again assume a one-dimensional situation. In the emitter region, where we have assumed a high concentration of impurity atoms, we have only a small density of excess minority carriers. The electrons injected from the base diffuse away from the junction to the emitter contact. Some recombination also occurs. In the base at the edge of the space-charge region of the emitter junction, the excess-hole concentration $p_{be}$ is

$$p_{be} = p_{bo}(e^{V_{EB}/V_T} - 1) \tag{7.1}$$

where $p_{bo}$ is the thermal equilibrium value of holes in the base and $V_{EB}$ is the (forward) bias voltage across the emitter junction. The excess-hole density at the collector edge of the base region (at the left of the collector junction) is

$$p_{bc} = p_{bo}(e^{V_{CB}/V_T} - 1) \tag{7.2}$$

where $V_{CB} < 0$, for a reverse bias of the collector junction. When the magnitude of $V_{CB}$ is several times larger than $V_T$, the "excess" concentration of holes is negative, that is, $p_{bc}$ becomes $-p_{bo}$. The minority-carrier profile in the base is then illustrated by the solid line in Fig. 7.6b, for the case of pure diffusion flow of minority carriers. Negligible recombination in the base is assumed. For this case the diffusion current is constant.

$$I_{hE} \simeq I_{hC} = -qAD_b\frac{dp}{dx} = qAD_b\frac{p_{be} - p_{bc}}{w}$$

$$\simeq qAD_b\frac{p_{be}}{w} \tag{7.3}$$

where only hole (minority carrier) currents are considered, $w$ is the base-width between the edges of the space-charge regions, $A$ is the junction area at the emitter, and $D_b$ is the diffusion constant for minority carriers in the base (in our case $D_b = D_h$). The last form of (7.3) is valid because $p_{be} \gg p_{bo}$ and, by (7.2), $p_{bc} < p_{bo}$. As in the case of a short-base diode, the derivative $dp/dx$ is constant. Thus the minority-carrier density profile in the base is the straight line as shown.

In reality, some recombination takes place in the base, resulting in a profile contour of minority-carrier density which is slightly concave as shown by the dashed line in Fig. 7.6b. This also means that the minority-carrier collector current is less than the minority-carrier emitter current, $I_{hC} < I_{hE}$. We call $\alpha_0' I_{hE}$ the current through the collector junction due to the emitter

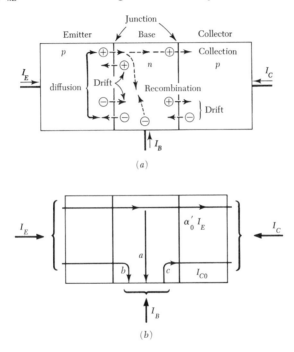

**FIGURE 7.7** *Particle flow and currents in the transistor.* (a) *Particle flow;* (b) *current components.*

hole current $I_{hE}$. This, however, is not all the current flowing through the collector junction. Other current components are present. In Fig. 7.7a, the significant components of actual charged-particle flow are shown. At the collector junction there is an emission (diffusion) flow of holes from the collector region into the base that is negligible for the reverse-biased junction and is not shown. At the collector, however, are the drift components of electrons from the collector region into the base and of holes from the base into the collector region. These drift components contribute to a component of the collector current which is called the *reverse saturation current* $I_{CO}$.

Note that $I_{CO}$ flows regardless of the value of $I_{hE}$ (even if $I_{hE} = 0$). The sum of the two components of the collector current is

$$I_C = -\alpha_0' I_{hE} - I_{CO} \qquad (7.4a)$$

At this point, we must stop to discuss the assumed positive direction for currents. By convention, each current *into* the transistor is *defined* positive as illustrated in Fig. 7.7b. For a *pnp* transistor or an *npn* transistor, the *actual* current flow may be in the opposite direction and may be a negative quantity. For the *pnp* transistor which is considered here, the current in the emitter lead actually flows into the transistor for the normal active-mode operation; therefore, $I_E > 0$. On the other hand, the actual current in the collector lead flows out of the transistor and is negative, that is, $I_C < 0$. The actual direction of the current components in each region is also shown in Fig. 7.7b and should be compared with the particle flow pattern in Fig. 7.7a.

**EMITTER EFFICIENCY**    In the emitter, there is, in addition to the hole emission considered above, the (net) current due to electron emission into the emitter. This current is supplied by one component of the base current, as shown in Fig. 7.7b, and can be assumed small because of the greatly different doping densities of the base and the emitter. Nonetheless, this component must be included when (7.4a) is modified to include the total emitter current, as is brought out below. (The drift flow of carriers through the emitter junction is masked by the diffusion flow component.) The base current includes two other components. One supplies majority carriers to satisfy recombination of holes traversing the base region and the other supplies the drift ($I_{CO}$) current of the collector junction.

Returning to (7.4a), note that the parameter $I_{CO}$ is defined as a positive number. Thus, the reverse saturation current of a *pnp* transistor is $-I_{CO}$. We next modify (7.4a) to include the total emitter current. In terms of the hole and electron components,

$$I_E = I_{hE} + I_{eE} = \frac{I_{hE}}{\gamma_0} \qquad (7.4b)$$

where

$$\gamma_0 = \frac{I_{hE}}{I_{hE} + I_{eE}} \qquad (7.4c)$$

The constant $\gamma_0$ is called the *emitter efficiency parameter* and is the ratio of the emitted minority-carrier current into the base region to the total emitter current. If (7.4b) is used in (7.4a), we obtain

$$I_C = -\alpha_0 I_E - I_{CO} \qquad (7.4d)$$

where

$$\alpha_0 = \alpha_0' \gamma_0 \qquad (7.4e)$$

The parameter $\alpha_0$ is the negative ratio of the change of the collector current to the change of emitter current.

$$\alpha_0 = -\frac{dI_C}{dI_E} \qquad (7.4f)$$

This value refers to the dc case only as is indicated by the subscript 0, but may be used for low-frequency ac situations.

**ACTIVE MODE IV CHARACTERISTIC**    It should be noted in (7.4d) that we estimate that $I_C$ is independent of $V_{CB}$ for a given value of $I_E$ since, from Chap. 5, the reverse saturation current of a $pn$ junction is largely independent of the reverse bias. Of course, (7.4d) is only valid if there is no breakdown phenomenon of the reverse-biased collector junction. From (7.4d) the collector-base, or *output characteristic*, can be sketched as in Fig. 7.8a. This is a plot of $I_C$ versus $V_{CB}$ with $I_E$ as a parameter.[1]

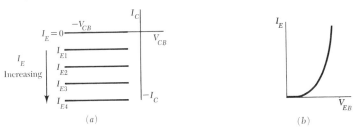

(a)                                                         (b)

**FIGURE 7.8**    *Idealized IV characteristics of a pnp transistor.* (a) *Output characteristic (incomplete for small $V_{CB}$);* (b) *input characteristic.*

The emitter current $I_E$ depends primarily on the excess-hole concentration at the emitter junction edge of the base $p_{be}$ and a corresponding density in the emitter $n_{ee}$. Both are exponentially related to $V_{EB}$ [from (7.1)], which is a result of the Maxwell-Boltzmann energy distribution of particles. Therefore, the emitter current must have the form

$$I_E = k_1(e^{V_{EB}/V_T} - 1) + k_2 \qquad (7.5)$$

where $V_{EB} > 0$ for the normal active mode, and where $k_1$ and $k_2$ are constants closely related to the constants of the two $pn$ junctions. In Fig. 7.8b the emitter-base, or *input characteristic*, is plotted as $I_E$ versus $V_{EB}$ for $V_{EB} > 0$. As expected, this characteristic is the same as that of a forward-biased $pn$ junction.

The three external currents of the transistor are not independent, but are related by Kirchhoff's current law. Thus, if we keep in mind that

[1] It is common practice, for a $pnp$ transistor, to plot $-I_C$ versus $-V_{CB}$ in order to obtain the output characteristic in the first quadrant.

Kirchhoff's current law applies not only to currents at a node in a circuit but also to all the currents into a device or a complete circuit, we obtain

$$I_E + I_B + I_C = 0 \tag{7.6}$$

Clearly, (7.6) can only be satisfied if the three currents do not all have the same sign. As mentioned above, for the *pnp*-junction transistor, the emitter current $I_E$ is principally a hole flow from emitter into the base and is positive (into the device). The collector current $I_C$ is a hole current out of the device and therefore it is negative. The base current $I_B$ is primarily an electron flow into the device which corresponds to a negative current out of the device. $I_B$ is then negative for the *pnp* transistor.

For the *npn* transistor, different polarities of the bias voltages are needed to achieve the normal active mode of operation. To forward bias the

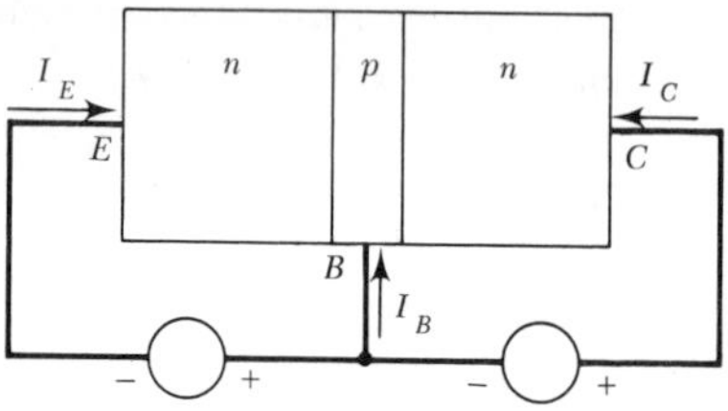

**FIGURE 7.9** *Bias voltages for an npn transistor for normal active mode operation.*

emitter-base junction, we need $V_{EB} < 0$ as shown in Fig. 7.9. To reverse bias the collector-base junction, we need $V_{CB} > 0$ as shown. The injected minority carriers into the base region from the emitter are electrons. The flow of these carriers toward the collector junction constitutes a current from the collector to the emitter. The emitter current flows out of the emitter and is negative ($I_E < 0$). The collector current component $I_{CO}$ is now a positive current into the collector. For the *npn* transistor, (7.4d) becomes

$$I_C = -\alpha_0 I_E + I_{CO} \tag{7.7}$$

Therefore, the collector current is positive, as is the base current.

The input and output characteristics for the *npn* transistor, corresponding to Fig. 7.8, appear in the first quadrant for $I_C$ versus $V_{CB}$ and in the third quadrant for $I_E$ versus $V_{EB}$.

## 7.3  power gain

With an understanding of the particle flow in the transistor, we next investigate the power gain that can be expected from a transistor in the normal active mode of operation. For this, we consider the circuit shown in Fig. 7.10 where a load resistance $R_L$ is connected between the collector terminal of the transistor and the bias voltage source $V_{CC}$. The input or signal voltage to be amplified is introduced between the bias voltage source $V_{EB}$ and the emitter of the transistor. (This is an idealized biasing arrangement; actual biasing is discussed later in this chapter and also in Chap. 9.) For the input voltage increment $\Delta V_{EB}$, an increment of emitter current $\Delta I_E$ flows. Consequently, at the collector, an increment $\Delta I_C$ is collected.

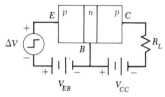

**FIGURE 7.10**   *Transistor with bias voltage supplies and load resistance.*

The current increment at the input can be related approximately to the input-voltage change by the use of Ohm's law:

$$\Delta I_E = \Delta V_{EB} g \tag{7.8}$$

where $g$ is the incremental conductance of the forward-biased emitter junction (see Sec. 6.3). From the values of Sec. 6.3, a typical value for $g$ is 0.2 mho if the bias point of the forward-biased junction is 5 mA. The incremental input power into the transistor $P_i$ is

$$P_i = \frac{(\Delta I_E)^2}{g} \tag{7.9a}$$

The output power $P_o$ supplied to the load resistance $R_L$ is

$$P_o = (\Delta I_C)^2 R_L \tag{7.9b}$$

We can now relate $\Delta I_C$ to $\Delta I_E$ using (7.4f). The result is $\Delta I_C = -\alpha_0 \Delta I_E$, where $\alpha_0$ is about 0.98 for a typical transistor. This leads to

$$P_o = \alpha_0^2 (\Delta I_E)^2 R_L \tag{7.9c}$$

The power gain of the device can now be defined as the ratio $P_o/P_i$:

$$\text{Power gain} = G_p = \frac{P_o}{P_i} = \alpha_0^2 g R_L \tag{7.10a}$$

To estimate a value of the power gain we need a value for $R_L$. $R_L$ may vary from very low to very high values. An appropriate value for an example is of the order of 10 k$\Omega$. The power gain becomes

$$G_p = (0.98)^2 0.2 (10 \cdot 10^3) = 2000 \tag{7.10b}$$

This is about 33 dB, a substantial amount of power gain. A device which can provide a power gain greater than unity is defined as an *active device*.

## 7.4   transistor configurations

We next consider the transistor as a 2-port device having one terminal pair or port for the input and another port for the output, as shown in

Fig. 7.11$a$.[1] As the transistor has only three terminals, one terminal must be common to both the input and the output ports. In our earlier discussions, we have used the base as the common terminal. This situation

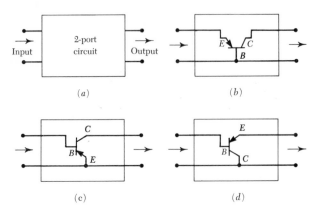

**FIGURE 7.11**   *Transistor connections.* (a) *2-port circuit;* (b) *common-base connection;* (c) *common-emitter connection;* (d) *common-collector connection.*

is referred to as the *common-base* (or c-b) configuration and is shown in Fig. 7.11$b$. Note that the emitter and base are the input terminals and that the collector and base terminals form the output. Clearly, this is only one way to connect the transistor. In Fig. 7.11$c$, the emitter terminal is shown as a common node. This connection is referred to as the *common-emitter* (c-e) configuration. The third possible configuration is shown in Fig. 7.11$d$ where the collector terminal is common to the input and output. This is the *common-collector* (c-c) configuration.

As we see later, the three configurations, c-b, c-e, and c-c, exhibit different amounts of current gain and voltage gain while at the same time providing useful amounts of power gain. In addition, the three configurations have different values of *input impedance* $Z_i$ (when looking from the signal source into the transistor) and *output impedance* $Z_o$ (when looking from the load back into the transistor). The configuration to be used depends on the required gains and impedance values needed for a given application. In the common-base connection we see that $\Delta I_C/\Delta I_E = -\alpha_0$. This is a current-gain magnitude of slightly less than unity. However, a substantial voltage gain can be obtained. In contrast, the common-emitter configuration can produce both current *and* voltage gain. The possibility of a large current gain is clear if we note that the base current is the input current for the c-e connection and if we recall that the base current is

[1]A terminal pair or port is defined as a two-terminal entry into a circuit or device in which the current *into* one terminal is equal to the current flowing *out* of the other terminal.

primarily the result of recombination and is only a small fraction of the collector current. Because of the possibility of both current and voltage gain, the common-emitter connection is the "workhorse." The common-base and common-collector connections are principally used when their special values of input or output impedance are needed.

In order to obtain a set of $IV$ relations for the c-e connection of Fig. 7.11c, we need to express the output current $I_C$ in terms of the input current $I_B$. This we obtain by solving (7.6) for $I_E$:

$$I_E = -(I_B + I_C) \qquad (7.11)$$

The result is used in (7.4d) to obtain

$$I_C = \frac{\alpha_0}{1 - \alpha_0} I_B - \frac{1}{1 - \alpha_0} I_{CO} \qquad (7.12a)$$

We define now a quantity $\beta_0$ which is the ratio $dI_C/dI_B$, that is, the current gain of the c-e connection.

$$\beta_0 = \frac{dI_C}{dI_B} \simeq \frac{\Delta I_C}{\Delta I_B} \qquad (7.12b)$$

If we perform the differentiation of (7.12a), we obtain

$$\beta_0 = \frac{\alpha_0}{1 - \alpha_0} \qquad (7.12c)$$

If $\alpha_0$ is 0.98, $\beta_0 = 49$. Clearly, we obtain a substantial amount of current gain with the c-e connection. We now rewrite (7.12a)

$$I_C = \beta_0 I_B - (\beta_0 + 1) I_{CO} \qquad (7.13)$$

Note that the output voltage $V_{CE}$ does not enter in (7.13). This is similar to the situation we encountered for the c-b configuration [see (7.4d)]. The output characteristic, $I_C$ versus $V_{CE}$ with $I_B$ as parameter, is sketched in Fig. 7.12a.

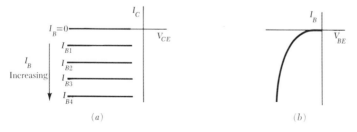

(a)                              (b)

**FIGURE 7.12**  *Idealized IV characteristics of pnp transistor in c-e connection. (a) Output characteristic (incomplete for small $V_{CE}$); (b) input characteristic.*

For the input characteristic, we need a relation between $I_B$ and $V_{BE}$. Clearly, it must be similar to (7.5) since an exponential relation must exist between $I_B$ and $V_{BE}$ because of the forward-biased emitter junction. Thus the form of the relation must be

$$I_B = k_1'(e^{-V_{BE}/V_T} - 1) + k_2' \tag{7.14}$$

where $k_1'$ and $k_2'$ are constants that are related to the coefficients of (7.5). For example, $k_1' = -k_1/(\beta_0 + 1)$. In (7.14) a change of notation for the emitter-base junction bias is introduced, namely, $V_{BE} = -V_{EB}$. This change is made because the bias voltage for the c-e connection is taken with respect to the emitter node. The exponential term in (7.14) is dominant in the input characteristic which relates $I_B$ and $V_{BE}$ so that we obtain a curve such as that shown in Fig. 7.12b.

For the npn transistor, the output characteristic for the normal active region occurs in the first quadrant since $V_{CE} > 0$ and $I_C > 0$. Similarly, the input characteristic also occurs in the first quadrant since $V_{BE} > 0$ and $I_B > 0$. In (7.13), the sign of $(\beta_0 + 1) I_{CO}$ is positive for the npn transistor and in (7.14), $+V_{BE}$ should be used.

## 7.5   mathematical model of the junction transistor

The developments to this point are restricted to the normal active mode of operation. We now obtain a complete mathematical model which can be used for any mode of operation, i.e., for any bias connection of the two junctions.

We start by considering the minority-carrier density and flow in the base region for a general bias situation for a pnp transistor. At each junction, the applied bias voltage governs the excess-minority-carrier-charge concentration at the base side edge of the space-charge regions. These excess

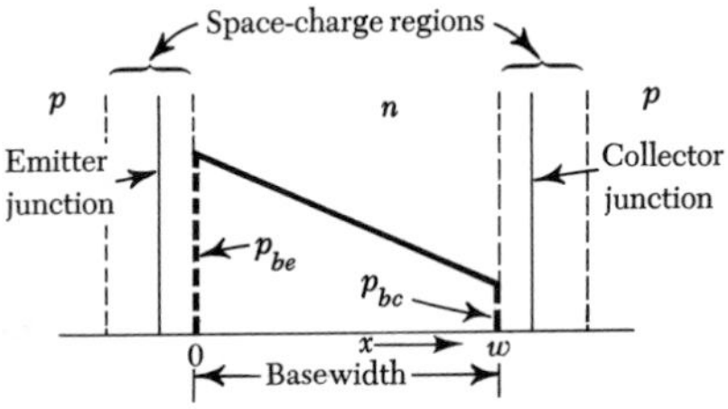

**FIGURE 7.13**  *Excess minority carrier densities at the edges of the base region.*

concentrations are labeled $p_{be}$ and $p_{bc}$ and are illustrated in Fig. 7.13 for the situations where both junctions are forward biased. The expressions for these edge densities are

$$p_{be} = p_{bo}(e^{V_{EB}/V_T} - 1) \tag{7.15a}$$

$$p_{bc} = p_{bo}(e^{V_{CB}/V_T} - 1) \tag{7.15b}$$

where $p_{bo}$ is the density of minority carriers in the base region in thermal equilibrium.[1] In (7.15), $V_{EB} > 0$ and $V_{CB} > 0$ is the condition which forward biases each junction of the *pnp* transistor. However, in both equations the voltages may be of either sign. That is, $V_{EB}$ and $V_{CB}$ are now algebraic quantities which can be either positive or negative. We return later to the distribution of minority carriers in the base region. For here, we can very quickly develop the mathematical form of the complete *IV* equations of the transistor. The hole current which is emitted into the base for a forward bias of the emitter junction is linearly related to (7.15a). Similarly, if the collector junction is forward biased, the emitted hole current into the base is linearly related to (7.15b). At the emitter edge of the base region, then, the total hole current must be the algebraic sum of the emitter hole current plus the hole current which has diffused from the collector junction. Using (7.15), we write these relations in the following form

$$I_E = a_{11}(e^{V_{EB}/V_T} - 1) + a_{12}(e^{V_{CB}/V_T} - 1) \qquad (7.16a)$$

where $a_{11}$ and $a_{12}$ are constants comparable to, but not equal to, the coefficients $k_1$ and $k_2$ of (7.5). Similarly, at the collector edge of the base region, we use the fact that the two current components of $I_C$ are proportional individually to (7.15).

$$I_C = a_{21}(e^{V_{EB}/V_T} - 1) + a_{22}(e^{V_{CB}/V_T} - 1) \qquad (7.16b)$$

Properly, our arguments above apply only to the hole components of the two currents. However, the electron components at each junction also follow relations such as (7.15). Therefore, we can use total currents in (7.16) and assume that the coefficients $a_{ij}$ include contributions from both hole and electron components. Of major importance here is the form of (7.16).

To verify the reasoning above, we can now return to the density of minority carriers in the base and obtain (7.16) on the basis of the solution of the continuity equation (see Sec. 5.5).

In the base, we consider the variations of excess holes in the $x$ direction only and choose, for convenience, $x = 0$ at the base edge of the emitter space-charge region (see Fig. 7.13). To find the excess holes anywhere between the emitter and collector space-charge regions, we use a simplified form of the continuity equation. The development leading to (5.25f) is followed. We also assume as a first-order approximation that recombination in the base can be neglected, as in the short-base diode of Sec. 6.3. This leads to a very simple form of the continuity equation:

$$D_b \frac{d^2 p_b}{dx^2} = 0 \qquad (7.17)$$

[1] We assume that the doping of the base is uniform; therefore, $p_{bo}$ is not a function of distance.

where $p_b$ is the concentration of excess holes in the base for any value of $x$, and $D_b$ is equal to $D_h$ for a *pnp* transistor. The solution of (7.17) is found by integration. The constants of the solution are found from the boundary values of (7.15). The solution is

$$p_b(x) = \frac{w - x}{w} p_{bo}(e^{V_{EB}/V_T} - 1) + \frac{x}{w} p_{bo}(e^{V_{CB}/V_T} - 1) \qquad (7.18)$$

This result tells us that the excess-hole concentration for any value of $x$ in the base region depends linearly on both the excess-hole concentrations $p_{be}$ and $p_{bc}$ at the edges of the base region. The excess density for the assumed absence of recombination is linear with $x$, as shown in Fig. 7.13.

To obtain expressions for the current at the boundaries of the base region, we note that at each junction the current is the sum of a hole current and an electron current, similar to those of the *pn* diode. Each of these currents is proportional to $dp/dx$ or $dn/dx$. Assuming neither generation nor recombination in the space-charge regions, we write

$$I_E = I_h(0) + I_e(0) \qquad (7.19a)$$

$$I_C = I_h(w) + I_e(w) \qquad (7.19b)$$

Note that the electron currents $I_e$ pertain to the emitter side of the space-charge region for $I_e(0)$ and on the collector side for $I_e(w)$. We assume that these currents are unchanged throughout their respective space-charge regions. The hole currents are found from $dp/dx$ using (7.18), if we assume that the current is due only to diffusion of holes. The electron currents are also proportional to exponential boundary values similar to (7.15a) or (7.15b). As a consequence, the total emitter and collector currents can be obtained and have the form of (7.16). This completes our verification.

Of particular importance is the fact that the final equations hold regardless of the bias (forward or reverse) of the junctions. Note again that equations (7.16) are the result of the linear relation of the carrier density in the base to the edge densities, the linear relation between the density and the current flow, and the exponential relationship between the edge density and the junction voltages.

The identification of the $a_{ij}$ parameters, in terms of the properties and dimensions of the transistor region, is seldom necessary except for device engineers. Instead we propose a special set of measurements, the results of which give the values of the $a_{ij}$ in terms of measurable currents and voltages.[1] If several transistors of one type are measured, averaged values of the $a_{ij}$ can be considered to characterize this transistor type and its

---

[1] This important concept, in terms of slightly different coefficients, was developed by J. J. Ebers and J. L. Moll in "Large-Signal Behavior of Junction Transistors," *Proc. IRE,* **42**:1761-1772 (1954).

mathematical model. For this, it is convenient to define an alternate set of four coefficients in place of the $a_{ij}$ of (7.16). The new coefficients are developed below and have the advantage of a physical interpretation in terms of simple experiments.

Consider the situation depicted in Fig. 7.14a, where a *pnp* transistor

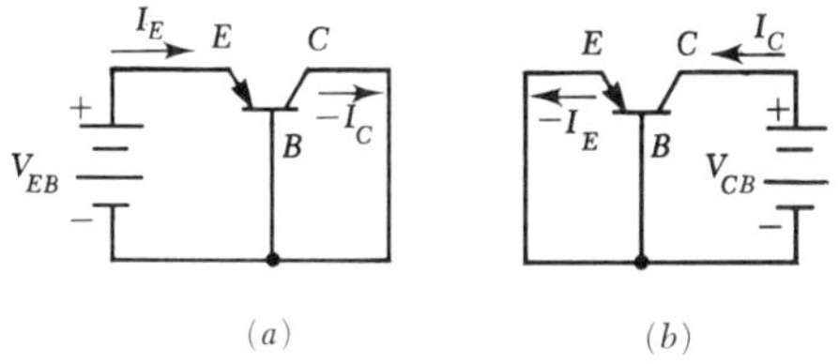

**FIGURE 7.14** *Transistor parameter measurement* (a) *for $I_{ES}$ and $\alpha_0$ and* (b) *for $I_{CS}$ and $\alpha_{r0}$.*

is shown with the output short-circuited, that is, $V_{CB} = 0$. If this is used in (7.16a), the second term becomes zero and $a_{11}$ can be identified as a diode-like saturation current $I_{ES}$.

$$I_E = I_{ES}(e^{V_{EB}/V_T} - 1) \qquad V_{CB} = 0 \qquad (7.20a)$$

Clearly, if $V_{EB}$ is large and negative, $I_{ES}$ is the emitter current that flows and $a_{11} = I_{ES}$. From (7.16a) and (7.16b), for $V_{CB} = 0$, we obtain the following relation:

$$I_C = \frac{a_{21}}{a_{11}} I_E = -\alpha_0 I_E \qquad (7.20b)$$

Note that we identify $\alpha_0$ as the forward-current gain for the short-circuit output. This follows because the $I_{CO}$ term of (7.4d) is absent if $V_{CB} = 0$; therefore,

$$\alpha_0 = -\frac{I_C}{I_E}\bigg|_{V_{CB}=0} = -\frac{dI_C}{dI_E} \qquad (7.20c)$$

and $\alpha_0$ has the same meaning as before. The subscript 0 again signifies that this is a dc or low-frequency relation. As before, we choose $\alpha_0$ to be a positive number; therefore, it is necessary to include a minus sign, as in (7.20c), because of the defined positive direction for the currents of the transistor. From (7.20b), we also identify $a_{21}$ as $-\alpha_0 I_{ES}$ since $a_{11} = I_{ES}$.

A second special measurement can be used to identify $a_{12}$ and $a_{22}$. We now operate the transistor in the *inverse sense*, i.e., the collector junction is forward biased and the emitter junction is shorted as shown in Fig. 7.14b. Because the impurity concentration and the geometry of the collector region are usually different from those of the emitter region, we obtain different values of currents for the new measurement. For

$V_{EB} = 0$, the first term in (7.16$b$) disappears. The collector current for this situation is

$$I_C = I_{CS}(e^{V_{CB}/V_T} - 1) \qquad V_{EB} = 0 \qquad (7.21a)$$

Therefore, $a_{22} = I_{CS}$. From (7.16$a$) and (7.16$b$), we also obtain for $V_{EB} = 0$

$$I_E = \frac{a_{12}}{a_{22}}I_C = -\alpha_{r0}I_C \qquad (7.21b)$$

where $\alpha_{r0}$ is the current gain for inverse (reverse) operation with the output short-circuited. Therefore, $a_{12} = -\alpha_{r0}a_{22}$. The minus sign again appears because $\alpha_{r0}$ is defined as a positive number. [The notation for normal (forward) operation could be $\alpha_{f0}$ in (7.20$b$); we do not, however, include the subscript $f$ because the parameter $\alpha_0$ appears so frequently for the normal active mode.]

With the new parameters, the mathematical model of the *pnp* transistor can be written as follows:

$$I_E = I_{ES}(e^{V_{EB}/V_T} - 1) - \alpha_{r0}I_{CS}(e^{V_{CB}/V_T} - 1) \qquad (7.22a)$$

$$I_C = -\alpha_0 I_{ES}(e^{V_{EB}/V_T} - 1) + I_{CS}(e^{V_{CB}/V_T} - 1) \qquad (7.22b)$$

Equations (7.16) and (7.22) satisfy a reciprocity condition for the transfer coefficients in that $a_{12} = a_{21}$.[1] This leads to

$$\alpha_{r0}I_{CS} = \alpha_0 I_{ES} \qquad (7.23)$$

Therefore, of the four parameters $I_{ES}$, $I_{CS}$, $\alpha_0$, and $\alpha_{r0}$, only three are independent and the fourth can be obtained from (7.23).

These above equations have been derived and hold for the *pnp*-junction transistor only. For the *npn* transistor, minus signs must be introduced for each component and for each exponent in order to obtain the correct polarity. The results are

$$I_E = -I_{ES}(e^{-V_{EB}/V_T} - 1) + \alpha_{r0}I_{CS}(e^{-V_{CB}/V_T} - 1)$$
$$I_C = \alpha_0 I_{ES}(e^{-V_{EB}/V_T} - 1) - I_{CS}(e^{-V_{CB}/V_T} - 1) \qquad (7.24)$$

As a final topic in this section, we relate the current parameter $I_{CS}$ of either (7.22) or (7.24) to the previously defined parameter $I_{CO}$. $I_{CS}$ is defined in terms of the collector current under the condition of a shorted

---

[1] A circuit obeys the reciprocity relation if the transfer function from one port to another is equal to the reverse transfer between the ports if the source is moved to the second port and if the new output is the same quantity (current or voltage) as at the original output. This reciprocity relation does not hold, in general, for active circuits which contain dependent voltage or current sources and for nonlinear circuits. Here we have both a nonlinear and an active device. Nonetheless, the equations above in terms of current and the exponential voltage factors exhibit the reciprocity relation.

emitter-base junction with a reverse bias for the collector-base junction. On the other hand, $I_{CO}$ is defined in terms of an open-circuited emitter-base junction ($I_E = 0$) with a reverse-biased collector-base junction. This is illustrated in Fig. 7.15a for a *pnp* transistor. We know from the results above that $I_{CS} = a_{22}$ for a *pnp* transistor. To obtain an expression for $I_{CO}$, we set $I_E = 0$ in (7.22) and eliminate the quantity $(e^{V_{EB}/V_T} - 1)$ from the second equation. For $V_{CB} << V_T$, we obtain $I_C = -I_{CO}$, where the minus sign is again used so that $I_{CO}$ is always a positive number. The result is

$$I_{CO} = I_{CS}(1 - \alpha_0\alpha_{r0}) \tag{7.25a}$$

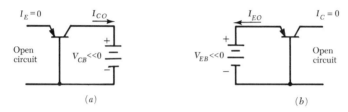

(a)                                        (b)

**FIGURE 7.15**  *Transistor parameter measurements* (a) *for* $I_{CO}$ *and* (b) *for* $I_{EO}$.

A similar procedure can be followed for inverse operation. $I_{EO}$ is the reverse current that flows when $I_C = 0$ and $V_{EB} << V_T$ for a *pnp* transistor. This is illustrated in Fig. 7.15b. The relation between $I_{EO}$ and $I_{ES}$ is

$$I_{EO} = I_{ES}(1 - \alpha_0\alpha_{r0}) \tag{7.25b}$$

where $I_{ES}$ is as defined earlier.

## 7.6  graphical characteristics

Graphical characteristics of the transistor can be plotted from the *IV* equations of (7.22) or (7.24). We have already considered, earlier in this chapter, simplified characteristics for the active mode. We are now able to plot the characteristics for any condition of bias (any mode of operation).

For a *pnp* transistor in the c-b connection, the *output IV* characteristic can be obtained from a rearrangement of (7.22). What is desired is the plot of $I_C$ versus $V_{CB}$ with $I_E$ as a parameter.[1] The relation $I_C = f(V_{CB}, I_E)$ is obtained from (7.22) by eliminating $(e^{V_{EB}/V_T} - 1)$ from the two equations. The result is

$$I_C = -\alpha_0 I_E + I_{CO}(e^{V_{CB}/V_T} - 1) \tag{7.26}$$

[1] We can also use $V_{EB}$ as a parameter; however, $I_E$ is usually the input variable that is easiest to deal with.

This, of course, is the generalization of the transfer expression for the normal active mode, (7.4$d$). A plot of (7.26) is shown in Fig. 7.16. As in the previous plot of Fig. 7.8, the normal active operation region appears in

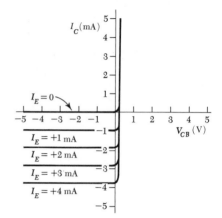

**FIGURE 7.16**   *Complete output IV characteristic for a pnp transistor in c-b connection. (After Searle et al., SEEC, vol. 3.)*

the third quadrant for this *pnp* transistor. It is to be noticed that the spacing between the $I_E$ parameter curves is a measure of $\alpha_0$. Finally, note that if $V_{CB} > 0$, for the *pnp* transistor, the output characteristic is similar to that of a forward-biased diode and is almost the characteristic of the forward-biased collector-base junction by itself. The effects of $I_E$ in the first quadrant are very small and the $I_E$ family in this quadrant only appears as a "fine structure" of the principal curve.

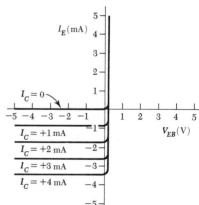

**FIGURE 7.17**   *Complete input IV characteristic for a pnp transistor in c-b connection. (After Searle et al., SEEC, vol. 3.)*

The *input* characteristic of a transistor in the c-b connection is a plot of $I_E$ versus $V_{EB}$ with $I_C$ as a parameter. The relation $I_E = f(V_{EB}, I_C)$ is found from (7.22) by eliminating $(e^{V_{CB}/V_T} - 1)$.

$$I_E = -\alpha_{ro} I_C + I_{EO}(e^{V_{EB}/V_T} - 1) \qquad (7.27)$$

This relation is plotted in Fig. 7.17. The normal active region is the first quadrant for a *pnp* transistor. Inverse active operation is obtained in the third quadrant where $V_{EB} < 0$, $V_{CB} > 0$. The spacing between parameter curves in the third quadrant is related to $\alpha_{r0}$.

As mentioned earlier, the common-emitter connection is used in the majority of applications. Therefore, it is usual to plot and compare the input and output *IV* characteristics for the c-e connection. The ideal *IV* characteristics for c-e are obtained from a rearrangement of (7.22) for a *pnp* transistor, or from (7.24) for an *npn* transistor. Using a development similar to that leading to (7.12a), we substitute $I_E = -(I_B + I_C)$ in (7.26) and (7.27). The results are

$$I_C = \frac{\alpha_0}{1 - \alpha_0} I_B + \frac{I_{CO}}{1 - \alpha_0} (e^{(V_{CE} - V_{BE})/V_T} - 1) \qquad (7.28a)$$

$$I_B = -I_C(1 - \alpha_{r0}) - I_{EO}(e^{-V_{BE}/V_T} - 1) \qquad (7.28b)$$

The above may be considered the mathematical model of the c-e connection. Note that the output voltage for the c-e connection is $V_{CE} = V_{CB} + V_{BE} = V_{CB} - V_{EB}$. The input voltage is $V_{BE} = -V_{EB}$. The output and input *IV* characteristics from these two equations are plotted in Figs. 7.18 and 7.19, respectively. In the output characteristic, the input parameter is $I_B$. Well inside the third quadrant, which corresponds to the normal active operating mode, the spacing of the curves is related to $\beta_0 = \alpha_0/(1 - \alpha_0)$. Note that a family of curves also exists in the first quadrant. This corresponds to inverse active operation in a common-collector connection.

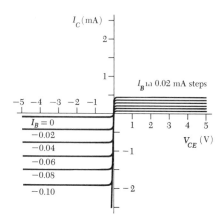

**FIGURE 7.18** *Complete output IV characteristic for a pnp transistor in c-e connection* (Ge transistor). (*After Searle et al., SEEC, vol. 3.*)

This aspect is discussed in greater detail in Chap. 9. From (7.13), the value of the collector current for $I_B = 0$ is $I_C = -I_{CO}/(1 - \alpha_0) = -(\beta_0 + 1) I_{CO}$. This value of $I_C$ can be reduced to approximately $-I_{CO}$ if the emitter-base junction is reverse biased. This is shown by letting $-V_{BE} = V_{EB} << 0$ and $V_{CB} = V_{CE} - V_{BE} << 0$ in (7.28) and by solving for $I_C$. The result is $-I_{CO}$ if $\alpha_{r0} << 1$.

In the input $IV$ characteristic of the c-e connection, the normal active operating region for a *pnp* transistor is the third quadrant. For $V_{BE} = 0$, a small current which is approximately $I_{CO}$ flows into the base. Note also

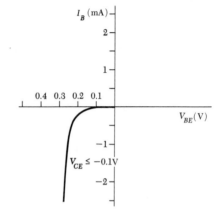

that for $I_B = 0$, a small input voltage is present. In essence, when $I_B = 0$ and with $V_{CE} << 0$, the transistor is still in the normal active region with a collector current of $-(\beta_0 + 1) I_{CO}$ and an emitter current of $+(\beta_0 + 1) I_{CO}$. Only when $V_{BE} = 0$ is the transistor turned "off," i.e., with both junctions at zero or reverse bias.

The characteristics shown in Figs. 7.16 to 7.19 are idealized ones. Actual characteristics deviate, sometimes considerably, from the ideal ones. Figure 7.20*a* shows a typical input characteristic for the normal active region of the c-e connection for an *npn* transistor, and Fig. 7.20*b*

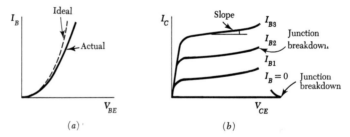

**FIGURE 7.20**   *Actual IV characteristics of npn transistor in the c-e connection for normal active operation.* (a) *Input IV characteristic;* (b) *output IV characteristic.*

shows the c-e output characteristic. As mentioned earlier, the normal active region of both the input and output characteristics for an *npn* transistor lie in the first quadrants of the $I_B V_{BE}$ plane and the $I_C V_{CE}$ plane, respectively. Note that the actual input characteristic does not rise as fast as the ideal one. This difference can be attributed to the voltage drop in the base region due to body resistance. In the output characteristic, we notice an increased slope, which is due to "basewidth modulation." As will be discussed in Chap. 8, this is the result of changes in the base-width as the collector junction voltage is changed. In the output character-istic, we also see the effects of voltage breakdown at large reverse bias of the collector junction. Finally, the ohmic resistance of the collector regions produces the finite slope of the "saturation" portion of the characteristic (small $V_{CE}$). This aspect is also discussed in greater detail in Chaps. 8 and 9.

## 7.7   load lines

The bias voltages to obtain normal active-mode operation at the input and output of a transistor are usually not obtained by the direct application of dc voltage sources as illustrated in Fig. 7.21a. One reason for this is

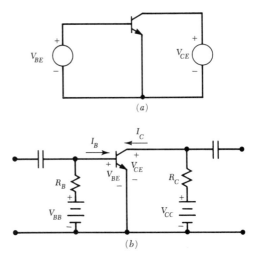

**FIGURE 7.21**   *Bias arrangements for c-e connection.* (a) *Voltage sources alone;* (b) *with bias resistors and ac coupling to source and load.*

that the necessary input bias $V_{BE}$ is a small value which is difficult to establish accurately. (Remember that a small change of $V_{BE}$ leads to an exponential change of $I_B$.) Second, if an input signal source is inserted in series with the input, either this source or the bias supply must be a "floating" supply with respect to the reference potential (ground). The same problem is present with respect to a load. Finally, both the source and the load usually have nonzero resistances which develop voltage drops. Thus the actual transistor voltages are different from the bias supply voltages. A basic bias arrangement is then as shown in Fig. 7.21b where two dc voltages, $V_{BB}$ and $V_{CC}$, are used together with two *bias resistors*, $R_B$ and $R_C$. In Chap. 9, we consider bias circuits and their design in greater detail. In this section, we only establish a graphical load-line technique to establish the bias condition of the transistor in a circuit such as Fig. 7.21*b* (refer also to load-line problems in Chaps. 3, 5, and 6).

At the input and at the output of the transistor, two coupling capacitors are shown. This indicates that the signal source and signal load are ac coupled to the transistor but are isolated for dc, and thus do not affect the bias condition. At the input of the *npn* transistor in Fig. 7.21*b*, the base current $I_B$ causes a voltage drop across $R_B$. Using Kirchhoff's voltage law, we find

$$R_B I_B + V_{BE} - V_{BB} = 0 \qquad (7.29a)$$

From this we obtain

$$I_B = \frac{V_{BB} - V_{BE}}{R_B} \qquad (7.29b)$$

This is a linear relation between $V_{BE}$ and $I_B$. We also have a second relation between $I_B$ and $V_{BE}$ of the transistor.

$$I_B = I_C(1 - \alpha_{r0}) + I_{EO}(e^{V_{BE}/V_T} - 1) \qquad (7.30)$$

This relation is similar to (7.28*b*), except that we are now dealing with an *npn* transistor. The operating or bias point can be obtained from the simultaneous solution of the last two equations. Because (7.30) is nonlinear and, in addition, is only a mathematical model of the input characteristic of a transistor, we usually use an alternate approach. For an actual transistor, the input characteristic can be plotted as in Fig. 7.22*a*. The

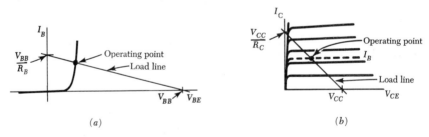

(a)                                                      (b)

**FIGURE 7.22** *Load line construction. (a) Load line on input IV characteristic; (b) load line on output IV characteristic.*

near-exponential curve is the plot of all possible values of $I_B$ and $V_{BE}$ in the first quadrant; that is, the operating point must be somewhere on this curve. However, the values of $I_B$ and $V_{BE}$ must also satisfy (7.29*b*). If we plot (7.29*b*) on the same plane, as in Fig. 7.22*a*, the intersection of the two curves must be the operating point of the input. The plot of (7.29*b*) is called the *load line* for the input characteristic. Notice that this line is easily drawn as a line through the two intersections $V_{BB}$ and $V_{BB}/R_B$ of the load line with the axes.

At the output side of the transistor of Fig. 7.21b, a graphical solution can also be used to establish the operating point. An output characteristic of the c-e transistor is shown in Fig. 7.22b. Kirchhoff's voltage law for the output circuit leads to

$$R_C I_C + V_{CE} - V_{CC} = 0 \tag{7.31}$$

or

$$I_C = \frac{V_{CC} - V_{CE}}{R_C} \tag{7.32}$$

This is a linear relation between $V_{CE}$ and $I_C$ and can be plotted as a load line on the output characteristic as in Fig. 7.22b. The intercepts of the load line with the coordinate axes are $V_{CE} = V_{CC}$ and $I_C = V_{CC}/R_C$. Again, all points of possible collector current and collector voltage must lie on the *load line*.

On the other hand, the operating point must also lie on an $I_B$ parameter curve in the $I_C V_{CE}$ plane as specified by the value of the input current. This is shown as a dashed curve in Fig. 7.22b. The operating point is then the intersection of this curve and the load line, as shown.

As a practical matter, since $V_{BB}$ and $V_{CC}$ in Fig. 7.21a have a common terminal and the same polarity, the same dc supply can be used for both. Usually, $V_{CC} \gg V_T$ in order to achieve adequate reverse bias of the collector junction. Thus $V_{CC} = V_{BB} \gg V_{BE}$. If this inequality is used in (7.29b), we obtain

$$I_B \simeq \frac{V_{BB}}{R_B} \tag{7.33}$$

Therefore, if $V_{BB}$ is much larger than $V_{BE}$ (which is of the order of a few tenths of a volt), the base current is independent of the transistor input characteristic and is determined only by the external input circuit.

## REFERENCES

P. E. Gray, D. De Witt, A. R. Boothroyd, and J. F. Gibbons, "Physical Electronics and Circuit Models of Transistors," SEEC, vol. 2, chaps. 1, 7, John Wiley & Sons, Inc., New York, 1964.

C. L. Searle, A. R. Boothroyd, E. J. Angelo, Jr., P. G. Gray, and D. O. Pederson, "Elementary Circuit Properties of Transistors," SEEC, vol. 3, chaps. 1, 2, John Wiley & Sons, Inc., New York, 1964.

## PROBLEMS

**7.1**   Explain why a transistor biased in the normal active mode can provide power gain.

**7.2**   Sketch the flow of particles and the current components in an *npn* transistor operated (*a*) in the normal active mode, (*b*) in the *off* mode where both junctions are reverse biased, (*c*) in the *saturated* mode where both junctions are forward biased, and (*d*) in the inverse active mode.

**7.3**   Plot the internal electrostatic potential diagrams for an *npn* transistor for all four modes of operation (see Prob. 7.2.)

**7.4**   For the basic *IV* equations for a *pnp* transistor, (7.22), determine the four constants $I_{CS}$, $I_{ES}$, $\alpha_0$, $\alpha_{r0}$, given the following data:

(*a*) With $V_{CB} = 0$ and $V_{EB} = 0.104$ V, $I_C$ and $I_E$ were measured and found to be $-0.74$ mA and $+0.8$ mA, respectively.

(*b*) With $V_{EB} = 0$ and $V_{CB} > 0$, $I_C$ and $I_E$ were again measured and found to be $+1.25$ mA and $-1$ mA, respectively.

**7.5**   From the measurements of Prob. 7.4, establish the values of the $a_{ij}$ coefficients of (7.16).

**7.6**   The currents for the three circuits shown were measured as follows: For the circuit of figure *a*, $I_E = +0.88$ mA, $I_C = -0.8$ mA; for figure *b*, $I_E = -0.5$ mA, $I_C = +1$ mA; for figure *c*, $I_C = -10$ $\mu$A. Use the results of these measurements to determine the coefficients of (7.22) and (7.16).

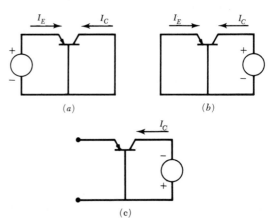

**Problem 7.6**

**7.7**   From the measurements of Prob. 7.4, determine the parameters $I_{CO}$ and $I_{EO}$. Check to see if (7.23) holds.

**7.8**   For a Si *npn* transistor, current measurements for a negative value of $V_{EB}$ and a shorted collector to base were $I_E = -1.2$ mA, $I_C = 1.15$ mA.

While the emitter current for $V_{EB}$ much greater than $V_T$ was 10 nA. The current measurements for a negative-collector base voltage and a short from emitter to base was $I_C = -4.0$ mA, $I_E = 0.8$ mA. Determine the coefficients of the $IV$ equations (7.24), and draw a diode circuit model showing all element values.

**7.9**   Using the $IV$ equations (7.22) for the c-b configuration, find (a) $I_C$ and $I_E$ for $V_{EB} = 0$; (b) $I_C$ and $V_{EB}$ for $V_B = 0$.

**7.10**   Describe the sequence of internal electronic behavior in an *npn* transistor, as well as the steady-state performance, if a small positive step function of base current is applied in the c-e connection. Why is the incremental input resistance larger for the c-e connection than for the c-b connection? (*Hint*: The voltages are the same.)

**7.11**   Convert the values given in the Sec. 7.3 to determine the power gain of the transistor connected in c-e.

**7.12**   Use an expression comparable to (7.18) to plot the minority-carrier density profile in the base region of an *npn* transistor under the conditions that $V_{EB} < -V_T$ and (a) $V_{CB} >> V_T$, (b) $V_{CB} < -V_T$.

**7.13**   Start from the $IV$ equations for an *npn* transistor, (7.24), to determine the value of base current for $V_{BE} = 0$ and the values of $V_{BE}$ when $I_B = 0$. What is the most negative value of $I_B$ that can flow for $V_{CB} \geqslant 0$.

**7.14**   Use the parameter values for Prob. 7.6 and draw a complete set of $IV$ characteristics (a) for the c-b connection and (b) for the c-e connection. Assume $T = 300°K$.

**7.15**   For the normal active region of an *npn* transistor, discuss how the output $I_C V_{CE}$ characteristic of the c-e connection varies with an increase of temperature (a) if $I_{CO}$ doubles for every 10°C increase, (b) if $\beta_0$ increases, and (c) if both $I_{CO}$ and $\beta_0$ increase.

**7.16**   A *pnp* transistor in c-e configuration of the figure has input and output characteristics as given in Figs. 7.19 and 7.18, respectively.

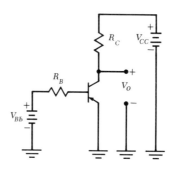

**Problem 7.16**

Assume that $V_{BB} = -1.0$ V, $V_{CC} = -5$ V, and $R_C = 2$ k$\Omega$. Plot the output load line.

(a) What is the range over which $\Delta V_o$ may vary?

(b) Choose a value of $I_B$ to obtain an operating point such that the maximum value of $+\Delta V_o$ equals the maximum value of $-\Delta V_o$.

(c) Find the value of $R_B$ to obtain the quiescent $I_B$ value of part b. Plot the input load line.

**7.17**   For the 2N914 transistor for which the $I_C V_{CE}$ characteristics are given in Prob. 9.4b, determine the operating point of the transistor if $V_{CC} = V_{BB} = 10$ V, if $R_B = 100$ k$\Omega$ and $V_{BE} = 0$. What change in the operating point occurs if $V_{BE}$ is 0.7 V?

**7.18**   An npn transistor has a dc voltage source of 15 V in series with a collector load of 1 k$\Omega$. Assume this is now driven in the common-emitter configuration with a current generator supplying base current

$$i_B = I_0 + I_m \sin \omega t$$

Utilizing the $I_C V_{CE}$ characteristics given in Prob. 7.17 for this type of transistor, (a) plot the load line, and (b) sketch the waveform of collector current versus $\omega t$ for $I_0 = 0.04$ mA and $I_m = 0.02$ mA.

**7.19**   A Ge npn transistor in the c-e configuration is used in the circuit shown. If $V_B$ is made sufficiently large, the transistor operates in the saturated mode of the transistor where both junctions are forward biased. In saturation, the output voltage $V_o$ becomes almost zero. The following data are used: $V_B = 10$ V; $I_C = 10$ mA; $I_{co} = 5$ mA; $\alpha_0 = 0.99$; $\alpha_{r0} = 0.30$; $R_B = 10$ k$\Omega$. Find (a) the current $I_B$ and (b) the voltage $V_{CE}$. (Hint: Use the basic IV equations to find an expression for the voltage.)

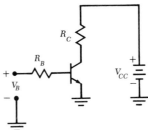

**Problem 7.19**

**7.20**   In the circuit shown, $V_{CC}$ is much larger than $V_T$. Using the basic IV equations for the transistor, determine and sketch the change of $I_C$ as $R_B$ is varied from $\infty$ to 0. (Hint: Establish first the values for the limiting conditions.)

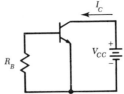

**Problem 7.20**

**7.21**  Develop expressions for the input and output $IV$ characteristics for the common-collector connection in the normal active region.

**7.22**  What is the current gain of the c-c connection? Why is the voltage gain of this connection almost unity?

**7.23**  Convert and use the values of Sec. 7.3 to estimate the power gain of the transistor in the c-c connection.

# chapter 8

# TRANSISTOR CIRCUIT MODELS

## 8.1 transistor models

Two different models for the transistor were proposed in the last chapter. Equations (7.22) and (7.24), or any of the equations derived from them for a particular operating point, constitute *mathematical* *models* of the transistor. Graphs of these *IV* relations can be considered to be *graphical IV models* and can be compared with actual *IV* characteristics to establish the accuracy of the models. A *circuit model*, consisting of ideal diodes and dependent current generators, can also be developed

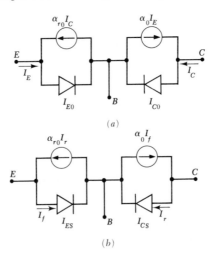

(a)

(b)

**FIGURE 8.1** *Diode circuit models for a pnp transistor* (a) *on* $I_{E0}$, $I_{C0}$ *basis and* (b) *on* $I_{ES}$, $I_{CS}$ *basis.*

from the mathematical model. This model is shown in Fig. 8.1a for a *pnp* transistor and is developed from (7.26) and (7.27). The equations are repeated below:

$$I_E = -\alpha_{ro}I_C + I_{EO}(e^{V_{EB}/V_T} - 1) \tag{8.1a}$$

$$I_C = -\alpha_0 I_E + I_{co}(e^{V_{CB}/V_T} - 1) \tag{8.1b}$$

The first equation can be considered to be a statement of Kirchhoff's current law at a node such as the input node of Fig. 8.1a. The first term on the right of (8.1a) represents a dependent current generator which depends on the collector current that flows. The second term of (8.1a) is the *IV* relation of an ideal *pn*-junction diode with a reverse saturation current of $I_{EO}$. Similarly, (8.1b) is the Kirchhoff current law at the output node of Fig. 8.1a. Thus, the circuit model of Fig. 8.1a is an alternate description for the equations (8.1).

A second diode, current-generator model can also be proposed as in Fig. 8.1b, which is a modification of Fig. 8.1a. For this model, we start with (7.22). The first term on the right of (7.22a) is identified as the *IV* relation of an ideal diode characterized by the saturation current $I_{ES}$. The forward-bias current through this diode is labeled $I_f$.

$$I_f = I_{ES}(e^{V_{EB}/V_T} - 1) \tag{8.2a}$$

Similarly, the second term on the right of (7.22b) is identified with

$$I_r = I_{CS}(e^{V_{CB}/V_T} - 1) \tag{8.2b}$$

Using Kirchhoff's current law at the input and the output nodes, we can propose the circuit model of Fig. 8.1b where the diodes are now characterized by $I_{ES}$ or $I_{CS}$ and the dependent current generators are proportional to $I_f$ or $I_r$ rather than $I_E$ or $I_C$. In passing, note that $I_f$ is the emitter current that flows when $V_{CB} = 0$ and $V_{EB} > 0$ and that $I_r$ is the current that flows when $V_{EB} = 0$ and $V_{CB} > 0$.

For *npn* transistors, the diodes and the current generators in Fig. 8.1a and b need to be reversed. Either type of the two circuit models is useful primarily for very low frequency variations since no charge-storage effects are included. To include charge-storage effects, one procedure is to choose an operating point, say for the normal active mode, and to include small-signal circuit models for the diodes of Fig. 8.1. These model small variations about a chosen operating point. For the active mode, if the results of Sec. 6.4 (Fig. 6.20) are used in Fig. 8.1a, we obtain the small-signal circuit model of the transistor shown in Fig. 8.2. Since the $I_{EO}$ (emitter) diode is forward biased, we need to include a diodelike conductance $g_d$ as well as a "diffusion" capacitance $C_d$. The latter element represents stored excess minority and majority carriers near the emitter junction. The junction (space-charge) capacitance $C_{je}$ is shown explicitly although it may be combined with $C_d$. Because the emitter region is usually much more heavily doped than the base, only the ohmic resistor in the base, $r_x$, is shown.

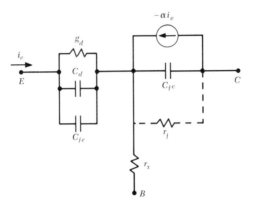

**FIGURE 8.2**  *Small-signal circuit model based on diode model.*

For the $I_{CO}$ (collector) diode, only the junction capacitance $C_{jc}$ is included since the collector-base junction is reverse biased. The dependent current source $\alpha i_e$ is retained from Fig. 8.1a and appears across $C_{jc}$. Because we are dealing only with small signals about an operating point, the dependence of this source is shown for $i_e$, the incremental emitter current, rather than $I_E$. In addition, the 0 subscript of $\alpha$ is dropped. This parameter is not independent of frequency because the transport of minority carriers through the base region is a dispersive phenomenon. Thus, $\alpha$ changes in magnitude and phase as the frequency of the input excitation is changed. Finally, a resistance $r_j$ is shown in dashed lines across $C_{jc}$. This element represents, in only a gross way, changes in the output current due to output-voltage changes. These changes are discussed in Sec. 8.3.

The circuit model of Fig. 8.2 seems appropriate at this time in that we have a collection of all the first-order effects occurring in the transistor. However, this circuit model does not provide a good representation of the transistor in the common-emitter (c-e) connection. A more detailed analysis shows that effects which are second order in the common-base (c-b) connection, become first-order effects for the c-e connection. In other words, these effects cause significant errors in the predicted small-signal performance or evaluation of the c-e transistor. We do not pursue this aspect further. Instead, a small-signal circuit model is developed directly for the c-e connection, i.e., with the base current as an input variable. Interestingly enough, the new circuit model is adequate for first-order prediction of the c-b connection as well as for the c-e connection, as is brought out in Sec. 8.9.

In the following section, we first develop the "circuit elements" for the minority-carrier flow and storage in the base region. Next, we add the elements due to the junctions and the "extrinsic" regions. Finally, after assembling a complete circuit model, we introduce simplifications to obtain a convenient working model. The circuit model is capable of representing the transistor in most small-signal applications up to the highest useful frequencies of interest.

## 8.2  charge flow and storage in the base region

The density profile of minority carriers with distance in the base region is developed in Sec. 7.2 for a transistor for the normal active mode of operation. For this case, the minority carriers move principally by diffusion flow from the emitter junction to the collector junction and the device is called a "pure diffusion" transistor. If recombination is small in the base, the profile of the minority-carrier density distribution is almost a triangle, as shown in Fig. 7.6 and as repeated as the solid line in Fig. 8.3. (For simplicity, we assume for a diffusion transistor that the density is described by the straight line, rather than the slightly concave curve which is shown in Fig. 7.6.)

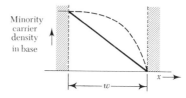

**FIGURE 8.3**  *Profile of minority-carrier density in the base; solid line for uniform base, dashed curve for graded base.*

Pure diffusion flow in the base of the transistor is obtained if the impurity concentration of the base region is uniform and if the density of minority carriers is much less than the density of majority carriers. By design, the majority carriers in the base can be much greater than the "residual" minority carriers. However, if the injection of minority carriers from the emitter junction is large, the density of minority carriers can become comparable to the original density of majority carriers, especially near the emitter junction. For this high-injection condition, an electric field is set up in the base region comparable to the situation described in Sec. 5.8 for the diode. This electric field affects the flow of minority carriers in the base and distorts the linear relation shown in Fig. 8.3.

Internal, built-in electric fields in the base also result if the impurity concentration (doping) of the base region is not uniform. For such a *graded-base* transistor, the profile of minority carriers is similar to the dashed curve in Fig. 8.3. Most transistors today are graded-base, *npn* transistors and are manufactured by the planar, diffusion processes mentioned in Secs. 5.1 and 7.1. Nonetheless, we consider first the simplest case of a linear minority-carrier profile in order to obtain the simplest analysis procedure. The nature of the results remains valid for the more general case.

For the uniform-base transistor, with low-level injection into the base, minority carriers flow because of diffusion only. An expression for this current is given in (7.3) for a *pnp* transistor. In the remainder of this chapter we restrict attention to an *npn* transistor. The collector current, determining the gradient from the edge conditions for the base, as in Fig. 7.6, is

$$I_C = qAD_e \frac{n_{be} + n_{bo}}{w} \qquad (8.3a)$$

where $w$ is the basewidth, $A$ is the cross-sectional area of the base, and $n_{be}$ is the excess-electron density at the emitter edge of the base region,

$$n_{be} = n_{bo}(e^{V_{BE}/V_T} - 1) \qquad (8.3b)$$

where $n_{bo}$ is the density of electrons (minority carriers) in the base in thermal equilibrium. For a small change of input voltage $dV_{BE}$ and with the collector voltage held constant, that is, $V_{CE} = $ constant or $dV_{CE} = 0$, we can use (8.3a) and (8.3b) to obtain the resulting change in $I_C$, that is, $dI_C$. The ratio of $dI_C$ to $dV_{BE}$ has the dimensions of conductance and is defined as the "transfer conductance" or more simply the *transconductance* $g_m$:

$$g_m = \left. \frac{dI_C}{dV_{BE}} \right|_{dV_{CE}=0} \simeq \frac{\Delta I_C}{\Delta V_{BE}} \qquad (8.4a)$$

As noted, the definition is properly made in terms of a derivative, but is useful for small but finite increments of $I_C$ and $V_{BE}$. Using the equations above, we obtain

$$g_m = \frac{qAD_e}{w} \frac{dn_{be}}{dV_{BE}}$$

$$= \frac{1}{V_T} \frac{qAD_e}{w}(n_{be} + n_{bo}) = \frac{1}{V_T} \frac{qAD_e}{w} n_{be}$$

$$= \frac{I_C}{V_T} \qquad (8.4b)$$

We use the last expression as our defined value of $g_m$. Notice that this transconductance has the same form as in the diode incremental conductance developed in Sec. 6.3.

From the above, we see that for the change in input voltage, the slope of the profile is changed and this changes the collector current. In addition, the area under the profile curve is increased or decreased. This area is a measure of the stored minority-carrier charge in the base region. At dc, there is a constant injection of charge into the base from the emitter and a constant flow of charge into the collector. On a time average, however, we have stored charge in the base which is represented by the area under the curve of Fig. 8.3. An expression for the *excess* stored charge $Q_B$ (over and above the minority-carrier charge in the base for thermal equilibrium) can be easily obtained because of the triangular shape. For $n_{b_e} \gg n_{b_o}$,

$$Q_B \simeq qAn_{b_e}\frac{w}{2} \qquad (8.5)$$

As brought out in Sec. 6.3 for the diode, an excess majority-carrier stored charge also is present in the base region. This charge has the same magnitude as (8.5) and the opposite sign because of the approximate charge neutrality in the base region. As $V_{BE}$ is changed, a change in current occurs which changes the minority-carrier stored charge. Therefore, a change in (majority carrier) base current also occurs to change the excess majority-carrier charge in the base. These changes of stored charge for a change of input voltage can be modeled with a capacitance, which we call the *base-charging capacitance* $C_B$.

$$C_B = \frac{dQ_B}{dV_{BE}}\bigg|_{dV_{CE}=0} \simeq \frac{\Delta Q_B}{\Delta V_{BE}}$$

$$= \frac{qAw}{2}\frac{dn_{be}}{dV_{BE}}$$

$$= g_m\frac{w^2}{2D_e} \qquad (8.6a)$$

where (8.4b) is used. Again, the form of this capacitance expression is the same as that of the diffusion capacitance of the short-base diode developed in Sec. 6.3. In the latter, the factor $w^2/2D_e$ is identified as the *average transit time* of minority carriers between emission and collection. We use the same identification where $\tau_t$ is now taken as the average transit time of minority carriers traversing the base from the emitter to the collector. Then

$$C_B = g_m\tau_t \qquad (8.6b)$$

where for a pure-diffusion transistor

$$\tau_t = \frac{w^2}{2D_e} \qquad (8.6c)$$

The two circuit elements developed to this point model the fundamental charge flow and charge storage in the base. We can now start to assemble a circuit model for the transistor. We do this by setting down three nodes as in Fig. 8.4, one representing an internal base "connection" or "node";

another, an internal emitter node; and the last, an internal collector node. We use the term *internal node* because we are only considering the base region at this time. Connections to the external (actual) nodes of the

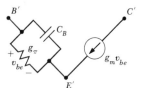

**FIGURE 8.4**    *Basic circuit model for internal base region.*

transistor are introduced shortly. Similar to the situation for a diode model, we must look later at extrinsic regions in order to connect the internal nodes with the actual outside device terminals or leads. The internal nodes are labeled $B'$, $E'$, and $C'$, as shown in Fig. 8.4.

We start to assemble the model by defining between $B'$ and $E'$ the voltage $v_{be} = dV_{BE} \simeq \Delta V_{BE}$ and also by inserting the capacitance $C_B$. (The use of primes on the subscripts is a correct notation but too cumbersome.) Between the $C'$ and $E'$, we next connect a *dependent* current generator $g_m v_{be}$. This current generator models the change of output current due to a change of input voltage as discussed in the derivation of (8.4b).

We have neglected recombination in developing the expressions for $g_m$ and $C_B$. We know that some recombination must occur even though it does not appreciably affect the minority-carrier profile or the expressions for $g_m$ and $C_B$. However, this recombination in the base causes a transverse majority-carrier current, which must increase if $V_{BE}$, and therefore $Q_B$, increases. To model this current-voltage relation we need to introduce a resistance, which we label $r_\pi$ for reasons which will be clear later. The reciprocal of $r_\pi$ ($g_\pi = 1/r_\pi$) is developed as follows:

$$g_\pi = \frac{dI_B}{dV_{BE}} \bigg|_{dV_{CE} = 0} \simeq \frac{\Delta I_B}{\Delta V_{BE}}$$

$$= \frac{dI_B}{dI_C} \frac{dI_C}{dV_{BE}}$$

$$= \frac{dI_B}{dI_C} g_m \qquad (8.7a)$$

In (8.7a), we have included a ratio of the change of $I_B$ to the change of $I_C$. We are interested here only in slow changes of the currents and their relationship with recombination. Therefore, this ratio is the reciprocal of the transistor parameter $\beta_0$, the low-frequency, short-circuit current gain of the c-e connection.

$$\beta_0 = \left.\frac{dI_C}{dI_B}\right|_{dV_{CE} = 0} \tag{8.7b}$$

Therefore

$$g_\pi = \frac{1}{\beta_0} g_m \tag{8.7c}$$

The $g_\pi$ element is also placed across the $B'$ and $E'$ nodes as shown in Fig. 8.4 since it relates base current changes to a $V_{BE}$ change.

To this point, only the changes in the input and output currents and the base stored charge due to changes of $V_{BE}$ have been considered. These quantities also change if the output voltage is changed. These changes are the result of the variation of the width of the base region and are discussed in the next section.

## 8.3   basewidth modulation

Let the base-to-emitter voltage $V_{BE}$ now be held constant, $dV_{BE} = v_{be} = 0$. A change in $V_{CE}$ is then also a change of $V_{CB}$, the collector-to-base-junction voltage, by Kirchhoff's voltage law. That is, $V_{EB} + V_{BC} + V_{CE} = 0$. So $dV_{BC} + dV_{CE} = 0$ if $dV_{BE} = 0$. If the collector-junction voltage is increased, the width of its space-charge region also increases as seen in Sec. 6.3 for the diode junction. Therefore, the width $w$ of the base region is decreased. This is shown in Fig. 8.5 for a transistor in which minority-carrier current in the

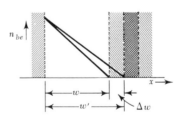

**FIGURE 8.5**   *Base-width modulation.*

base is due only to diffusion flow. With a change of $w$, both the slope and area of the profile of minority carriers in the base are affected. Thus, both the output current and the stored charge in the base are changed, and we need to introduce circuit elements to model these changes.

First, we introduce a capacitance to model the change in the stored charge in the base.

$$C_{cb} = \left.\frac{dQ_B}{dV_{CB}}\right|_{dV_{BE} = 0} = \frac{dQ_B}{dw}\frac{dw}{dV_{CB}} \tag{8.8a}$$

The first factor we obtain from the derivative of (8.5):

$$\frac{dQ_B}{dw} = \frac{qA}{2} n_{be} \tag{8.8b}$$

For $n_{be}$ we can use the value obtained in the development of (8.4b) where we again let $n_{be} \gg n_{bo}$. The result is

$$\frac{dQ_B}{dw} = \frac{g_m w}{2D_e} V_T \tag{8.8c}$$

This expression is used in (8.8a). If we also multiply and divide by $w$, and recognize from (8.6) that $w^2/2D_e$ is $\tau_t$ and that $g_m \tau_t$ is $C_B$, (8.8a) can be written as

$$C_{cb} = \eta C_B \tag{8.8d}$$

$$\eta = \frac{V_T}{w} \frac{dw}{dV_{CB}} \tag{8.8e}$$

The *basewidth modulation factor* $\eta$ typically has a value of the order of $10^{-3}$. The element $C_{cb}$ is connected between the internal base and collector terminals as shown in Fig. 8.6 because changes in $V_{CB}$ lead to basewidth modulation.

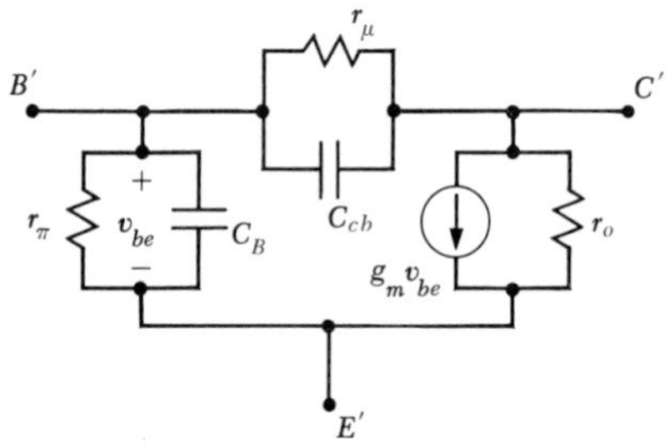

**FIGURE 8.6** *Circuit model for internal base region.*

Two resistances are now introduced to model the change in the dc output current for a change in $V_{CE}$. We need two resistances (or conductances) because both the emitter and base currents must change and we must connect the internal collector node to both of the other internal nodes. Remember that both the profile slope and the recombination must change. The sum of the base-current and emitter-current changes must, from (7.6), be the negative of the change in the collector current

$$dI_C = -(dI_B + dI_E) \tag{8.9a}$$

It is also convenient to express this relation in terms of the incremental currents $i_e = dI_E$, etc.

$$i_c = -(i_b + i_e) \tag{8.9b}$$

Again the change in $V_{CE}$ is equal to the change in $V_{CB}$ because $V_{BE}$ is held constant. The change in emitter current due to a change in $V_{CB}$ leads us to the resistance $r_o$. The value of its conductance is

$$\frac{1}{r_o} = \frac{dI_E}{dV_{CB}}\bigg|_{dV_{BE}=0} = \frac{\beta_0 + 1}{\beta_0}\frac{dI_C}{dw}\frac{dw}{dV_{CB}} \tag{8.10a}$$

where we have used $dI_E = [(\beta_0 + 1)/\beta_0]dI_C$, which follows from (8.7b) and (8.9a). If $dI_C/dw$ is established using (8.3a) and (8.4b), we obtain

$$\frac{1}{r_o} = \frac{\beta_0 + 1}{\beta_0}g_m\eta \simeq g_m\eta \tag{8.10b}$$

where $\eta$ is given in (8.8e). The resistance $r_o$ is connected between the $C'$ and $E'$ nodes in Fig. 8.6 because it models the change in emitter current. It is usually referred to as the short-circuit output resistance.

In a similar manner, a resistance $r_\mu$ is proposed to model the changes in the base current due to $dV_{CE} = dV_{CB}$.

$$\frac{1}{r_\mu} = \frac{dI_B}{dV_{CB}}\bigg|_{dV_{BE}=0} = \frac{dI_B}{dI_E}\frac{dI_E}{dV_{CB}} = \frac{1}{\beta_0 + 1}\frac{1}{r_o} \tag{8.11a}$$

$$r_\mu \simeq \beta_0 r_o \tag{8.11b}$$

This element is shown in Fig. 8.6. The circuit model of Fig. 8.6 for the internal base region is now complete.

## 8.4 additional elements

The regions outside of the base region store charge and provide voltage drops. Thus we need to include additional capacitances and resistances to complete the circuit model of the transistor.

In Chap. 6, the changes in stored charge in the space-charge region of a junction are modeled with a capacitance. In the transistor, then, we need to include two such capacitances, $C_{jc}$ for the collector-base junction and $C_{je}$ for the emitter-base junction. These capacitances are placed between the $C'$ and $B'$ nodes and $B'$ and $E'$ nodes, respectively, in Fig. 8.7.

The finite conductivity of the three transistor regions, and the resulting voltage drops when current flows, lead to three "ohmic" resistances: $r_b'$ in the base lead, $r_e'$ in the emitter lead, and $r_c'$ in the collector lead. These resistances are included in the leads between the internal nodes and the external connections of the transistor as shown in Fig. 8.7. The last two resistances are usually very small and will be neglected in the work to follow. In contrast to $r_e'$ and $r_c'$, the area pertaining to $r_b'$ is the narrow section shown in Fig. 8.8a and b. Because the value of the resistance $r_b'$ is inversely proportional to the area of current flow, $r_b'$ is much larger than $r_e'$ and $r_c'$.

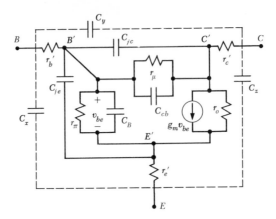

**FIGURE 8.7**   *Circuit model for complete transistor.*

The final three elements which we will include in building up a circuit model of the transistor are the "can and lead" capacitances $C_x$, $C_y$, and $C_z$, as shown by the dashed lines in Fig. 8.7. These model the capacitances between the leads and from the leads to the enclosure of the transistor,

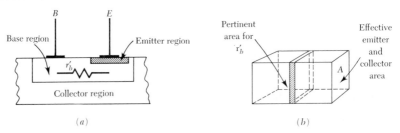

**FIGURE 8.8**   *Base resistance.* (a) *Cross section of planar structure;* (b) *pertinent area for calculation of $r_b'$.*

which is usually metal. These capacitances are shown in dashed lines because they can be neglected in almost all instances since they have values typically of the order of 1 pF $= 10^{-12}$ F. For similar reasons, we do not include any inductances to model the inductive effect of the leads.

The complete circuit model of Fig. 8.7 is a formidable configuration. If we neglect $C_x$, $C_y$, and $C_z$, however, as well as $r_e'$ and $r_c'$, and if we combine capacitances in parallel where possible, we obtain the much simpler configuration shown in Fig. 8.9. In this figure, we have labeled the combination of $C_B$ and $C_{je}$ as $C_\pi$.

$$C_\pi = C_B + C_{je} \qquad (8.12)$$

The parallel combination of $C_{jc}$ and $C_{cb}$ is called $C_\mu$,

$$C_\mu = C_{jc} + C_{cb} \qquad (8.13)$$

The ohmic base resistance is relabeled $r_x$ to avoid the prime.

$$r_b' = r_x \qquad (8.14)$$

The circuit of Fig. 8.9 can be considered to be the basic circuit model for the transistor. It is often called the "hybrid $\pi$" model.

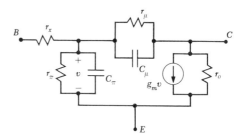

**FIGURE 8.9** *Basic small-signal circuit model of transistor.*

For our purposes, the circuit of Fig. 8.9 is still too complicated to work with easily in the study and evaluation of electronic circuit functions. Consequently, we introduce simpler circuit models either by restricting the range of the frequency spectrum over which a model is to be valid or by relaxing the accuracy with which the model can predict performance of the transistor.

## 8.5 circuit-model simplifications

In place of the circuit model of Fig. 8.9, we show in this section that one of two simplified circuit models can be used in most useful situations. These two models are shown in Figs. 8.10b and 8.12. The first is used for calculations for dc and low frequencies. The second simplified model provides one equivalent capacitance to model all charge-storage effects in the transistor. In this section, we develop these simplifications starting from the model of Fig. 8.9.

In the circuit of Fig. 8.9 there are two parallel resistance-capacitance combinations: $r_\mu$ and $C_\mu$, and $r_\pi$ and $C_\pi$. We know from Chap. 3 that the susceptances of the capacitances vary linearly with frequency. Therefore, it is possible to neglect the capacitances at low frequencies and to neglect the resistances at high frequencies. For example, the admittance of $r_\mu$ and $C_\mu$ in parallel is

$$y_\mu = \frac{1}{r_\mu} + j\omega C_\mu \qquad (8.15)$$

At very low frequencies, the susceptance of $C_\mu$, that is, $\omega C_\mu$, is much smaller than the fixed conductance $g_\mu = 1/r_\mu$. A good "bench mark" to establish the edge of the frequency range where one element is more important than the other is the frequency where the susceptance of $C_\mu$ equals the conductance.

$$\omega_\mu = \frac{1}{r_\mu C_\mu} \tag{8.16}$$

For frequencies considerably less than $\omega_\mu$, say $\omega < \frac{1}{3}\,\omega_\mu$, $C_\mu$ can be neglected in relation to $r_\mu$.

In a similar manner, a frequency can be established for the $r_\pi$ and $C_\pi$ combination.

$$\omega_\pi = \frac{1}{r_\pi C_\pi} \tag{8.17}$$

For frequencies well below $\omega_\pi$, $C_\pi$ can be ignored. (Note, $\omega_\mu$ and $\omega_\pi$ are not break frequencies for a gain function which is derived using the circuit model.)

It is helpful to introduce values of the elements for a typical transistor. From these values we can calculate the values of (8.16) and (8.17) and ascertain which circuit elements are more important in a given frequency region. For a silicon transistor operated at $I_C = 5$ mA and $V_{CE} = 5$ V,

$$r_\pi = 250\ \Omega \qquad\qquad r_\mu = 1\ M\Omega$$

$$g_m = 0.2\ \text{mho} \qquad r_o = 20\ k\Omega$$

$$r_x = 50\ \Omega \qquad\qquad C_\mu = 5\ \text{pF}$$

$$C_\pi = 100\ \text{pF}$$

From these values,

$$\omega_\mu = (2\pi)\ 32\ \text{kHz} \qquad \omega_\pi = (2\pi)\ 6.4\ \text{MHz}$$

For this transistor $\omega_\mu$ is 200 times lower than $\omega_\pi$. Thus, at frequencies below 32 kHz both $C_\pi$ and $C_\mu$ can be omitted, i.e., the charge-storage effects of the transistor can completely be neglected. The circuit model for very low frequencies then becomes that shown in Fig. 8.10$a$.

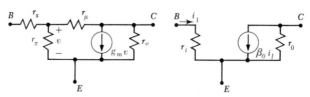

**FIGURE 8.10**  *Circuit models for dc and very low frequencies.* (a) *Complete circuit;* (b) *simplified circuit.*

The low-frequency model can be simplified even further since $r_\mu$ is usually very large. As is brought out below, the "feedback" from the output to the input and the "transmission" from the input to the output due to this element are both very small. This leads us to neglect $r_\mu$ as in Fig. 8.10$b$. In this circuit, it is often convenient to think of the series combination of $r_x$ and $r_\pi$ as a single input resistance $r_i$.

$$r_i = r_x + r_\pi \tag{8.18}$$

For the values above, $r_i = 300\ \Omega$. Notice in the figure that the dependent current generator can also be modified to be a function of the input current $i_i$ together with the current gain parameter, $\beta_0$. This follows since

$$g_m r_\pi = \beta_0 \tag{8.19a}$$

$$g_m v = \beta_0 i_i \tag{8.19b}$$

At this point, we could go back and find frequency ranges over which $C_\mu$ must be included but not $C_\pi$, etc. However, we now introduce an analysis which indicates that not only can $r_\mu$ and $r_o$ be neglected over the entire useful frequency interval for which the model is valid, if $R_L$ is sufficiently small, say much less than $r_o$, but also the major effects of $C_\mu$ can be included as an equivalent capacitance added to $C_\pi$. For the analysis we use the circuit of Fig. 8.11$a$. If $R_L \ll r_o$, then $r_o$ can

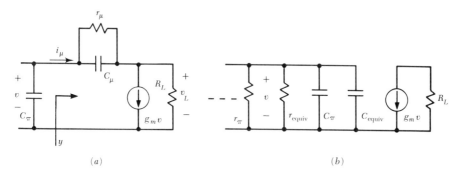

(a)                                            (b)

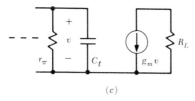

(c)

**FIGURE 8.11** *Equivalent feedback effects of $r_\mu$ and $C_\mu$. (a) Admittance loading; (b) use of $r_{equiv}$ and $C_{equiv}$; (c) use of a combined total capacitance, $C_t$.*

be neglected as shown. The presence of $r_\mu$ and $C_\mu$ affects, in general, the input and output of the circuit, the forward transmission of current to the load, and the reverse transmission (feedback) from the output to the input. The last effect is by far the most important. The forward transmission through $r_\mu$ and $C_\mu$ is much smaller than the transmission due to the dependent current source $g_m v$ (see Prob. 8.23). The reverse transmission is also small, but it must be kept in mind that because of the current gain of the c-e transistor, the feedback current can be of the same order of magnitude as the current through $r_\pi$ and $C_\pi$ due to the actual input.

We investigate the loading and feedback effects of $r_\mu$ and $C_\mu$ on the input of the circuit by calculating the input admittance $y$ looking from $C_\pi$ toward $r_\mu$, $C_\mu$ and the output (see Fig. 8.11a). This admittance is

$$y = \frac{I_\mu}{V} \tag{8.20a}$$

where sinusoidal variables are assumed and a phasor notation is used. This is found as follows:

$$I_\mu = \left(\frac{1}{r_\mu} + j\omega C_\mu\right)(V - V_L) = \left(\frac{1}{r_\mu} + j\omega C_\mu\right)V\left(1 - \frac{V_L}{V}\right) \tag{8.20b}$$

Because the forward transmission through $r_\mu$ and $C_\mu$ can be neglected

$$V_L \simeq -g_m R_L V \tag{8.20c}$$

This leads to an approximate expression for $y$.

$$y = \left(\frac{1}{r_\mu} + j\omega C_\mu\right)(1 + g_m R_L) \tag{8.20d}$$

This is the admittance of a shunt combination of an equivalent resistance and an equivalent capacitance. Therefore, input effects due to $r_\mu$ and $C_\mu$ can be modeled with a resistance $r_{\text{equiv}} = r_\mu/(1 + g_m R_L)$ and a capacitance $C_{\text{equiv}} = C_\mu(1 + g_m R_L)$ as shown in Fig. 8.11b. From our earlier results, (8.10) and (8.11), it is clear that $r_{\text{equiv}} \gg r_\pi$ if $R_L \ll r_o$. Therefore, $r_{\text{equiv}}$ can be neglected as shown in Fig. 8.11c. It is convenient to combine $C_\pi$ and $C_{\text{equiv}}$ as shown in Fig. 8.11c.

$$C_t = C_\pi + C_{\text{equiv}} = C_\pi + C_\mu(1 + g_m R_L) \tag{8.21}$$

The final simplified circuit model of the transistor becomes that of Fig. 8.12 and it is sometimes referred to as the $C_t$ approximation.

The upper-frequency limit of the model of Fig. 8.12 depends on the validity of the modeling of the individual processes. The most fundamental limitation is due to the finite time of transport of minority carriers across the base. This time we called the average transit time $\tau_t$. It is reasonable to expect, then, that as the period of an input-signal frequency approaches $\tau_t$, our simple modeling of the base transport phenomenon will be in serious

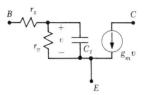

**FIGURE 8.12** *Simplified circuit model for a resistance load, the $C_t$ approximation.*

error. To be on the conservative side the average transit time should be less than a quarter of the period of the sinusoidal input signal.

$$\frac{T}{4} \geqslant \tau_t \qquad (8.22a)$$

The input-signal frequency is the reciprocal of the period. Thus the constraint on the input frequency is

$$f \leqslant \frac{1}{4\tau_t} \qquad (8.22b)$$

or

$$\omega \leqslant \frac{2\pi}{4} \frac{1}{\tau_t} \qquad (8.22c)$$

For a numerical example, we use the values of the transistor above. If for simplicity we neglect $C_{je}$, then $C_\pi \simeq C_B$. From (8.6b),

$$\tau_t = \frac{C_B}{g_m} = 5 \cdot 10^{-10} \text{ second} = 0.5 \text{ nanosecond}$$

This leads to an upper-frequency limit of this transistor of approximately

$$f_\tau = \frac{1}{4\tau_t} = 500 \text{ MHz} \qquad (8.22d)$$

In summary, the linear circuit models shown in Figs. 8.10 and 8.12 are simple accurate models with which to study or evaluate the performance of the transistor for very low frequencies (Fig. 8.10) or for the entire frequency spectrum up to the transit-time limitation frequency (Fig. 8.12). Of course, being small-signal models, they are valid only for small variations about an operating point.

## 8.6 characterization of the circuit model

The values for the elements of a circuit model obtained from the geometry or electrical properties of the transistor regions are useful for first-order transistor design. However, in the use of actual transistors, special electrical measurements are made to obtain element values.[1] These measurements include resistance, capacitance, and current-gain measurements, and from the measurements calculations can be made to determine the values of the elements.

It is easiest to introduce the measurements with the circuit model of Fig. 8.9 immediately at hand. First, we measure the values of dc collector current $I_C$ and the collector-to-emitter voltage $V_{CE}$ to insure that the desired operating point is achieved. The element $g_m$ depends on $V_T$ and $I_C$. The former is defined in terms of temperature, and so can be calculated. With the measured value of $I_C$, $g_m$ is given by (8.4b). The values of $\beta_0$ and $(C_\pi + C_\mu)$ are obtained from a measurement of a special current-gain characteristic with frequency. For this measurement we use the arrangement shown in Fig. 8.13a. The input source is chosen to be a pure,

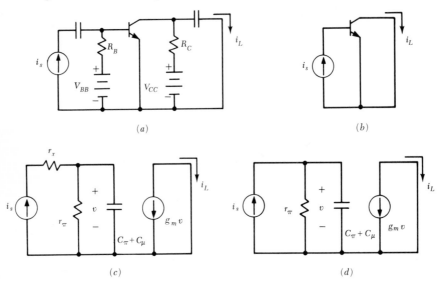

(a)

(b)

(c)

(d)

**FIGURE 8.13**  *Experimental setup for the measurement of short-circuit current gain.*  (a) *Measurement circuit;* (b) *equivalent circuit for variational response;* (c) *circuit model;* (d) *omission of* $r_x$.

sinusoidal current source $i_s$, the frequency of which can be varied. The output is taken to be the current through a short circuit. Coupling capacitors are used to introduce the source and load to the transistor without disturbing the dc operating point. If we do not consider the very low frequencies, the capacitors can be assumed to be short circuits for signals.

---

[1] Measured values depart from those of the physical model because simplifications have been used to establish the descriptions for the elements, e.g., the one-dimensional situation and pure-diffusion flow.

The circuit for variations about the operating point can then be drawn as in Fig. 8.13b where the loading effects of $R_C$ can also be neglected with respect to the ac short-circuit load. The loading effect of $R_B$ is also usually negligible. If the circuit model of the transistor from Fig. 8.12 is now introduced, we obtain the circuit shown in Fig. 8.13c for variations about the operating point where $C_t = C_\pi + C_\mu$ because $R_L = 0$. Notice that $r_\mu$ and $r_o$ are negligible because of the short-circuit load. Finally, $r_x$ plays no part since it is in series with the input current source as in Fig. 8.13c. The current-gain function for the final circuit is found by solving the circuit equation using phasor notation for the variables,

$$V = \frac{I_s}{g_\pi + j\omega(C_\pi + C_\mu)} \tag{8.23a}$$

$$I_L = -g_m V \tag{8.23b}$$

where $g_\pi = 1/r_\pi$. The short-circuit current-gain function $\beta(j\omega)$ is found by solving for the short-circuit load current $-I_L$ and by dividing through by the source current $I_s$. The minus sign is introduced to conform with our earlier definition of $\beta_0$.

$$\beta(j\omega) = \frac{-I_L}{I_s}\bigg|_{\substack{\text{short-circuit} \\ \text{output}}} = \frac{g_m}{g_\pi + j\omega(C_\pi + C_\mu)} = \frac{g_m r_\pi}{1 + j\omega r_\pi(C_\pi + C_\mu)} \tag{8.24a}$$

If we use $r_\pi = \beta_0/g_m$, the result has the form

$$\beta(j\omega) = \frac{\beta_0}{1 + j\omega/\omega_\beta} \tag{8.24b}$$

where

$$\omega_\beta = \frac{1}{r_\pi(C_\pi + C_\mu)} \tag{8.24c}$$

Notice that the gain function appears to include frequencies down to dc since the circuit of Fig. 8.13d appears to be valid to dc. In reality, we must neglect the very low frequencies where the effects of the coupling capacitors become important. In (8.24b), the parameter $\beta_0$ appears as expected, since $\beta_0$ is the low-frequency, short-circuit current gain of the c-e connection. The magnitude and phase of $\beta(j\omega)$ are

$$|\beta(j\omega)| = \frac{\beta_0}{\sqrt{1 + (\omega/\omega_\beta)^2}} \tag{8.24d}$$

$$\text{Phase of } \beta(j\omega) = -\tan^{-1}\frac{\omega}{\omega_\beta} \tag{8.24e}$$

These quantities as a function of the frequency of the input sinusoidal excitation are shown in Fig. 8.14a and b. A log-log plot is used for $|\beta(j\omega)|$ in order to emphasize the low-frequency and high-frequency asymptotes of the function. A semilog plot is used for the phase. Note from the definition of $\beta(j\omega)$ in (8.24a) that this plot shows the phase of $-I_L$. A factor of $\pi$ must be added if one wants the phase of $I_L$ itself.

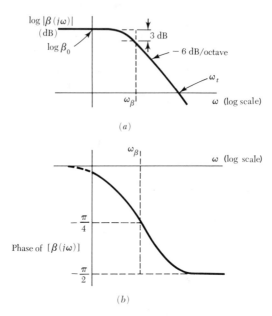

(a)

(b)

**FIGURE 8.14**   *Short-circuit current gain.* (a) *Magnitude* $|\beta(j\omega)|$ *versus* $\log \omega$; (b) *phase of* $\beta(j\omega)$ *versus* $\log \omega$.

As observed in Chap. 3, a function such as (8.24d) reaches a magnitude which is 0.707 of its low-frequency value at the break frequency $\omega = \omega_\beta$. At this frequency the magnitude is "down" $-3$dB and this frequency is called the 3-dB bandedge since it defines, in one sense, the edge of the passband of the gain function. The phase of $\beta(j\omega)$ at $\omega = \omega_\beta$ is $-\pi/4$ rad $= -45°$. In mathematical form, these results are

$$\beta(j\omega_\beta) = \frac{1}{\sqrt{2}} \beta_0 \qquad (8.25a)$$

$$\text{Phase of } \beta(j\omega_\beta) = -\frac{\pi}{4} \text{ rad} = -45° \qquad (8.25b)$$

In terms of cycles per second, the $-3$ dB frequency of $|\beta(j\omega)|$ is

$$f_\beta = \frac{\omega_\beta}{2\pi} \qquad (8.25c)$$

If for an actual transistor, we have obtained a gain-magnitude curve such as that of Fig. 8.14a, the low-frequency value of the curve provides us with a value of $\beta_0$. The $-3$ dB frequency is also known and this value leads to a value of $(C_\pi + C_\mu)$. From a rearrangement of (8.24c),

$$C_\pi + C_\mu = \frac{1}{r_\pi \omega_\beta} = \frac{g_m}{\beta_0 \omega_\beta} \tag{8.26}$$

The second expression is obtained from $r_\pi = \beta_0/g_m$. $C_\mu$ is primarily the space-charge capacitance of the collector-base junction. It is usually measured with a capacitance bridge by measuring the capacitance of the collector-base junction at the desired reverse bias with the emitter lead not connected. This is illustrated in Fig. 8.15. The bias resistor is chosen to be very large, say of the order of megohms. As shown, the capacitance

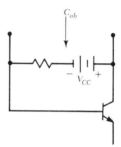

**FIGURE 8.15**  *Measurement setup for $C_{ob}$.*

obtained from this measurement is labeled $C_{ob}$ since it is also the output capacitance of the c-b connection if the collector is reverse biased. This capacitance is not a function of the current through the junction. Therefore, the measurement can be made with only the collector-base junction biased. If we neglect the capacitances $C_x$, $C_y$, $C_z$ of Fig. 8.7, and if $r_\pi \ll r_\mu$

$$C_\mu \simeq C_{ob} \tag{8.27}$$

Using a measured value of (8.27) in (8.26), we obtain a value of $C_\pi$.

$$C_\pi = \frac{g_m}{\beta_0 \omega_\beta} - C_\mu \tag{8.28}$$

Manufacturers usually do not provide typical values for $f_\beta$ or $\omega_\beta$. Instead, a value corresponding to the product $\beta_0 f_\beta$ or $\beta_0 \omega_\beta$ is given. The rationale for this is as follows. The measurement of $f_\beta$ to find exactly the $-3$ dB frequency can be time-consuming. On the other hand, a function such as $\beta(j\omega)$ in (8.24b) has the property that the product of the magnitude at a frequency well above the break frequency $\omega_\beta$, and the value of this frequency is approximately equal to the product $\beta_0 \omega_\beta$ (the product of the low-frequency magnitude and the $-3$ dB frequency). To prove this, we start with the gain-magnitude function (8.24$d$). For a frequency $\omega_1$ well above $\omega_\beta$, we obtain

$$|\beta(j\omega_1)| = \frac{\beta_0}{\sqrt{1 + (\omega_1/\omega_\beta)^2}} \simeq \frac{\beta_0}{\omega_1/\omega_\beta} = \frac{\beta_0\omega_\beta}{\omega_1} \tag{8.29a}$$

or
$$|\beta(j\omega_1)|\omega_1 = \beta_0\omega_\beta \tag{8.29b}$$

Therefore, from a measured curve such as Fig. 8.14$a$, the value of $\beta_0\omega_\beta$ can be easily obtained.

The product $\beta_0\omega_\beta$ is also approximately equal to the frequency at which the short-circuit current gain is unity. This frequency is labeled $\omega_t$ (or $f_t$) which is, of course, much larger than $\omega_\beta$.

$$|\beta(j\omega_t)| = 1 = \frac{\beta_0}{\sqrt{1 + (\omega_t/\omega_\beta)^2}} \simeq \frac{\beta_0\omega_\beta}{\omega_t} \tag{8.30a}$$

or
$$\omega_t = \beta_0\omega_\beta \tag{8.30b}$$

Unity gain corresponds to a gain of 0 dB. In terms of this 0 dB frequency, $C_\pi$ becomes

$$C_\pi = \frac{g_m}{\omega_t} - C_\mu \tag{8.31}$$

A numerical example is given shortly, but first we turn to the determination of the other resistance elements of the circuit model. The output resistance of Fig. 8.9, $r_o$, is either measured with a resistance bridge with the base an ac short circuit or is estimated from the slope of the $I_E V_{CE}$ characteristics at the desired operating point. The slope of the $I_C V_{CE}$ characteristic with $I_B$ equal to a constant is approximately $r_o/2$ (Prob. 8.11). The feedback resistance $r_\mu$ is usually calculated from the relation

$$r_\mu = \beta_0 r_o \tag{8.32}$$

The resistance $r_x$ is estimated from measurements of the input impedance of the c-e transistor with the output shorted as in Fig. 8.13$a$ and $b$.

$$Z_{in} = \frac{V_{in}}{I_s} = r_x + \frac{1}{1/r_\pi + j\omega(C_\pi + C_\mu)} \tag{8.33a}$$

At high frequencies, the second term on the right is negligible. The break frequency of this term is $\omega_\beta = 1/[r_\pi(C_\pi + C_\mu)]$. Thus,

$$Z_{in}\Big|_{\omega >> \omega_\beta} \simeq r_x \tag{8.33b}$$

A problem sometimes arises with this measurement, however. We have neglected the stray and header capacitances. These provide a shunting path to ground at high frequencies which leads to an erroneous estimate of $r_x$. Fortunately, an exact value for $r_x$ is often not of too great importance and a rough estimate is sufficient.

It is proper now to ask: Why not determine $r_x$ from measurements and calculations of input resistance at low frequencies? This value is approximately

$$R_{in}\bigg|_{\omega<<\omega_\beta} = r_i = r_x + r_\pi \qquad (8.34)$$

Since we have a value of $r_\pi$, it can be subtracted from a measured value of $r_i$ to obtain $r_x$. The trouble with this approach is that two numbers of about the same magnitude must be subtracted. Thus, the chance for error is great. Consequently, the direct measurement above is preferable.

We now summarize in Table 8.1 the measurements and calculations to establish the element values of the circuit model of Fig. 8.9.

**TABLE 8.1**

| | |
|---|---|
| $g_m$ | Calculated from $I_C/V_T$, $V_T = kT/q = 0.026$ V at $T = 300°$K |
| $\beta_0$ | Measured, i.e., obtained, from short-circuit current-gain measurements |
| $r_\pi$ | Calculated from $\beta_0/g_m$ |
| $C_\mu$ | Measured with capacitance bridge $C_{ob}$ |
| $C_\pi$ | Obtained from short-circuit current-gain measurements $g_m/\omega_t - C_\mu$ |
| $r_o$ | Estimated from the reciprocal of the slope of $I_C V_{CE}$ characteristics |
| $r_\mu$ | Calculated from $\beta_0 r_o$ |

## 8.7   example of circuit-model characterization

To illustrate the determination of the element values for the circuit model of the transistor, we start with selected data obtained from a manufacturer's data sheet for a typical silicon planar transistor, the 2N708. In Table 8.2,

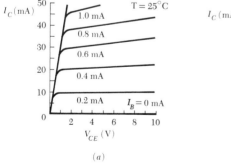

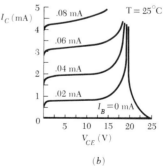

**FIGURE 8.16**  $I_C V_{CE}$ *characteristics for* 2N708. (a) *Large values of* $I_C$; (b) *small values of* $I_C$. (*From Fairchild Semiconductor data sheets.*)

the maximum values or the minimum values are given for several transistor parameters. In Fig. 8.16a and b, two $I_E V_{CE}$ characteristics of the c-e connection are given, one for large values of $I_C$ and low values of $V_{CE}$, and the other for smaller values of $I_C$ and large values of $V_{CE}$. In Fig. 8.17a and b, graphs of $\beta_0$ and $f_t$ are given versus $I_C$ with either temperature or $V_{CE}$ as a parameter.

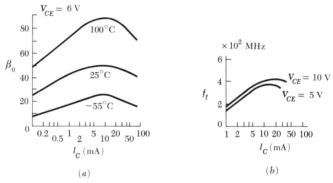

(a)                          (b)

**FIGURE 8.17** *Plots of $\beta_0$ and $f_t$ for the 2N708. (a) $\beta_0$ versus $I_C$ with T as a parameter; (b) $f_t$ versus $I_C$ for two values of $V_{CE}$. (From Fairchild Semiconductor data sheets.)*

Let us assume that the desired operating point is $I_C = 5$ mA, $V_{CE} = 6$ V. From the values of Table 8.2 and from Figs. 8.16 and 8.17, we can now obtain the necessary information. Keeping Table 8.1 in mind, we first calculate $g_m$ assuming a temperature of $25°C = 298°K$

$$V_T \simeq 0.026 \text{ volt} \qquad (8.35a)$$

$$g_m = \frac{5 \cdot 10^{-3}}{0.026} = 0.19 \text{ mho} \qquad (8.35b)$$

From Fig. 8.17a, we then obtain $\beta_0$:

$$\beta_0 \simeq 50 \qquad (8.36a)$$

From the last two values

$$r_\pi = \frac{\beta_0}{g_m} = 260 \ \Omega \qquad (8.36b)$$

From Table 8.2, the maximum value of $C_\mu = C_{ob}$ is 6 pF at a reverse bias of 10 volts. Since we desire an operating point of 6 V, we need to adjust this value. We do not have information on the change of $C_{ob}$ with

**TABLE 8.2**   *Characteristics of the 2N708 Transistor*

MAXIMUM POWER DISSIPATION

Total dissipation, case temperature 25°C .............. 1.2  W
Total dissipation, case temperature 100°C ............ 0.68 W
Total dissipation, ambient temperature 25°C.......... 0.36 W

MAXIMUM VOLTAGES

$V_{CB}$, collector-to-base voltage ........................ 40 V
$V_{CE}$ $(R_{BE} \leqslant 10\ \Omega)$................................... 20 V
$V_{CE}$, collector-to-emitter voltage ..................... 15 V
$V_{EB}$, emitter-to-base voltage ......................... 5 V

ELECTRICAL CHARACTERISTICS (25°C UNLESS OTHERWISE NOTED)

| Symbol | Characteristics | Min. | Max. | Test Conditions |
|---|---|---|---|---|
| $\beta_0$ | Short-circuit current gain | 30 | 120 | $I_C = 10$ mA, $V_{CE} = 1.0$ V |
| $\beta_0(-55°C)$ | Short-circuit current gain | 15 | | $I_C = 10$ mA, $V_{CE} = 1.0$ V |
| $\beta_0$ | Short-circuit current gain | 15 | | $I_C = 0.5$ mA, $V_{CE} = 1.0$ V |
| $V_{BE,\text{sat}}$ | Base saturation voltage, V | 0.72 | 0.80 | $I_C = 10$ mA, $I_B = 1.0$ mA |
| $V_{CE,\text{sat}}$ | Collector saturation voltage, V | | 0.40 | $I_C = 10$ mA, $I_B = 1.0$ mA |
| $V_{BE,\text{sat}}$ | Base saturation voltage (−55°C), V | | 0.90 | $I_C = 7.0$ mA, $I_B = 0.7$ mA |
| $V_{CE,\text{sat}}$ | Collector saturation voltage (−55°C to +125°C), V | | 0.40 | $I_C = 10\ I_B$ |
| $|\beta|$ | High-frequency short-circuit current gain, $f = 100$ MHz | 3 | | $I_C = 10$ mA, $V_{CE} = 10$ V |
| $C_{ob}$ | c-b output capacitance, pF | | 6 | $I_E = 0$, $V_{CB} = 10$ V |
| $r_x$ | Base resistance, $f = 300$ MHz, $\Omega$ | | 50 | $I_C = 10$ mA, $V_{CE} = 10$ V |
| $I_{CO}$ | Collector cutoff current, nA | | 25 | $I_E = 0$, $V_{CB} = 20$ V |
| $I_{CO}(150°C)$ | Collector cutoff current, $\mu$A | | 15 | $I_E = 0$, $V_{CB} = 20$ V |
| $V_{CB,\text{max}}$ | Collector-to-base breakdown voltage, V | 40 | | $I_C = 1.0\ \mu$A, $I_E = 0$ |
| $V_{CE,\text{sust}}$ | Collector-to-emitter sustaining voltage, V | 15 | | $I_C = 30$ mA, $R_{BE} \leqslant 10\ \Omega$ (pulsed) |
| $V_{EB,\text{max}}$ | Emitter-to-base breakdown voltage, V | 5 | | $I_C = 0$, $I_E = 10\ \mu$A |
| $I_{EO}$ | Emitter cutoff current, $\mu$A | | 0.1 | $I_C = 0$, $V_{EB} = 4.0$ V |
| $t_s$ | Saturation time, ns | | 25 | $I_C = I_{B1} = -I_{B2} = 10$ mA |
| $T_{\text{on}}$ | Turn-on time, ns | | 40 | $I_C = 10$ mA, $I_{B1} = 3.0$ mA, $V_{BE} = -2$ V |
| $T_{\text{off}}$ | Turn-off time, ns | | 75 | $I_C = 10$ mA, $I_B = 3.0$ mA $I_{B2} = -1.0$ mA |

SOURCE: Fairchild Semiconductor Division, Fairchild Camera and Instrument Corporation.

$V_{CB}$. Therefore, as a first guess, we assume the previous square-law relation (6.7a). This leads to

$$C_{\mu} \simeq 6 \text{ pF} \sqrt{\frac{10}{6}} = 7.75 \text{ pF} \tag{8.37}$$

This is still a maximum estimate. A typical value might then be 7 pF.

From Fig. 8.17b, we obtain $f_t = 320$ MHz. Notice that the change in $f_t$ from $V_{CE} = 5$ V to 6 V should be small. Using (8.31), we obtain

$$C_{\pi} = \frac{0.19}{(2\pi)(3.2 \cdot 10^8)} - 7 \cdot 10^{-12} \text{ farad} = 87 \text{ pF} \tag{8.38}$$

We do not have a quoted estimate of $r_o$. Further, we do not have a parameter curve of the $I_C V_{CE}$ characteristics of Fig. 8.16 at precisely our operating point. However, we note from (8.10) that $r_o$ is inversely proportional to $I_C$. From Fig. 8.16a at $I_C = 20$ mA and $V_{CE} = 6$ V, we measure a slope of

$$\frac{2}{r_o}\bigg|_{20 \text{ mA}} = 0.25 \cdot 10^{-3} \text{ mho} \tag{8.39a}$$

At 5 mA, the slope should then be 5/20 of this value. Therefore, our estimate of $r_o$ is

$$r_o = \frac{2 \cdot 10^3}{0.25} \frac{20}{5} = 32 \text{ k}\Omega \tag{8.39b}$$

The estimate of $r_{\mu}$ is then

$$r_{\mu} = (50)(32) \text{ k}\Omega = 1.6 \text{ M}\Omega \tag{8.39c}$$

Finally, from Table 8.2, the maximum value of $r_x$ is

$$r_x = r_b' = 50 \ \Omega \tag{8.40}$$

The element values of our model are shown in Fig. 8.18.

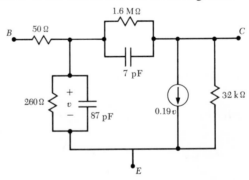

**FIGURE 8.18**  *Small-signal circuit model of 2N708 for $I_C = 5$ mA, $V_{CE} = 6$ V.*

## 8.8 the $h_{ij}$ parameters

Over the years, a particular notation scheme from circuit theory has come into use for transistors. This is the *hybrid* or *h parameter* description. For any connection of the transistor, we can in general relate the (small-signal) variations of input and output currents and voltages about an operating point by writing linear relations in which we assume sinusoidal quantities and use a phasor notation

$$V_1 = h_{11}I_1 + h_{12}V_2 \tag{8.41a}$$

$$I_2 = h_{21}I_1 + h_{22}V_2 \tag{8.41b}$$

where $I_1$ is the input current and $V_1$ is the input voltage of the transistor considered as a 2-port as shown in Fig. 8.19. The output voltage and current

**FIGURE 8.19**  *2-port circuit.*

are also defined in this figure. These linear equations relate the input-voltage variation to the input-current and output-voltage variations, etc. The individual parameters or coefficients can be identified as follows: if the output is shorted for ac variations, say with a large capacitor, $V_2$ is zero. From (8.41a), it is clear that $h_{11}$ is the ratio of input voltage to input current under this output short-circuit condition:

$$h_{11} = \left. \frac{V_1}{I_1} \right|_{V_2 = 0} \tag{8.42a}$$

Also, $h_{21}$ is the ratio of output current flowing through the ac short circuit and the input current:

$$h_{21} = \left. \frac{I_2}{I_1} \right|_{V_2 = 0} \tag{8.42b}$$

Similarly, $h_{22}$ is the ratio of the output current to the output voltage if the input is open circuited, $I_1 = 0$,

$$h_{22} = \left. \frac{I_2}{V_2} \right|_{I_1 = 0} \tag{8.42c}$$

Finally,
$$h_{12} = \left. \frac{V_1}{V_2} \right|_{I_1 = 0} \tag{8.42d}$$

The parameter $h_{11}$ is a special input impedance, i.e., the input impedance under a special measurement condition; $h_{22}$ is an output admittance; $h_{21}$

is a forward-transfer current ratio; and $h_{12}$ is a reverse-transfer voltage ratio.

We can represent (8.41) by the circuit shown in Fig. 8.20. The first equation of (8.41) can be identified as Kirchhoff's voltage law around the input loop of the circuit. The second equation is identified as Kirchhoff's current law for the top node of the output port. Notice that we have a circuit which

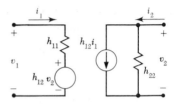

**FIGURE 8.20** *Equivalent circuit using $h_{ij}$ parameters.*

is equivalent to a set of equations in terms of measurable parameters.

In representing the transistor in Fig. 8.20 we must designate in which configuration it is connected. That is, is the emitter the common node for the input and output ports, or is it the base node or the collector node? If we introduce a new subscript for the common node, we have a cumbersome three-subscript notation scheme. By convention, this is avoided by the following notation:

$$h_{11} = h_i \qquad h_{21} = h_f \qquad h_{12} = h_r \qquad h_{22} = h_o \qquad (8.43a)$$

where the subscript $i$ indicates input; $f$, forward; $r$, reverse; and $o$, output. Therefore, the common-emitter $h$ parameters are written

$$h_{ie} \qquad h_{fe} \qquad h_{re} \qquad h_{oe} \qquad (8.43b)$$

Similarly, the common-base parameters are designated

$$h_{ib} \qquad h_{fb} \qquad h_{rb} \qquad h_{ob} \qquad (8.44)$$

For the common-emitter connection, note that $h_{fe}$ is the ratio of the output current and the input current for a short-circuit load. Therefore

$$h_{fe} = \beta \qquad (8.45)$$

Some manufacturers use uppercase subscripts to denote low-frequency measurements and lowercase subscripts to denote high-frequency measurements. In this scheme, $h_{FE} = \beta_0$, $h_{fe} = \beta|_{\omega \geqslant \omega_\beta}$. This scheme is not generally accepted, however. In this book, we use lowercase subscripts and indicate the frequency of interest as a functional notation, for example, $h_{fe}(0) = \beta_0$.

## 8.9 a circuit model for c-b

The transistor model developed in the last few sections for the c-e connection can also be used if another node is taken as the common node of both input and output ports. For example, for the c-b connection, the circuit model appears as in Fig. 8.21a. In many cases, the much simpler model of Fig. 8.21c can be used. To verify this, we first note that $r_x$ and $r_o$ are the common elements between the output and the input. It can be shown that

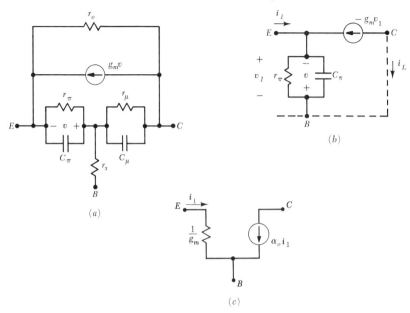

FIGURE 8.21 *Development of small-signal circuit model for c-b connection.* (a) *Reorientation of circuit model for emitter input;* (b) *simplified circuit model;* (c) *elementary circuit model.*

the "coupling" due to both is small if the load resistance is not too large, say less than $r_o$. If $r_x$ and $r_o$ are neglected, the combination of $r_\mu$ and $C_\mu$ appears in shunt with the load and can usually be neglected. The much reduced circuit model is shown in Fig. 8.21b. To obtain the circuit of Fig. 8.21c, we write the circuit equations using Kirchhoff's current law. At the E and C nodes, where the (sinusoidal) input current is denoted $I_1$ and the load current is denoted $I_L$,

$$I_1 = \left(\frac{1}{r_\pi} + j\omega C_\pi\right) V_1 + g_m V_1 \qquad (8.46a)$$

$$I_L = g_m V_1 \qquad (8.46b)$$

Rearranging (8.46), we obtain

$$\frac{I_1}{V_1} = \left(1 + \frac{1}{\beta_0}\right) g_m + j\omega C_\pi \simeq \frac{\beta_0 g_m}{\beta_0 + 1} \simeq g_m \qquad (8.47a)$$

$$I_L = \frac{g_m I_1}{(1 + 1/\beta_0) g_m + j\omega C_\pi} \simeq \frac{\beta_0}{\beta_0 + 1} I_1 = \alpha_0 I_1 \qquad (8.47b)$$

For a frequency range

$$\omega << \frac{(1 + 1/\beta_0)g_m}{C_\pi} \simeq \omega_t$$

where $\omega_t$ is defined in (8.30), the $j\omega C_\pi$ terms are neglected in the last two terms of (8.47a) and (8.47b). The first equation, then, is the input conductance of the model shown in Fig. 8.21c and is approximately equal to $g_m$. The second equation, in its reduced form, can be considered the description of a dependent current source, as shown. Note that the parameter $\alpha_0$ appears, as can be expected, since the ratio of output current to input current in the c-b connection is $\alpha$. If this circuit model is compared with that of Fig. 8.2, it is clear that we have arrived at a much simplified version of Fig. 8.2.

It is sometimes useful to include the frequency dependence of the dependent current generator of Fig. 8.21c. From (8.47b), we define

$$\alpha = \left. \frac{I_L}{I_1} \right|_{\substack{\text{short-circuit} \\ \text{load, c-b}}} = \frac{\alpha_0}{1 + j\omega/\omega_\alpha} \qquad (8.48a)$$

where
$$\alpha_0 = \frac{\beta_0}{\beta_0 + 1} \qquad \omega_\alpha = \frac{(1 + 1/\beta_0)g_m}{C_\pi} \qquad (8.48b)$$

The important feature of the above simplified development is the form of (8.48a). The value of the break frequency $\omega_\alpha$ as given by (8.48b) can be as small as one-third of the measured value.

### REFERENCES

P. E. Gray, D. DeWitt, A. R. Boothroyd, and J. F. Gibbons, "Physical Electronics and Circuit Models of Transistors," SEEC, vol. 2, John Wiley & Sons, Inc., New York, 1964, chaps. 7-10.

C. L. Searle, A. R. Boothroyd, E. J. Angelo, Jr., P. E. Gray, and D. O. Pederson, "Elementary Circuit Properties of Transistors," SEEC, vol. 2, John Wiley & Sons, Inc., New York, 1964, chaps. 1-4.

### PROBLEMS

**8.1** For very low frequency variations, the charge-storage effects in the transistor can be neglected. For this condition, (a) use the two-diode model of Fig. 8.1a to develop a small-signal model of a transistor in the c-e connection in the normal active region, (b) convert the dependent current source to be a function of the input current, and (c) convert the dependent current source to be a function of the input voltage.

**8.2** For the transistor circuit model shown, explain what process is modeled by $r_\pi$. In what parameter or element of the circuit model of Fig. 8.2 is the same process modeled?

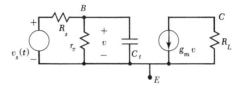

**Problem 8.2**

**8.3** Calculate the value of excess stored charge of minority carriers in the base of an *npn* transistor in the normal active mode of operation if the resistivity of the base region is 1 $\Omega$-cm, the base width is 4 $\mu$, the emitter dimensions are 25 by 100 $\mu$, and $V_{BE} = 10V_T$. What is the value of the base-charging capacitor $C_B$? ($1\mu = 10^{-6}$ m.)

**8.4** The dimensions of an *npn* transistor are shown in the cross-sectional view. The length of the emitter (into the paper) is 100 $\mu$. All three regions are assumed to be uniformly doped, and the junctions are abrupt. The resistivity of the collector region is 1 $\Omega$-cm, that of the base region is 300 $\Omega$-cm, and that of the emitter region 0.001 $\Omega$-cm. For a collector current of 5 mA and a collector-emitter voltage of 5 V, establish the element values of the circuit model for $g_m$, $C_B$, $C_{je}$, $C_{jc}$, and $C_\pi$. Note that the area of the collector junction is not the same as that for the emitter junction.

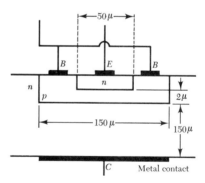

**Problem 8.4**

**8.5** What is the average transit time of minority carriers in the base region of the transistor of Prob. 8.4? What is an estimate of the upper frequency limit of the transistor?

**8.6** For the transistor of Prob. 8.4, estimate the values of $r_c'$ and $r_e'$. What is your estimate of $r_b'$, where it should be noted that two base contacts are used?

**8.7** One component of the dc base current of a transistor supplies the majority carriers to supply recombination. If the time average of excess minority carriers "stored" in the base (in transit in the base) is $Q_B$ and the lifetime of minority carriers in the base is $\tau_b$, the dc or time-average base current is

$$I'_B = \frac{Q_B}{\tau_b}$$

The time-average collected component of the collector current is $Q_B$ divided by the average transit time $\tau_t$ for minority carriers to cross the base region:

$$I'_C = \frac{Q_B}{\tau_t}$$

The ratio of this component of collector current to this component of base current is the current gain of the base region of the transistor:

$$\beta'_0 = \frac{I'_C}{I'_B} = \frac{\tau_b}{\tau_t}$$

If the $\tau_b$ for the transistor of Prob. 8.4 is 50 ns, what is the value of $\beta'_0$? For the operating point of 5 mA and 5 V, what is the value of the resistance $r_\pi$?

**8.8**   Which elements in the circuit model shown represent the process of base-width modulation?

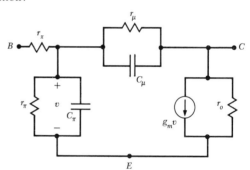

**Problem 8.8**

**8.9**   If the change of base width with collector-base junction voltage in the transistor of Prob. 8.4 is 0.05 $\mu$/V, what is the value of the output resistance for a short-circuit input? What is the value of the base-width-modulation contribution to $C_\mu$?

**8.10**   When a load resistance $R_L$ is connected to the transistor output, under what condition can the resistance $r_0$ in the c-e circuit model be omitted?

**8.11**   For very low frequencies, determine the resistance looking into the output terminals (a) with the input a short circuit and (b) with an open-circuit input. Use the circuit model of Fig. 8.10a, assuming $r_x = 0$. (c) Show that the output resistance for an input short circuit with $r_x > 0$ is approximately equal to

$$\frac{r_x + r_\pi}{2r_x + r_\pi} r_0$$

**8.12**   Given the values below, determine the loading effects of $r_\mu$ on the input of a transistor for $R_L = 0$, $10\ \Omega$, $100\ \Omega$, $1\ \mathrm{k}\Omega$, and $10\ \mathrm{k}\Omega$ [see (8.20$d$) and Fig. 8.11$b$].

$$g_m = {}^1\!/_5\ \mathrm{mho} \qquad \beta_0 = 100 \qquad r_o = 20\ \mathrm{k}\Omega$$

**8.13**   From Table 8.2 and Figs. 8.16 and 8.17, establish a circuit model for the transistor (a) for $I_C = 1$ mA and $V_{CE} = 10$ V and (b) for $I_C = 6$ mA and $V_{CE} = 10$ V.

**8.14**   Determine the circuit models for Prob. 8.13 if it is assumed that the values of $\beta_0$ and $f_t$ do not change with operating point and compare with the results of Prob. 8.13.

**8.15**   In figure $a$, an *npn* transistor is connected in the common-emitter configuration and is biased to obtain $I_C = 5$ mA and $V_{CE} = 5$ V. A sinusoidal current source $I_s$ and a resistive load are ac coupled with capacitors; the values of the coupling capacitors are sufficiently large to be considered short circuits for all frequencies of interest. Similarly, the appropriate values of $R_B$ and $R_C$ are sufficiently large that their shunting effect on the signal can be neglected. The value of $R_L$ is $10\ \Omega$. Determine the element values of the circuit model of the transistor shown in figure $b$ if

(a) The magnitude of the current gain $|I_L/I_s|$ is equal to 1 at an input frequency of 200 MHz.

(b) The peak magnitude of the input voltage at 200 MHz is 1.4 mV for a magnitude of the sinusoidal input current of 20 $\mu$A.

(c) The value of the load current is 1.2 mA for a source current of 20 $\mu$A at low frequencies.

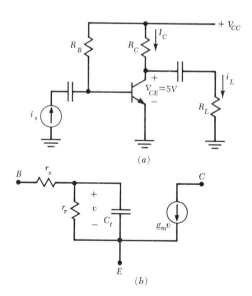

(a)

(b)

**Problem 8.15**

**8.16** Over a narrow band of frequencies, the circuit model of a transistor in the common-emitter configuration can be taken as the simple $R_1$, $C_1$, $g_m v$ combination shown. In the figure, a load resistance $R_L$ and a signal source with sinusoidal voltage $v_s(t)$ and internal resistance $R_s$ are also shown.

(a) Assume that it is desired to produce voltage $V_L \sin \omega t$ across the load. Use circuit equations to find the required signal-source voltage $v_s(t)$.

(b) For $g_m = 0.04$ mhos and $R_1 = 1.250$ kΩ, find the time-average ac power in the load resistance, as well as that dissipated in the input resistance of the transistor. Assume $R_L = 300$ Ω.

(c) Determine the ratio of load to input power both for very low frequencies and for a frequency $5 \cdot 10^5$ Hz.

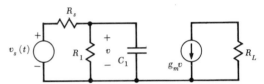

**Problem 8.16**

**8.17** The input portion of the circuit model of the transistor shown in Prob. 8.15 is repeated below in figure $a$.

(a) Find the values of the equivalent $R_1 C_1$ circuit in figure $b$ at a frequency $\omega$. One way to obtain the equivalent is to determine the admittance of the circuit of figure $a$:

$$Y = \cfrac{1}{r_x + \cfrac{1}{1/r_\pi + j\omega C_t}}$$

This is then manipulated to obtain

$$Y = G + jB = \frac{1}{R_1} + j\omega C_1$$

where the conductance $G$ is identified as $1/R_1$ and the susceptance $B$ is set equal to $\omega C_1$.

(b) If $r_x = 50$ Ω, $r_\pi = 250$ Ω, and $C_t = 100$ pF, what are the values of $R_1$ and $C_1$ if $f = 1$ MHz.

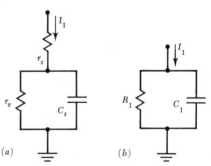

**Problem 8.17**    $(a)$                     $(b)$

**8.18** The circuit model for a transistor with a resistive load is shown in Prob. 8.2, the $I_C V_{CE}$ characteristics are shown in figure $a$, and measurements of the current gain $|\beta|$ for the transistor are shown graphically in figure $b$ for a particular operating point.

(*a*) Under what signal condition does this model apply?

(*b*) On the $I_C V_{CE}$ characteristics for the transistor, shade the portion over which the model applies.

(*c*) From the graph of the short-circuit current gain $|\beta|$, determine the numerical values of $\beta_0, f_t,$ and $f_\beta$ for the given operating point.

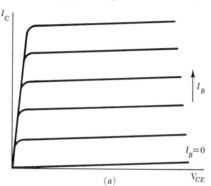

(*a*)

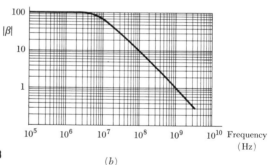

**Problem 8.18**

(*b*)

**8.19** In the circuit shown, the series combination of the base resistance $r_x$ and the source resistance $R_s$ are combined as the resistor for $R_1 = R_s + r_x$. $C_\mu$ is assumed to be zero.

(*a*) If $V_i$ is a sinusoidal source of frequency $\omega$, find the magnitude function $|V_o/V_i|$ as a function of frequency.

(*b*) Find the frequency $\omega_u$ at which

$$\left|\frac{V_o}{V_i}\right|_{\omega = \omega_u} = 0.707 \left|\frac{V_o}{V_i}\right|_{\omega = 0}$$

(*c*) Find the frequency of $\omega_{0\,dB}$ at which

$$\left|\frac{V_o}{V_i}\right|_{\omega = \omega_{0\,dB}} = 1$$

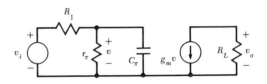

**Problem 8.19**

**8.20** For a Ge transistor, $f_t$ at a given operating point in the normal active mode is 400 MHz. The value of $C_{ob}$ for this transistor is 3 pF. Plot the value of $C_t$ as $R_L$ is increased from 0 to 1 kΩ.

**8.21** Determine the $h_{ij}$ parameters for the circuits below, and develop equivalent circuits in the configuration of Fig. 8.20.

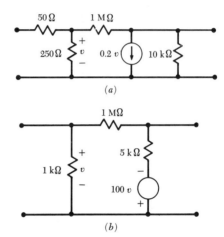

**Problem 8.21**

**8.22** Develop an expression for the output resistance of the c-b circuit model of Fig. 8.21a at very low frequencies, with a short-circuit and an open-circuit input. Compare these expressions with the results of Prob. 8.11.

**8.23** For the circuit model of Fig. 8.9 and for a current source input, determine the current in a short-circuit load. Compare the magnitude of the current component from $C_\mu$ with that from $g_m$. At what input frequency are the two components equal in magnitude?

**8.24** Note that $\omega_\tau \, (= 2\pi f_\tau)$ from (8.22d) is equal to $g_m/C_B$. Compare $f_\tau$ and $f_t$ for the circuit model of Fig. 8.18 if $C_{je} = C_\mu$.

# chapter 9

# SIMPLE TRANSISTOR APPLICATIONS

## 9.1 uses of transistors

The amplification property of the junction transistor leads to the use of this element as the basic active device in a large variety of system building blocks, i.e., electronic circuit functions. For example, transistors are widely used in amplifiers, oscillators, modulators, switches, and logic circuits. For the amplifier function, we usually desire very linear performance from the transistor. For other functions, however, we may need both the amplification property and the nonlinear characteristics provided by the transistor. To illustrate these points, we consider in this chapter several elementary applications of the transistor: (1) transistor amplifiers, (2) a simple transistor switch, and (3) several transistor logic circuits.

In investigating these applications, the material from the last chapter on small-signal models is used to establish the gain performance of an amplifier over its useful frequency spectrum. For the simple switch and the logic circuits, where large signals are encountered, we depend primarily on the graphical and diode models which are developed in Chaps. 7 and 8, e.g., the models of Figs. 7.18 and 8.1.

## 9.2 a simple transistor amplifier

An amplifier consisting of a single transistor in the c-e connection is shown in Fig. 9.1a. In this section, we analyze the performance of this circuit using a typical silicon planar transistor, the 2N708, data for which are given in Sec. 8.7. For the complete amplifier we need, in addition to the transistor, the bias voltage supplies $V_{BB}$ and $V_{CC}$, the associated bias resistors $R_B$ and $R_C$, and the coupling elements. The signal source is represented by the ideal voltage source $v_s$ and a

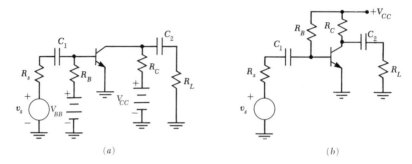

(a)                                                (b)

**FIGURE 9.1**    *A one-transistor amplifier* (a) *with two bias voltage sources and* (b) *with one supply voltage.*

series resistance $R_s$. The load is assumed to be a pure resistance $R_L$. Usually, in order to simplify the schematic diagram of an amplifier, we do not show the dc voltage supplies explicitly. Instead, the voltage-supply node which is not connected to the common node of the circuit ("ground") is shown with a plus- or minus-sign designation implying the battery or other dc source. This situation is shown in Fig. 9.1$b$ where the single supply voltage $V_{CC}$ is used instead of two separate supply sources. It is understood that a constant voltage source of value $+V_{CC}$ is connected from this node to ground. The use of a single bias-supply voltage is usually desired for convenience.

**SIMPLE BIASING**    In order to achieve the inherent amplification of the transistor in the circuit shown in Fig. 9.1, we need to choose first suitable values for $R_B$ and $R_C$ (that is, to design the bias circuit) in order to achieve a desired operating point for the transistor. We use an example to illustrate the design procedure for the bias circuit of Fig. 9.1$b$.

For the transistor, we first choose an operating point which provides adequate gain performance for the application. The $I_C V_{CE}$ characteristics for the 2N708 and a plot of $\beta_0$ versus collector current are shown in Figs. 8.16 and 8.17$a$. We can see immediately from Fig. 8.16$a$ that $V_{CE}$ should be less than 20 V since voltage breakdown occurs near this value. From Fig. 8.17$a$ it is seen that $\beta_0$ is not a constant and has a maximum value at $I_C \simeq 10$ mA. However, the curve has a broad peak. Therefore, we can initially assume that the desired output signal will not exceed a volt or so and we can choose an operating point with relatively low values of $I_C$ and $V_{CE}$. This choice minimizes the power consumption in the transistor. The following choice of operating point is made:

$$I_C = 5 \text{ mA} \qquad V_{CE} = 5 \text{ volts} \qquad (9.1)$$

The value of $\beta_0 \simeq 50$ from Fig. 8.17a for $V_{CE} = 6$ V can also be used here. For this unit, we see from Table 8.2 that $I_{CO} (= I_{CBO})$ is typically of the order of $10^{-8}$ A (10 nA). This is certainly negligible with respect to $I_C$. Therefore, the necessary dc base current to achieve $I_C$ is

$$I_B \simeq \frac{1}{\beta_0} I_C = 0.1 \text{ mA} \qquad (9.2)$$

We now determine $R_B$ and $R_C$ using Kirchhoff's voltage law at the input and output of the transistor. (Remember that $C_1$ and $C_2$ act as open circuits for very low frequencies; that is, $C_1$ and $C_2$ "block" any dc currents flowing to or from $R_s$ and $R_L$.)

$$R_B = \frac{V_{CC} - V_{BE}}{I_B} \qquad (9.3)$$

$$R_C = \frac{V_{CC} - V_{CE}}{I_C} \qquad (9.4)$$

To obtain values for $R_B$ and $R_C$, a choice of $V_{CC}$ must be made. Usually, we choose a convenient value which must be larger than the desired value of $V_{CE}$. A large value of $V_{CC}$ leads to a large value of $R_C$ and, consequently, only a small loss of output signal power in this resistor (which is in parallel with the load $R_L$ for ac signals). Of course, we cannot make $V_{CC}$ too large or the necessary power drain from the supply ($I_C V_{CC}$) will become excessive. Commonly, $V_{CC}$ is chosen from one to several times greater than $V_{CE}$. Here we choose $V_{CC} = 15$ V. From (9.4), we then obtain $R_C = 2$ k$\Omega$.

To obtain $R_B$, we need a value for $V_{BE}$. We could use a load-line construction on an $I_B V_{BE}$ characteristic such as that of Fig. 7.22a. However, since $V_{BE}$ will be of the order of 0.7 V for a Si transistor in the normal, active operating mode (0.3 V for a Ge transistor) and because $V_{CC}$ is of the order of several volts, an exact value of $V_{BE}$ is not critical. Using $V_{BE} = 0.7$ V, we obtain $R_B = 147$ k$\Omega$. (If $V_{BE}$ is completely neglected, we obtain $R_B = 150$ k$\Omega$.)

**COUPLING ELEMENTS**  We next turn to the choice of the coupling capacitors $C_1$ and $C_2$. These capacitors are used to introduce the source and the load to the transistor without disturbing the dc operating point of the transistor; the source and the load are primarily important in respect to the "variational response" of the complete amplifier about the operating point. That is, we are now primarily interested in the small-signal response. For such a variational response, we consider the dc voltage sources to be ac short circuits. Thus, the resistors $R_B$ and $R_C$ can be returned to ac ground. In addition, we introduce a small-signal circuit model for the transistor. To make the proper choice of $C_1$ and $C_2$, the frequency region of interest is the very low frequency range near dc. For the transistor, we use the simple circuit model of Fig. 8.10$b$ and obtain the amplifier circuit of Fig. 9.2$a$.

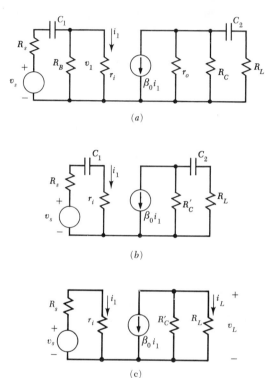

**FIGURE 9.2** *Amplifier small-signal circuit model.* (a) *Complete circuit model for very low frequency variations about the bias point;* (b) *simplified circuit for very low frequencies;* (c) *circuit model for midfrequency calculations.*

From the developments of Sec. 8.7 for the 2N708 transistor, $r_x$ is typically 50 $\Omega$. An appropriate value for $r_o$ at the chosen operating point is 32 k$\Omega$. (Since $r_\mu = \beta_0 r_o = 1.6$ M$\Omega$, the omission of $r_\mu$ as in the circuit model of Fig. 9.2$a$ appears well justified.)

In the model, $r_i$ is $r_x + r_\pi$, where $r_\pi = \beta_0 / g_m$. For $I_C = 5$ mA and for $T = 300°$K,

$$g_m = \frac{I_C}{V_T} = \frac{5 \cdot 10^{-3}}{0.026} = 0.19 \text{ mho} \tag{9.5}$$

With a value of $\beta_0 = 50$, $r_\pi$ is 260 $\Omega$, and $r_i$ ($= r_x + r_\pi$) is 310 $\Omega$. Parallel combinations of $R_B$ and $r_i$ and of $R_C$ and $r_o$ can now be made to obtain the simpler circuit of Fig. 9.2$b$. The value of $R_B = 150$ k$\Omega$ is completely negligible in relation to $r_i$. Therefore, we retain only $r_i$. The element $R_C'$ is made up of $r_o$ and $R_C$ in parallel (denoted $r_o \parallel R_C$) and equals 1.9 k$\Omega$.

In the figure, we see two simple highpass circuits such as those analyzed in Chap. 3. Each coupling circuit provides a break frequency above which transmission occurs virtually unimpeded. For the input circuit

$$\omega_i = \frac{1}{(R_s + r_i)C_1} \tag{9.6}$$

For the output circuit

$$\omega_o = \frac{1}{(R_C' + R_L)C_2} \tag{9.7}$$

For our example, let $R_s = 500$ $\Omega$ and $R_L = 300$ $\Omega$. In addition, we choose both break frequencies to occur at $f = 100$ Hz, that is, $\omega = 2\pi \cdot 10^2$ rad/s.[1] Using these values above, we obtain the necessary values of capacitors.

$$C_1 \simeq 2 \ \mu\text{F} \qquad C_2 \simeq 0.7 \ \mu\text{F}$$

For both the biasing and the coupling elements, we usually do not attempt to realize (provide) actual elements which have the exact design value. For reasons of economy, readily available values near the design value are used. Because of tolerances in the values of components and the characteristics of transistors, it is unrealistic to attempt better accuracy anyway. The electronic industry has standardized on a set of values, with a color code system of designating the element values, which are commercially available. This information is presented in Appendix E. For the circuit at hand, we choose the following values:

$$R_B = 150 \text{ k}\Omega \qquad R_C = 2 \text{ k}\Omega$$
$$C_1 = 2 \ \mu\text{F} \qquad C_2 = 1 \ \mu\text{F}$$

## 9.3 midfrequency gain calculations

For frequencies above the low-frequency cutoff provided by the coupling capacitors of Fig. 9.2$b$, we neglect these elements (consider them short

---

[1]The actual $-3$ dB frequency, which we denote $f_l = \omega_l/2\pi$, for transmission through the complete circuit is higher than 100 Hz. Each highpass circuit starts the "rolling off" toward zero above its break frequency. At the break frequency each circuit provides a response which is down 3 dB from the value at high frequencies. Therefore, at 100 Hz the overall response is down $-6$ dB counting the two $RC$ circuits. If one defines an overall $-3$ dB frequency $\omega_l$ as one for which response of the combination is down by 3 dB from the maximum, it is higher than 100 Hz and can in fact be calculated as 155 Hz.

circuits) and use a midfrequency circuit model for the transistor amplifier as shown in Fig. 9.2c. The term "midfrequency" is used since we neglect both the charge-storage effects of the coupling capacitors at very low frequencies and the charge-storage effects in the transistor ($C_\pi$ and $C_\mu$) at high frequencies. We continue to use $R_s = 500\ \Omega$ and $R_L = 300\ \Omega$, as well as the other values of the preceding section.

**MIDFREQUENCY GAIN DEFINITIONS**    It is now a simple matter to calculate the voltage and current gains of the amplifier. The midfrequency voltage gain of the circuit of Fig. 9.1 (or Fig. 9.2c) can be defined as the ratio of the phasor output voltage $V_L$ to the "available open-circuit" source voltage $V_s$, also expressed as a phasor, where an input sinusoidal signal is assumed. In the midfrequency region all phasors are real quantities since the charge-storage effects are negligible. From Fig. 9.2c,

$$a_V = \frac{V_L}{V_s} = -\beta_0 \frac{R_L'}{R_s + r_i} \tag{9.8}$$

where $R_L' = R_L \| R_C \| r_o$. (We again use the symbol $\|$ to denote resistances in parallel.) In the case of the values of our example, $R_L' = 259\ \Omega$ and $a_V = -16.0$.

The midfrequency current gain of the amplifier can be defined as $I_L/I_i$, where $I_i$ is the (phasor) signal input current to the transistor.

$$I_i = \frac{V_s}{R_s + r_i} = \frac{V_i}{r_i} \tag{9.9a}$$

The load, or output, current is the current through $R_L$ as shown in Fig. 9.2c.

$$I_L = \frac{V_L}{R_L} \tag{9.9b}$$

For the current-gain notation, we use $a_I$

$$a_I = \frac{I_L}{I_i} = \frac{V_L/R_L}{V_s/(R_s + r_i)} = \frac{R_s + r_i}{R_L} a_V \tag{9.9c}$$

For the values above

$$a_I = -43.2 \tag{9.9d}$$

It is to be noted that if $R_L \ll R_C \| r_o$ then $-a_I$ is equal to $\beta_0$, the short-circuit current gain of the transistor in the c-e connection.

The power gain of the amplifier can also be simply defined. For the overall circuit, the ratio of the power developed in $R_L$ to the power flowing out from $V_s$ is as below. In this calculation, we take each power as the instantaneous power. In Sec. 9.7, power calculations are considered in greater detail.

$$G_p = \frac{v_L i_L}{v_s i_i} = a_V a_I = (16.0)(43.2) = 690 \qquad (9.10a)$$

This value of power gain is very much lower than the maximum available midfrequency power gain of the transistor. From the work in the earlier chapters, this maximum value is approximately as follows:

$$G_{p,\max} \simeq \frac{\beta_0^2}{4} \frac{r_o}{r_i} = \frac{50^2}{4} \frac{32{,}000}{310} \simeq 64{,}600 \qquad (9.10b)$$

Clearly, the amplifier is not achieving optimum performance from the transistor. This illustrates what occurs when the values of the source and load resistances do not "match" the values of the input and output resistances of the transistor. The conditions for optimum power transfer from a source to a load are discussed shortly.

**AVAILABLE OUTPUT VOLTAGE AND CURRENT EXCURSIONS** It is interesting now to establish the largest output voltage and current excursions that can be obtained from our amplifier. For this we again use the $IV$ characteristics and plot load lines. For the amplifier in Fig. 9.1, we need two load lines on the $I_C V_{CE}$ characteristic. One is the dc load line as used previously. This load line is the locus of possible dc operating points. For ac operation, i.e., for input variations with a frequency spectrum above $\omega_l$ defined in Sec. 9.2, the actual load is $R_L$ in parallel with the collector bias resistor $R_C$. Therefore, the ac load line is a line through the dc operating point in the $I_C V_{CE}$ plane but having a slope equal to $-1/(R_L \| R_C)$. From this load line and its intersection with the edges of the active operating region of the $IV$ characteristic, we can establish the maximum output excursions.

For the 2N708 example, the dc load line is drawn through the points $V_{CE} = V_{CC} = 15$ V and $I_C = V_{CC}/R_C = 7.5$ mA, as shown in Fig. 9.3. The actual load resistance is 300 $\Omega$ and the total ac load is $300\|2{,}000 = 261$ $\Omega$. The ac load line is simply constructed by noting that from the point $I_C = 5$ mA, at the dc operating point, to $I_C = 0$, the load must develop a voltage of $(261)(5 \times 10^{-3}) = 1.3$ V. The intersection of the ac load line with the $V_{CE}$ axis must then be at $(1.3 + 5)$ V $= 6.3$ V. A line through this point and the dc operating point is the ac load line. From the load line, we see that because $I_{CO} \simeq 0$, the maximum positive voltage now across $R_L$ is 1.3 V, and the maximum negative current excursion through $R_L$ is 5 mA. These excursions are obtained as the input signal is made negative by an amount equal to $I_B$. Ideally, for a large-enough positive input signal, the collector voltage can approach zero and the collector current can be very large. Usually, however, the ac load line crosses the maximum-power-dissipation hyperbola. This hyperbola, shown dashed in Fig. 9.3, denotes the boundary where the product of $I_C$ and

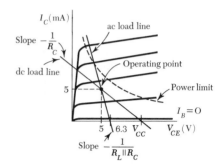

**FIGURE 9.3** $V_C I_{CE}$ *characteristic with dc and ac load lines.*

$V_{CE}$ just equals the maximum power dissipation permitted for the given transistor type.[1] Although operation to the right of the hyperbola is permissible for short-time durations, it is usually better to restrict ourselves to the region below the dashed curve. Thus, the intersection of the ac load line with this hyperbola fixes the maximum positive collector-current excursions and the maximum negative voltage excursion.

For the case at hand the positive and negative maximum excursions are not equal. In some situations, the operating point should be adjusted to provide equal excursions. As a final matter, if the input in its negative excursion exceeds a change of $|I_B|$, the transistor is turned *off*, i.e., the emitter junction is reverse biased. The output waveform is then "clipped" as shown in Fig. 9.4. Clipping can also occur for positive-going inputs, as shown in a later section. A Fourier analysis of such a waveform, as in Chap. 2, would yield higher harmonics of the signal frequency. This represents distortion and is undesirable if the amplifier is intended to be a linear amplifier.

## 9.4 gain versus frequency calculations

We now return to the small-signal situation and assume that the input signal is a sinusoid. If we inspect the gain of the single transistor amplifier as the frequency of the sinusoid is increased from a low value, the magnitudes of the voltage, current, and power gains change with frequency. The plot of voltage gain $|a_V|$ versus frequency, is shown in Fig. 9.5. A log-log (Bode) plot is used to emphasize the low-frequency, midfrequency,

---

[1] From Table 8.2, the maximum power dissipation of the 2N708 transistor in an ambient temperature of 25°C is 0.36 W. Thus, at $V_{CE} = 5$ V, the maximum-power-dissipation hyperbola passes through $I_C = 72$ mA. In Fig. 9.3, the dashed curve to represent the hyperbola is placed closer to the origin to show more clearly the point being made.

and high-frequency asymptotes. The gain magnitude drops at low frequencies with a slope of $-12$ dB per octave ($-40$ dB per decade). This loss of transmission is due to the increasing reactance of the coupling capacitors.

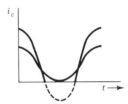

**FIGURE 9.4** *Collector waveform with and without clipping.*

The drop in the gain magnitude at the high-frequency end is due to the increasing susceptance of the capacitances $C_\mu$ and $C_\pi$, that is, due to the charge-storage effects in the transistor. Over the initial portion of the decrease, the slope falls at $-6$ dB per octave.

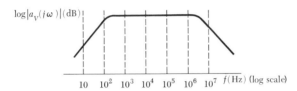

**FIGURE 9.5** *Relative magnitude of voltage gain versus frequency.*

Our previous calculations have provided values of the midfrequency gain magnitude and the value of the (combined) lower break frequency. To obtain the value of the upper break frequency, we introduce a new circuit model for the transistor. Since the load of the transistor is purely

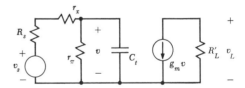

**FIGURE 9.6** *Amplifier circuit model.*

resistive, we use the simplified circuit model of Fig. 8.12. The circuit model of the complete amplifier for both midfrequency and high-frequency calculations is shown in Fig. 9.6. Note that as in Sec. 8.5, an equivalent capacitance $C_t$ is used to model the effects of $C_\mu$ across $C_\pi$. In this circuit, the equivalent load resistance $R'_L$, as used earlier, is the parallel combination of $r_o$, $R_C$, and $R_L$. From our earlier circuit calculations in Chaps. 3 and 8, we recognize that this is a lowpass circuit for which the magnitude of the voltage gain decreases with frequency, as shown in Fig. 9.7, where a log-log or Bode plot is again used. As the shunting effects of $C_t$ become increasingly important, the gain drops to zero. We expect the lowpass transmission function, as shown, with a slope of the high-frequency

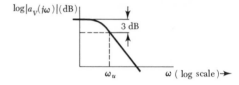

**FIGURE 9.7** *Frequency dependence of* $|a_V(j\omega)|$.

asymptote of $-6$ dB per octave since only one capacitance, $C_t$, is involved in the circuit of Fig. 9.6.

**UPPER BANDEDGE FREQUENCY** As a measure of the width of the frequency spectrum which can be transmitted and amplified adequately by the amplifier, we determine the upper bandedge, i.e., the upper break frequency of the response. This is also the "$-3$ dB frequency" of the curve as calculated. From our earlier circuit results, the gain function of the circuit of Fig. 9.6 is (Prob. 9.11)

$$a_V = \frac{V_L}{V_s} = \frac{-a_{V0}}{1 + j(\omega/\omega_u)} \tag{9.11a}$$

where

$$a_{V0} = \frac{\beta_0 R'_L}{R_s + r_x + r_\pi} \tag{9.11b}$$

$$\omega_u = \frac{1/(R_s + r_x) + 1/r_\pi}{C_t} \tag{9.11c}$$

The constant $a_{V0}$ is the gain magnitude at zero frequency for the simplified model of Fig. 9.6 but is the midfrequency gain magnitude for the actual amplifier. This expression for $a_{V0}$ is equivalent to (9.8). The $-3$ dB bandedge frequency $\omega_u$ is the frequency at which the susceptance of $C_t$ is equal to the conductance which appears across it.

For a numerical example, typical values for the 2N708 transistor are $C_\pi = 100$ pF, $C_\mu = 5$ pF, and $g_m = 0.2$ mho. From our previous values $R'_L = r_o \| R_C \| R_L \simeq R_L \| R_C = 261 \ \Omega$. From (8.21)

$$C_t = C_\pi + C_\mu(1 + g_m R'_L)$$

$$= 100 + 5(1 + 0.2 \cdot 261) \tag{9.12}$$

$$= 365 \text{ pF}$$

Notice that the contribution of $C_\mu(1 + g_m R'_L)$ is larger than that of $C_\pi$. We now introduce $r_\pi = 250 \ \Omega$, $r_x = 50 \ \Omega$, $R_s = 300 \ \Omega$. With these values in (9.11c), the upper bandedge is

$$f_u = \frac{\omega_u}{2\pi} = 2.54 \text{ MHz} \tag{9.13}$$

This value is smaller than the frequency $f_\pi$ where the conductance $g_\pi$ equals the susceptance of $C_\pi$. From (8.17), $f_\pi = 6.4$ MHz. From (9.11c) and (9.12) we can see that the feedback effects of $C_\mu$ lead to a smaller value of $f_u$, whereas the shunt conductance due to $R_s + r_x$ tends to produce a larger value. That is, the upper break frequency of the gain-magnitude curve moves to the left for an increase of $R_L$, but moves to the right for a decrease in $R_s$.

**BANDWIDTH** The gain-magnitude plot of Fig. 9.7 indicates how the gain magnitude drops as the frequency of an input sinusoid is varied. In addition, this plot indicates the width of the frequency spectrum of a general input which is preserved relatively unchanged in passing through the amplifier. Thus, we commonly refer to the *bandwidth* of the amplifier. Very often, the bandwidth is defined as the frequency range, in hertz, from the lower $-3$ dB frequency $f_l = (1/2\pi) \omega_l$ (due to the coupling elements) to the upper $-3$ dB frequency $f_u = (1/2\pi) \omega_u$ (due to $C_\pi$ and $C_\mu$):

$$BW = \frac{1}{2\pi}(\omega_u - \omega_l) \simeq \frac{1}{2\pi}\omega_u \qquad (9.14)$$

The second, approximate form for the bandwidth is appropriate since the upper $-3$ dB frequency is so much larger than the lower $-3$ dB frequency for lowpass amplifiers such as the present example. This difference is clear from an inspection of the values of the bandedges of Fig. 9.5. Because of the difference in the values of these frequencies, the desirability of using log-log graphs over several decades in order to show both cutoff frequencies is clear. Although the shape of such a curve recalls a bandpass characteristic, we must remember that the low-frequency bandedge is so much smaller than the high-frequency bandedge that we have in reality a lowpass amplifier in spite of the dc blocking.

## 9.5 a special bias circuit

Although the bias arrangement of Fig. 9.1b is both simple and practical for many transistor applications, problems arise with this biasing scheme, e.g., when the value of $I_{CO}$ is not negligible with respect to the value of $I_B$ at the desired operating point. To illustrate the problem, consider the bias circuit of Fig. 9.1b as temperature is changed. For a given value of $R_B$ and $V_{CC}$, the base bias current is approximately fixed.

$$I_B \simeq \frac{V_{CC}}{R_B} \qquad (9.15)$$

Even though $V_{BE}$ changes with temperature ($-2.3$ mV/°C, ideally), this effect is masked by the value of $V_{CC}$ which is much larger than $V_{BE}$. The collector current, including the $I_{CO}$ component and using (9.15), is, for an *npn* transistor,

$$I_C \simeq \beta_0 \frac{V_{CC}}{R_B} + (\beta_0 + 1) I_{CO} \qquad (9.16)$$

Now $I_{CO}$ is a strong function of temperature since it depends on the electron-hole generation in the semiconductor. $I_{CO}$ doubles approximately for every 10°C increase in temperature. From (9.16), it is clear that if $I_{CO}$ is of the order of magnitude of $I_B(\simeq V_{CC}/R_B)$ and if temperature increases, then $I_C$ increases and the operating point is changed.

The gain parameter $\beta_0$ also is a function of temperature, as illustrated in Fig. 8.17a. The temperature dependence of $\beta_0$ is not as strong as that of $I_{CO}$; however, the change is significant. An approximate rate of change for silicon transistors is 7 percent per 10°C. This increase of $\beta_0$ with temperature also increases $I_C$ as seen from (9.16). If we refer to a dc load-line plot on the output characteristic of a c-e transistor, as in Fig. 9.8, it is seen that the

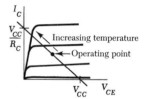

**FIGURE 9.8** $I_C V_{CE}$ *characteristic with dc load line.*

operating point moves up and to the left and toward the edge of the active operating region of the transistor. For a sufficiently large change of temperature, the maximum excursions of unclipped output voltage and current are greatly reduced.

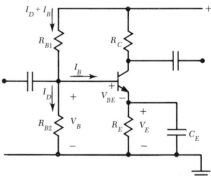

**FIGURE 9.9** *Self-compensating bias circuit.*

The change of the operating point can be minimized through the use of a self-compensating bias circuit such as that shown in Fig. 9.9. To understand the compensating action of this bias circuit, it is helpful to follow through the sequence of effects as a change is introduced. By design, an emitter-to-ground voltage $V_E$ is developed across $R_E$ which is proportional to $I_E \simeq [(\beta_0 + 1)/\beta_0]I_C$. At the input, a current, $I_D > I_B$, flows through $R_{B1}$ and $R_{B2}$. Starting from a given operating point, assume that $I_C$ tends to increase. $V_E$ also tends to increase. However, the base-to-ground voltage $V_B$ stays approximately constant since $I_D > I_B$. Therefore, $V_{BE} = V_B - V_E$ tends to decrease. A small decrease of $V_{BE}$ produces a large decrease of $I_C$ which opposes the original tendency to increase. Thus a self-compensating effect is obtained and the circuit tends to hold $I_C$ and $V_{CE}$ constant.

The details of the amount of compensation can be analyzed, most conveniently, from the viewpoint of a feedback amplifier. However, conventional circuit equations can be established and solved for the ratio of $\Delta I_C/I_C$. We do not take this up here except to note the results. For good compensation, choose $R_E$ such that $\beta_0 R_E > R_{B1} \| R_{B2}$.

We illustrate the design of the bias circuit by an example. For a Si transistor at $I_C = 5$ mA, $V_{CE} = 5$ V, we assume the following values: $\beta_0 = 100$, $I_{CO} = 10$ nA, and $V_{BE} \simeq 0.7$ V. If $V_{CC} = 18$ V, and if we choose $V_E = 3$ V, we obtain

$$R_C = \frac{V_{CC} - V_{CE} - V_E}{I_C} = 2 \text{ k}\Omega \tag{9.17a}$$

$$R_E = \frac{V_E}{I_E} = 0.6 \text{ k}\Omega \tag{9.17b}$$

$$I_B = \frac{1}{\beta_0}I_C - \frac{\beta_0 + 1}{\beta_0}I_{CO} = \frac{1}{100} 5 \cdot 10^{-3} - 10^{-8} = 50 \ \mu\text{A} \tag{9.17c}$$

We now choose $I_D$ through $R_{B2}$ to be larger than $I_B$, for example, ten times $I_B$.

$$I_D = 0.5 \text{ mA} \tag{9.17d}$$

Since $V_B = V_{BE} + V_E \simeq 3.7$ V, the lower bias resistor $R_{B2}$ is

$$R_{B2} = \frac{V_B}{I_D} = 7.4 \text{ k}\Omega \tag{9.17e}$$

The current through $R_{B1}$ is $I_D + I_B = 0.55$ mA. This leads to

$$R_{B1} = \frac{V_{CC} - V_B}{I_D + I_{B1}} = \frac{14.3}{0.55 \text{ mA}} \simeq 26 \text{ k}\Omega \tag{9.17f}$$

The shift in the operating point as $I_{CO}$ and $\beta_0$ change with temperature, or with aging, is left to a problem (Prob. 9.18). Note that the design criterion mentioned above is well satisfied: $\beta_0 R_E = 60 \text{ k}\Omega >> R_{B1} \| R_{B2} = 5.75 \text{ k}\Omega$.

The compensation described above is desired only for direct current and very low frequencies. This effect is not desired for the frequency spectrum of the input signal and is eliminated for higher frequencies by using the bypass capacitor $C_E$ as shown in Fig. 9.9. The proper choice of this capacitor in conjunction with the coupling capacitors to achieve a desired overall low-frequency break frequency is not simple because of the complexity of the total circuit. We can, however, pick a value which will provide a desired break frequency $\omega_E$ if $C_E$ is considered alone. This is comparable to what we did earlier in choosing values of the coupling capacitors $C_1$ and $C_2$ and does provide a guide for selection of $C_E$. For a specified value of $\omega_E$

$$C_E \simeq \frac{1}{\omega_E R_E \| (1/g_m + R'_s/\beta_0)} \tag{9.18}$$

where $R'_s$ is the value of the source resistance presented to the transistor. Equation (9.18) is established by considering $C_1$ to be a short circuit and by neglecting $r_\mu$ of the transistor. For an assumed sinusoidal input signal, an expression for the current $g_m V$ is obtained. The break frequency of the gain function $g_m V / V_s$ is then $\omega_E$. The resistance terms in the denominator of (9.18) represent approximately the input resistance looking back into the circuit from $C_E$. For our example, if we choose $R'_s = 500 \ \Omega$ and $\omega_E = 2\pi \cdot 10^2$ rad/s, $C_E$ should be approximately 63 $\mu$F. Note that this value of capacitance is much larger than the corresponding value of $C_1$ and $C_2$ from (9.6) and (9.7) in Sec. 9.2.

## 9.6   the thévenin and norton theorems

Two important theorems are useful in working with both active and passive circuits. These theorems, which make possible shortcuts in analyzing such networks, are the Thévenin and Norton theorems. Special cases of these were mentioned in Sec. 3.2. We now give more general forms for these theorems, using phasor notation together with complex impedances and admittances. Both theorems are concerned with linear time-invariant networks having an arbitrary interconnection of elements and one or more voltage and/or current sources. The point of view in both theorems is that a combination of elements and sources can be replaced (modeled) with respect to a load with an equivalent single source or generator including its internal impedance.

**THÉVENIN'S THEOREM**   This theorem states that a network which feeds a load impedance $Z_L$ behaves, insofar as the load is concerned, as a single voltage source having a phasor voltage $V_s$ in series with a single source impedance $Z_s$. This network is illustrated in Fig. 9.10. Voltage $V_s$ is the voltage at the output terminals with $Z_L$ removed (i.e., the output open circuited). $Z_s$ is the impedance seen looking back into the network from the load terminals, with all independent voltage sources shorted and all independent current sources open circuited, i.e., with all independent sources reduced to zero.

Although the proof of the theorem is straightforward, we will not give it here since it is most conveniently done by a more general network formulation than needed for this book. We illustrate the theorem by two

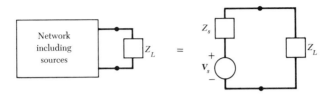

**FIGURE 9.10**   *Thévenin equivalent for a circuit.*

examples. As a first example, an equivalent of the base bias circuit of Fig. 9.9 is developed in order to simplify the analysis of this bias system. The input portion of the circuit is repeated in Fig. 9.11$a$, where the actual voltage presented to the transistor is labeled $V_B$ and the actual current flowing to the base is labeled $I_B$. The Thévenin equivalent source voltage is that obtained if the load is removed. For this example, this is the open-circuit

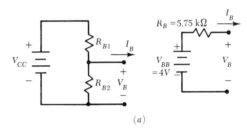

$(a)$

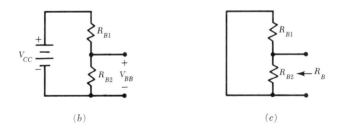

$(b)$                    $(c)$

**FIGURE 9.11**   *Thévenin equivalent for base bias circuit.* (a) *Initial circuit and equivalent;* (b) *circuit for open-circuit voltage;* (c) *circuit for input resistance.*

voltage obtained for Fig. 9.11$b$ ($I_B$ is set equal to zero) and is labeled $V_{BB}$.

$$V_{BB} = \frac{R_{B2}}{R_{B1} + R_{B2}} V_{CC} \qquad (9.19a)$$

For the values of the design of the last section, $V_{BB} = 4$ V. The Thévenin equivalent source resistance is the resistance looking back into the circuit, as in Fig. 9.11c, with all independent sources reduced to zero. We obtain

$$R_B = R_{B1} \| R_{B2} = \frac{R_{B1}R_{B2}}{R_{B1} + R_{B2}} \qquad (9.19b)$$

For the values of the preceding section, $R_B = 5.75$ kΩ. The remaining analysis of the complete bias circuit is left to Prob. 9.18.

As a second example, we return to the circuit of Fig. 3.22 which was analyzed in Secs. 3.7 and 3.9. In this circuit the resistor $R_2$ is taken as the load. The "source" circuit with $R_2$ removed, i.e., with the load terminals open circuited, is shown in Fig. 9.12a. The voltage appearing across these

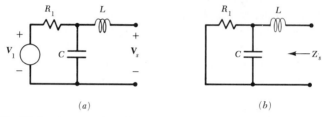

*(a)*        *(b)*

**FIGURE 9.12**   *Thévenin equivalent for circuit of Fig. 3.22 with respect to $R_2$. (a) $V_s$; (b) $Z_s$.*

terminals is just that across $C$, as there is no current in $L$ under this open-circuit condition. $V_s$ is then

$$V_s = \frac{1}{j\omega C} \frac{V_1}{R_1 + 1/j\omega C} = \frac{V_1}{1 + j\omega C R_1} \qquad (9.20a)$$

To obtain the source impedance for the Thévenin equivalent of Fig. 9.12a, we look back into the network from the load terminals with $V_1$ short-circuited, as illustrated in Fig. 9.12b. The impedance seen is

$$Z_s = j\omega L + \frac{1}{j\omega C + 1/R_1} = \frac{R_1(1 - \omega^2 LC) + j\omega L}{1 + j\omega C R_1} \qquad (9.20b)$$

We now have the elements of the Thévenin equivalent, as in Fig. 9.10. For the complete circuit of Fig. 3.22, we obtain the output voltage $V_2$ by including the load impedance that is equal to $R_2$

$$V_2 = \frac{R_2 V_s}{Z_s + R_2} = \frac{R_2 V_1}{[R_1(1 - \omega^2 LC) + R_2] + j\omega(L + CR_1R_2)} \qquad (9.21)$$

This result is the same as that of (3.84). The method may save little work for one calculation, but can be very helpful when a variety of loads are to be considered, and it may also be useful in the measurement of networks.

**NORTON'S THEOREM** This theorem is similar to the above, but provides an equivalent current source $I_s$ in parallel with a source admittance $Y_s$ as illustrated in Fig. 9.13. The current $I_s$ is the current through the output

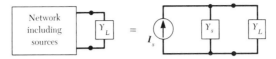

**FIGURE 9.13** *Norton equivalent for circuit.*

terminals if the load is replaced by a short circuit. $Y_s$ is the admittance seen looking back into the network from the load terminals with all independant voltage sources shorted and all independent current sources open circuited, i.e., with all independent sources reduced to zero. Clearly, the Norton and Thévenin equivalent circuits (Figs. 9.10 and 9.13) are related as follows:

$$Y_s = \frac{1}{Z_s} \tag{9.22}$$

$$I_s = \frac{V_s}{Z_s} \tag{9.23}$$

(The discussion of Sec. 3.2 is a special case of the above, in which the source impedance is a pure resistance.)

It should be stressed that the circuit simplifications of these theorems are intended for use in calculating relations between the source and the load. In general, we lose information about the internal behavior of the coupling network. Further, the input impedances seen by the sources of the actual network are not in general the impedances seen by the equivalent sources $V_s$ or $I_s$ in the Thévenin or Norton equivalent circuits. Finally, the power dissipated within the actual network is not in general given by the power loss in the resistance or conductance portions of $Z_s$ or $Y_s$.

## 9.7 power transfer and impedance matching

As stressed in Chap. 2 in the discussion of amplifiers, output power is required for movement of a loudspeaker coil, the driving of a recorder, or for any real loads to be actuated by amplified signals. Ultimately, then, we must be concerned with the power transfer to a useful output of a circuit. In our work to this point, we have considered the average power only at low frequencies, i.e., power in purely resistive circuits. In this section, we take up first average power in a general, linear, time-invariant circuit. This is followed by a development of the condition to transfer the maximum power to a load.

The instantaneous power into or out of a port (terminal pair) of a network is given by the product of voltage and current at the port.

$$P(t) = v(t)i(t) \tag{9.24}$$

Here, we restrict attention to the case where voltage and current are sinusoids of the same frequency but of different phase,

$$v(t) = V_m \cos \omega t \tag{9.25a}$$

$$i(t) = I_m \cos (\omega t + \theta) \tag{9.25b}$$

The instantaneous power is then

$$P(t) = V_m I_m \cos \omega t \cos (\omega t + \theta) \tag{9.25c}$$

This can be expanded by the use of trigonometric identities to obtain

$$P(t) = \frac{V_m I_m}{2} \cos \theta + \frac{V_m I_m}{2} \cos(2\omega t + \theta) \tag{9.25d}$$

As shown in Fig. 9.14, the power has an average part given by the first

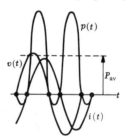

**FIGURE 9.14**   *Instantaneous power.*

term of (9.25d). It also has a time-varying part of zero average, given by the second term. The average power is more important to us here and is

$$P_{av} = \frac{1}{2} V_m I_m \cos \theta \tag{9.26a}$$

The average power can thus be obtained directly from phasor analysis by multiplying one-half the product of current and voltage peak magnitudes by the cosine of the phase angle between them. Using phasor notation, one can easily show that

$$P_{av} = \frac{1}{2} \text{Re} \, (VI^*) \tag{9.26b}$$

where $I^*$ is the complex conjugate of $I$.

It is essential to realize that (9.24) is a nonlinear expression. Phasors or complex forms cannot be substituted directly in it to obtain *instantaneous* power. Thus, when instantaneous power is desired, it is safest in beginning studies to convert complex forms to sinusoids in time before using (9.24).

We now illustrate power calculations by a simple but useful example.

Suppose a sinusoidal voltage source of magnitude $V_m$ has an internal resistance $R_s$ and is connected to the load $R_L$ as shown in Fig. 9.15. What

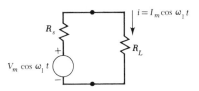

**FIGURE 9.15**   *Resistance matching.*

value of $R_L$ gives maximum power transfer to the load? The current magnitude in the circuit is

$$I_m = \frac{V_m}{R_s + R_L} \tag{9.27a}$$

The voltage across the load is

$$V_{Lm} = I_m R_L = \frac{V_m R_L}{R_s + R_L} \tag{9.27b}$$

For this simple example, the voltage and the current are in phase; therefore, in (9.26), $\cos \theta = 1$.

$$P_{av} = \frac{1}{2} \frac{V_m^2 R_L}{(R_s + R_L)^2} \tag{9.28}$$

In order to maximize power with respect to $R_L$, we differentiate (9.28):

$$\frac{dP_{av}}{dR_L} = \frac{V_m^2}{2} (R_s + R_L)^{-2} - 2R_L (R_s + R_L)^{-3} \tag{9.29a}$$

Setting this derivative equal to zero yields the result

$$R_L = R_s \tag{9.29b}$$

The result (9.29b) shows that to obtain the maximum power available from a source with internal resistance, we must make the load resistance equal to the internal source resistance. [Inspection of (9.28) shows that this is clearly a maximum—not a minimum.]

   In the general case when the source and load are complex impedances, maximum power is transferred if the source impedance is equal to the complex conjugate of the load impedance,

$$Z_s^* = Z_L \tag{9.29c}$$

The process described is called resistance or impedance *matching* and is a critical aspect of the interconnection of electronic circuits. If we have an amplifier with a high output resistance, it will not deliver much of its available power if connected to a load of low resistance. Thus we should look for another equally good amplifier of low output resistance to match the load, or else provide a transformer between amplifier and load to change the resistance level for matching. (Note from Sec. 3.2 that an ideal transformer changes impedance level by $n^2$.) Impedance levels of amplifiers and other building blocks are thus most important when the blocks are to be interconnected.

As an example to illustrate maximum power transfer, we consider the single transistor amplifier of Fig. 9.1b. In the midfrequency regions, the circuit model of the amplifier is that of Fig. 9.2c. The output portion of the circuit is repeated in Fig. 9.16. Note that the portion of this circuit

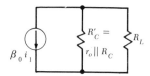

**FIGURE 9.16**  *Output circuit of Fig. 9.2c.*

to the left of $R_L$ is already in the form of a Norton equivalent source for $R_L$. Clearly, (9.29b), which is derived for a Thévenin equivalent, also holds for a Norton equivalent [see (9.22) and (9.23)]. Thus, for maximum power transfer, the load resistance $R_L$ should be chosen to equal $R'_C = r_o \| R_C$. In many cases, such as an audio amplifier, the load is fixed, say by the value of the resistance of the voice coil of the loudspeaker. A typical value of this resistance is 8 Ω while the parallel combination of $r_o$ and $R_C$ might be 2 kΩ. To achieve a resistance match for maximum power transfer, we introduce an output transformer as illustrated in Fig. 9.17a. For the resistance match

$$r_o \| R_C = n^2 R_L \tag{9.30a}$$

$$n = \sqrt{\frac{r_o \| R_C}{R_L}} \tag{9.30b}$$

For the values above, $n = 15.8$.

An actual transformer has both series and shunt inductances. The former attenuates signals at high frequencies and the latter inhibits the transmission of very low frequencies. Thus an actual transformer provides a bandpass transmission characteristic in itself. This aspect must be considered in the selection of the transformer. A transformer also has the advantage that it can provide dc blocking if two separate windings are used. Therefore the output coupling capacitor of the amplifier is not needed as illustrated in Fig. 9.17b. Also note that the collector bias resistor can also be omitted. The dc load line on the $I_C V_{CE}$ characteristic for this transformer-coupled case is a vertical line through $V_{CC}$.

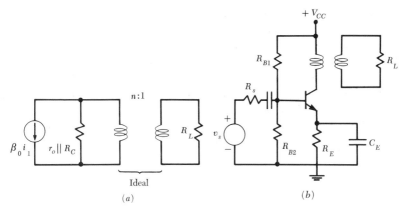

**FIGURE 9.17** *Transistor amplifier with transformer coupling.* (a) *Output circuit model;* (b) *complete circuit.*

## 9.8 a cascaded amplifier

Usually the current, voltage, or power gain that is provided by a single transistor amplifier is not sufficient to meet or to exceed the required level of amplification. In order to obtain larger amplification, a cascade connection of two or more single transistor stages is used. A cascade connection of two 2-ports is shown in Fig. 9.18a and should be compared with the parallel connection of two 2-ports as in Fig. 9.18b and with the

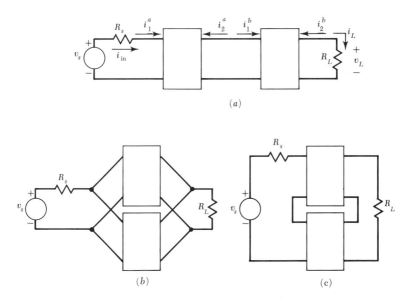

**FIGURE 9.18** *2-port connections.* (a) *Cascade;* (b) *shunt;* (c) *series.*

series connection in Fig. 9.18c. Each connection has its special advantages. For example, the parallel connection provides a load current in $R_L$ which is the sum of the output currents from each stage under the condition that each stage has the same voltage. This parallel connection can provide twice as much power output as one of its stages. However, the power and current gain are not changed since the input levels must be doubled to obtain the increased output.

In the cascade connection, a product type of overall gain function is obtained. This can be seen in terms of the current definitions shown in Fig. 9.18a. The overall current gain, in phasor notation, is

$$a_I = \frac{I_L}{I_{\text{in}}} = \frac{-I_2^{(b)}}{I_1^{(a)}} \qquad (9.31a)$$

If we multiply and divide by $I_2^{(a)} = -I_1^{(b)}$, we obtain

$$a_I = \frac{-I_2^{(b)}}{I_1^{(b)}} \quad \frac{-I_2^{(a)}}{I_1^{(a)}} \qquad (9.31b)$$

Note that we factor the result into two terms, each pertaining to a current gain function for each 2-port. The product nature of the overall gain function is clear although it is to be emphasized that the gain for each 2-port is that for which the source and load are the same as supplied in the cascade connection.

To illustrate the cascade connection, the two-transistor amplifier shown in Fig. 9.19a is studied in greater detail. The values of the bias elements are taken to be those developed in Sec. 9.5. The value of the source and load resistance is taken to be 300 $\Omega$. In the midfrequency region, the coupling and bypass capacitors can be neglected and we obtain the reduced circuit of Fig. 9.19b. Note that equivalent resistors are introduced for the several parallel combinations, the approximate values of which are

$$R_B = R_{B1} \| R_{B2} = 5.75 \text{ k}\Omega \qquad (9.32a)$$

$$R_I = R_B \| R_C \quad = 1.5 \text{ k}\Omega \qquad (9.32b)$$

$$R_L' = R_C \| R_L \quad = 260 \ \Omega \qquad (9.32c)$$

Finally, we introduce a midfrequency circuit model for the transistor, where the capacitors $C_\pi$ and $C_\mu$ are neglected for simplicity. The final circuit model of the complete amplifier is then as shown in Fig. 9.19c where a Thévenin equivalent for the source is also used.

$$V_s' = \frac{R_B}{R_B + R_s} \, V_s = 0.95 \, V_s \qquad (9.33a)$$

$$R_s' = R_s \| R_B = 285 \ \Omega \qquad (9.33b)$$

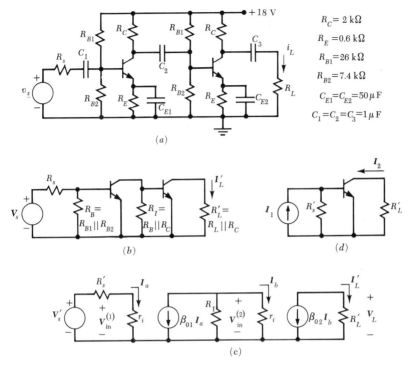

$R_C = 2\,\text{k}\Omega$

$R_E = 0.6\,\text{k}\Omega$

$R_{B1} = 26\,\text{k}\Omega$

$R_{B2} = 7.4\,\text{k}\Omega$

$C_{E1} = C_{E2} = 50\,\mu\text{F}$

$C_1 = C_2 = C_3 = 1\,\mu\text{F}$

**FIGURE 9.19**  *A two-transistor amplifier. (a) Complete circuit; (b) midfrequency simplified circuit; (c) circuit model for midfrequencies; (d) source and load for upper break-frequency calculations.*

The final circuit is suitable for calculations of the midfrequency gain of the amplifier.

The current gain of the circuit $a_I = I_L/I_{in}$ can be developed in many ways. Taking one step at a time, we obtain

$$I_L = \frac{V_L}{R_L} = \frac{R'_L}{R_L}I_L = \frac{R'_L}{R_L}(-\beta_{02}I_b) = \frac{R_C}{R_C + R_L}(-\beta_{02}I_b) \qquad (9.34a)$$

$$I_b = \frac{V_{in}^{(2)}}{r_i} = \frac{-\beta_{01}I_a}{r_i}(R_I\|r_i) = \frac{R_I}{r_i + R_I}(-\beta_{01}I_a) \qquad (9.34b)$$

$$I_{in} = I_a \qquad (9.34c)$$

$$a_I = \frac{I_L}{I_{in}} = +\frac{R_I}{r_i + R_I}\beta_{01}\frac{R_C}{R_C + R_L}\beta_{02} \qquad (9.34d)$$

For the values above and for $\beta_{01} = \beta_{02} = 100$ and $r_i = 550\,\Omega$,

$$a_I = (0.76)(100)(0.87)\ 100 = (76)(87) = 6600 \qquad (9.34e)$$

The two stages each provide approximately the same level of midband current gain. The midband voltage gain $V_L/V_s$, can be found directly or by converting the value of (9.34e). For the latter, we first obtain

$$V_s = \frac{R_s + R_B}{R_B} V_s' = \frac{R_s + R_B}{R_B} (R_s' + r_i) I_{\text{in}} \qquad (9.35a)$$

$$\frac{V_L}{V_s} = \frac{R_L I_L}{\dfrac{R_s + R_B}{R_B} (R_s' + r_i) I_{\text{in}}}$$

$$= \frac{R_L R_B}{(R_s + R_B)(R_s' + r_i)} a_I$$

$$= (0.34)(6600)$$

$$\simeq 2200 \qquad (9.35b)$$

In passing, note that only a $1:2$ resistance match occurs at the input of the transistor, that is, $R_s' = 285\ \Omega$, $r_i = 550\ \Omega$. However, a larger resistance mismatch occurs at the output $R_C = 2000\ \Omega$, $R_L = 300\ \Omega$.

The calculation of the lower and upper bandedges of the overall gain function is not a simple task if exact values are needed. The difficulty is due to the complexity of the overall circuit model with its several capacitances both for the very low frequency region and for the upper frequency region. As a first (and gross) approximation for the lower bandedge, we use the formulas developed earlier to estimate the break frequencies when each capacitor is considered alone. In these calculations, the other coupling and bypass capacitors are considered to be short circuits. A combined sketch of a Bode plot (log-log coordinates) incorporating the different asymptotes is next made to estimate the $-3$ dB lower bandedge.

For the upper bandedge, we follow a similar procedure. An upper break frequency of the gain function is estimated for each stage considered separately, as in Fig. 9.19d. That is, for each transistor the equivalent source and load resistances are calculated shorting out all coupling and bypass elements for this upper frequency region and neglecting the $C_\pi$ and $C_\mu$ capacitors of the other stage. From these values of resistance, the break frequency of the gain function for an individual stage is calculated as in Sec. 9.4. A sketch of the Bode plot again leads to a first estimate of the upper bandedge of the overall gain function.

To continue with our example, in the very low frequency region, we use (9.6) and (9.7) to estimate the break frequencies for $C_1$, $C_2$, and $C_3$ with the values of Fig. 9.19a.

$$\omega_{C1} \simeq \frac{1}{(R_s + R_B \| r_i) C_1} = 125 \text{ rad/s} \qquad (9.36a)$$

$$\omega_{C2} \simeq \frac{1}{(R_C + R_B \| r_i)C_2} = 400 \text{ rad/s} \tag{9.36b}$$

$$\omega_{C3} \simeq \frac{1}{(R'_C + R_L)C_3} = 435 \text{ rad/s} \tag{9.36c}$$

where $R'_C = R_C \| r_o$. For the bypass elements, we use (9.18) to obtain

$$\omega_{CE1} \simeq \frac{1}{R_E \|\left(\dfrac{1}{g_m} + \dfrac{R_B \| R_s}{\beta_{01}}\right)C_{E1}} \simeq 2500 \text{ rad/s} \tag{9.37a}$$

$$\omega_{CE2} \simeq \frac{1}{R_E \|\left(\dfrac{1}{g_m} + \dfrac{R_B \| R_C}{\beta_{02}}\right)C_{E2}} \simeq 1000 \text{ rad/s} \tag{9.37b}$$

Clearly, the highest break frequency is that due to $C_{E1}$. Therefore this break frequency and its low-frequency asymptote is dominant in determining the lower $-3$ dB bandedge of the amplifier. From a graphical sketch and a visual resolution of the five asymptotes, the lower $-3$ dB bandedge of the amplifier $\omega_l$ is

$$\omega_l \simeq 2700 \text{ rad/s} \tag{9.38a}$$

$$f_l = \frac{\omega_l}{2\pi} = 430 \text{ Hz} \tag{9.38b}$$

For the upper bandedge, the break frequency for the first transistor is found from (9.11c) and (9.12) using $R'_s = R_s \| R_B = 285 \ \Omega$, $R'_L = R_C \| R_B \| r_i \simeq 400 \ \Omega$, $r_x = 50 \ \Omega$, and $r_\pi = 500 \ \Omega$.

$$\omega_{u1} = \frac{\dfrac{1}{R'_s + r_x} + \dfrac{1}{r_\pi}}{C_{t1}} \simeq 10 \cdot 10^6 \text{ rad/s} \tag{9.39a}$$

where $\qquad C_{t1} = C_\pi + C_\mu(1 + g_m R'_L) = 505 \text{ pF} \tag{9.39b}$

In (9.39b), $C_\pi = 100$ pF and $C_\mu = 5$ pF have been used. For the second transistor, $R'_s = R_B \| R_C = 1.5 \text{ k}\Omega$ and $R'_L = 260 \ \Omega$.

$$C_{t2} = 365 \text{ pF} \tag{9.40a}$$

$$\omega_{u2} \simeq 7.3 \cdot 10^6 \text{ rad/s} \tag{9.40b}$$

From a sketch of the high-frequency asymptotes for these two break frequencies, we estimate for the overall response

$$\omega_u \simeq 6 \cdot 10^6 \text{ rad/s} \tag{9.41a}$$

$$f_u = \frac{\omega_u}{2\pi} \simeq 0.95 \text{ MHz} \tag{9.41b}$$

## 9.9 a transistor switch

We turn now from small-signal amplifier applications to large-signal or switch applications. The c-e transistor can serve as an excellent "controlled switch with gain." To illustrate this, we consider the circuit shown in Fig. 9.20. Here the load is the resistor $R_C$ and the drive, or input, is the

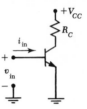

**FIGURE 9.20** *A transistor switch.*

voltage $v_{in}$ (or the current $i_{in}$). If $v_{in}$ is zero, the point of operation is point $a$ on the load line in Fig. 9.21. It has been brought out earlier on page 240 that $i_{in} = -I_{CO}$ for this case and that $I_C = I_{CO}$. [Remember, however, that if $i_{in} = I_B = 0$, $I_C = (\beta_0 + 1)I_{CO}$.] For an input of $v_{in} \leqslant 0$, the emitter-base junction is reverse biased, as is the collector-base junction, and we say the

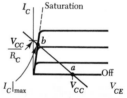

**FIGURE 9.21** $I_C V_{CE}$ *characteristic with load line.*

transistor is in the *off mode* or *off state*. The output resistance of the device is, of course, very large in the off state ($r_o \propto 1/I_C$). In Fig. 9.21, note that the *off* line and the $V_{CE}$ axis are almost coincident and at point $a$, $V_{CE} \simeq V_{CC}$.

As $v_{in}$ is increased from zero, collector current flows and this current develops a voltage across $R_C$. Thus, the operating point moves up the load line. At point $b$ we encounter transistor saturation. At this point $V_{CB} = 0$. As we increase $v_{in}$ further, $i_{in}$ ($= I_B$) increases and there is a tendency for $I_C$ to increase. However, this produces a tendency for $V_{CB}$ to become negative, since

$$V_{CB} = V_{CE} - V_{BE} = V_{CC} - I_C R_C - V_{BE} \qquad (9.42)$$

where $v_{in} = V_{BE}$ is a few tenths of a volt positive. A negative value of $V_{CB}$ represents forward bias for the collector junction of this $npn$ transistor. But with a forward bias, the collector junction will inject minority carriers into the base region while it continues to collect minority carriers which travel across the base from the emitter. Note potential barriers of Fig. 7.6a. Thus a self-compensating action is obtained since the emitted component of $I_C$ is in the opposite direction to the collected component.

The flow of the various components of minority carriers in the base region of the transistor in the *saturated state* is shown in Fig. 9.22a. At both the emitter and collector junctions, we have emitted and collected components of minority carriers (electrons for the *npn* transistor). In terms of currents, as shown in Fig. 9.22b,

$$-I_E = I_{Ee} - I_{Ec} \tag{9.43a}$$

$$I_C = I_{Cc} - I_{Ce} \tag{9.43b}$$

where the various components are defined as having positive directions in the direction of actual current flow. In (9.43a), $I_{Ee}$, for example, is the emitted current at the emitter, $I_{Ec}$ is the collected component at the

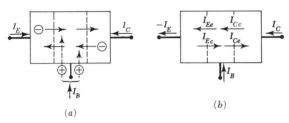

(a)

(b)

**FIGURE 9.22**   *Saturated npn transistor.* (a) *Principal charge-carrier flow;* (b) *current components and directions of actual flow.*

emitter, etc. In effect, we propose to separate the actual emitter and collector currents (including the contribution due to electron and holes) into the components which flow for normal active mode operation and inverse active mode operation. The total currents are then the superposition of these components. The base current in saturation must supply recombination majority carriers (holes) to satisfy both the "normal" flow of minority carriers from emitter to collector and the "inverse" flow from collector to emitter. Clearly, in saturation, we have a greater storage of minority carriers than in the active mode, since both junctions inject minority carriers into the base region. For the case at hand, the emitter junction has a larger value of forward bias than has the collector junction; therefore, $V_{BE} > V_{BC}$. The difference, however, which is $V_{CE}$ from (9.42), can be of the order of millivolts. Because $V_{CE}$ is so small, the collector current $I_C$ remains almost constant. Hence the term "saturation."

The dynamic resistance from collector to emitter is also very small. In fact, the ohmic resistance of the collector region is usually dominant. For a properly designed switching transistor, this resistance can be of the order of ohms. Thus the *saturation* line can be almost coincident with the $I_C$ axis of the $I_C V_{CE}$ characteristic. Therefore the current at point *b* of Fig. 9.21 is almost equal to $V_{CC}/R_C$ and the maximum current that flows in the output is

$$I_C \Big|_{max} \simeq \frac{V_{CC}}{R_C} \tag{9.44}$$

The developments above indicate that the c-e transistor can make a good electronic switch. In the open, or off, state, the switch has a large resistance and small leakage current. In the closed, or saturated, state, the switch resistance is low and a large current can flow with only a very small voltage drop. Finally, a large output current can be held *on* by a much smaller drive or control current. The input current to maintain the saturated state must be at least $1/\beta_0$ times the value of (9.44)

$$i_{\text{in}} = I_B \geqslant \frac{1}{\beta_0} \frac{V_{CC}}{R_C} \tag{9.45}$$

Even if (9.45) is well satisfied, the ratio of $I_C|_{\text{max}}$ and $I_B$ can be large. Therefore the switch can provide current gain.

The c-e transistor switch can also be used with a negative supply potential, as shown in Fig. 9.23a, with the same polarity input. With a negative

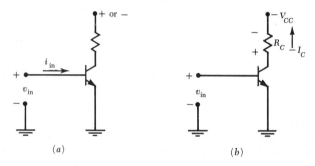

$(a)$ $(b)$

**FIGURE 9.23** *Transistor switch* (a) *with positive or negative supply voltage;* (b) *with negative supply voltage.*

supply voltage, $-V_{CC}$, and for $v_{\text{in}}$ positive from base to emitter, we may obtain inverse saturated operation. This is better understood using Fig. 9.23b. The positive $v_{\text{in}}$ from base to emitter provides a forward bias for the emitter junction. With a negative supply source, $-V_{CC}$, the collector current is negative. If the magnitude of $V_{CC}$ is larger than $v_{\text{in}}$, the collector junction is also forward biased and we obtain saturated operation. If $V_{CC}$ is sufficiently large and negative, the collector junction is more forward biased than the emitter junction. Therefore we have inverse saturated operation.

The complete $I_C V_{CE}$ characteristic for both positive and negative dc supplies is shown in Fig. 9.24. To obtain this characteristic, we assume that the input is now a dc current source $I_B$ of whatever level desired.

The output load line is drawn on this characteristic in either the first or third quadrant depending on whether the dc supply voltage is positive or negative, respectively. Operation in the interior of the third quadrant must be commented on further. In the interior of this quadrant, we have inverse operation, i.e., the collector junction is forward biased and the emitter junction is reverse biased. To see the latter, note that the forward

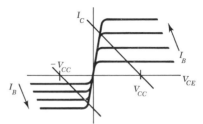

**FIGURE 9.24** *Complete $I_C V_{CE}$ characteristic with load lines for $+V_{CC}$ and $-V_{CC}$.*

bias of the collector junction clamps the base voltage to a value near $-V_{CC} + |I_C|R_C$. Thus $V_{BE}$ can be negative and the emitter junction can be reverse biased with a positive value of $I_B$. In the interior of the third quadrant, the operation corresponds to common-collector operation since the output current through $R_L$ is an effective "emitter" current. The separation between the $I_B$ parameter curves in the third quadrant is less than in the first quadrant since $\beta_{r0} < \beta_0$ where $\beta_{r0} = \alpha_{r0}/(1 - \alpha_{r0})$. The base current $I_B$ and the collector current $I_C$ in inverse operation are related as follows, if $I_{CO}$ and $I_{EO}$ are negligible with respect to $I_B$:

$$I_B \simeq \frac{1}{\beta_{r0} + 1} I_C \qquad (9.46a)$$

The factor $\beta_{r0} + 1$ is used in (9.46a), rather than $\beta_{r0}$ alone, because of the effective "common-collector" connection for inverse operation of Fig. 9.23b. To obtain inverse saturation, the necessary base current is obtained by including the maximum value of $I_C$ in (9.46a).

$$i_{\text{in}} = I_B > \frac{1}{\beta_{r0} + 1} \frac{|V_{CC}|}{R_C} \qquad (9.46b)$$

The control currents mentioned above are for the static situation. To change the state of the switch, control currents must also flow to establish or to remove the stored charges in the base and in the junctions. This leads to finite switching times as shown in Fig. 9.25. A fast rise for the onset of collector current is obtained by supplying an input current in excess of $(1/\beta_0)(V_{CC}/R_C)$ (for a positive supply potential). In Table 8.2, $T_{\text{on}}$ is the rise time, where $V_{BE} = -2V$ is the initial bias of the transistor, $I_{B1} = 3$ mA is the magnitude of the input pulse, and $I_C = 10$ mA is the maximum value of $I_C$. A similar fast drop, or fall, time can be obtained if the input is returned to a negative potential. In Table 8.2, the fall time is labeled $T_{\text{off}}$, where $I_B = 3$ mA and $I_C = 10$ mA is the initial bias point of the transistor, $I_{B2} = -2$ mA is the initial (negative) base current after switching to the negative control voltage. If the control voltage is returned to zero, a slow return to zero is obtained, as illustrated by the dashed curve of Fig. 9.25. In the figure, it should also be noticed that there is a

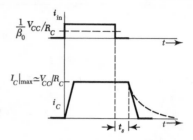

**FIGURE 9.25** *Input and output currents waveforms.*

delay time $t_s$ between the turnoff of the control and the initial drop in collector current. This delay is the time it takes to reduce the base stored charge to a level corresponding to operation at the saturation edge of the normal active region. After this delay, the collector current can fall as the remaining stored charge is removed to complete the turnoff. In Table 8.2, a typical saturation delay time is given where the initial saturated condition is $I_C = I_{B1} = 10$ mA. $I_{B2} = -10$ mA is the initial base current that flows when the base is switched to a negative voltage. The switching times can be extremely small. For the 2N708, we see from Table 8.2 that typical values for the rise, storage, and fall times are of the order of 50 ns.

A simple application of the transistor switch is shown in Fig. 9.26.

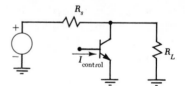

**FIGURE 9.26** *Transistor used as inhibit switch $V_s$ may be positive or negative.*

Here the switch acts as an inhibit switch. In the absence of a control current, the switch is open and power from the source flows to the load. With a sufficient control current, i.e., with

$$I_B\big|_{Vs>0} > \frac{1}{\beta_0} \frac{V_s}{R_s} \quad \text{and} \quad I_B\big|_{Vs>0} > \frac{1}{\beta_{r0} + 1} \frac{|V_s|}{R_s} \quad (9.47)$$

the transistor switch is closed, and almost all current from the source flows through the switch rather than through $R_L$.

## 9.10 transistor logic circuits

The transistor switch of the last section can also be used as the inverter in diode logic circuits. In Chap. 6, it was shown that the NAND or NOR logical operation can be obtained by cascading a diode logic circuit with an inverter. The combined circuit is referred to as a *diode-transistor logic* circuit.[1] A NAND circuit iş shown in Fig. 9.27. In the absence of

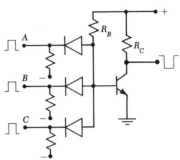

**FIGURE 9.27**  *Diode-transistor* NAND *circuit.*

any input, the transistor is biased off by a proper choice of the supply potentials. The output is thus in the high voltage or 1 state. Only if all the inputs are present will all of the diodes be cut off and will current flow through $R_B$ to saturate the transistor and to drop the output to a low voltage or 0 state. By proper design, inversion action and amplification can be obtained. A NOR circuit is shown in Fig. 9.28.

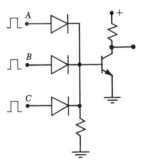

**FIGURE 9.28**  *Diode-transistor* NOR *circuit.*

Because of the diodelike nonlinear *IV* characteristic of the input and the output of a transistor, transistors alone can be used to obtain logic circuits. Very simple, *direct-coupled transistor logic* can be realized because of the low voltage drop in the saturated state. Consider first the circuit of Fig. 9.29a, where one c-e switch, or inverter, is directly connected to another. If the input to the first transistor saturates this stage, the output voltage of this transistor is very low, say of the order of millivolts. But this voltage is also the input voltage of the second stage. For a silicon transistor, the input voltage must be of the order of 0.7 V for reasonable collector-

---

[1]It is common to refer to the different types of logic circuits by the initials. Therefore, DTL circuit refers to diode-transistor logic circuits, DCTL to direct-coupled transistor logic circuits, TRL to transistor-resistor logic circuits, etc.

current flow. Therefore the second transistor is (almost) off and the output is in the high-voltage state. Conversely, if the first transistor is off, current can flow to the base of the second transistor to turn it on.

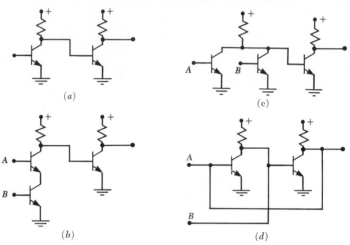

**FIGURE 9.29** *Direct-coupled transistor logic circuits.* (a) *Two inverters in cascade;* (b) AND *circuit;* (c) OR *circuit;* (d) *memory circuit.*

Because of the difference between transistor output voltages of the order of millivolts and input voltages of the order of tenths of volts, an AND circuit can be formed as shown in Fig. 9.29b. Only if both A and B inputs are present does the output-voltage state change. An OR circuit is shown in Fig. 9.29c. Finally, a memory circuit is shown in Fig. 9.29d. This is a bistable circuit, i.e., it has two different states in which the circuit is stable. If the first transistor is on (saturated), the second is off. However, the reverse is also true, hence the two stable states. The bistable circuit can serve as a memory element. Memory circuits are necessary in logic circuits in order to remember past data and instructions.

The direct-coupled circuits of Fig. 9.29 place a heavy dependency on the correct $IV$ characteristics of the input and the output of the transistors. It is often preferable to introduce an additional resistor and a second voltage source as shown in Fig. 9.30 for a basic inverter cascade. This type of transistor logic circuit is called *transistor-resistor logic*. With the second

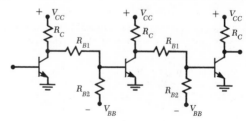

**FIGURE 9.30** *Transistor-resistor inverter cascade.*

voltage supply, it is a simple matter to ensure that a transistor is off if the preceding transistor is on. Thus, the close specification on, say, the value of $V_{CE}$ is removed for the modified circuits in relation to direct-coupled circuits.

A closed loop of two resistance-coupled inverters leads to the bistable circuit of Fig. 9.31a. This circuit has two stable states comparable to the circuit of Fig. 9.29d. In Fig. 9.31a, capacitors across $R_{B1}$ are introduced

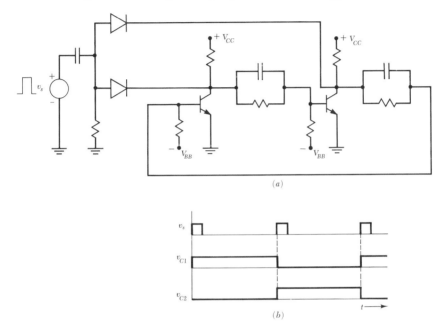

(a)

(b)

**FIGURE 9.31**   *Resistance-capacitance coupled bistable circuit.* (a) *Circuit diagram;* (b) *collector voltage waveforms.*

to provide a low impedance path for the fast switching transients. In addition, a two-diode AND circuit is introduced. This AND circuit, as connected, routes a positive input pulse to whichever collector is in the low-voltage state. The input pulse to this collector initially increases the collector current of this transistor and pulls it out of saturation since the base current is fixed. The input signal then is transferred to the base of the other transistor through the coupling capacitor. The base input turns the second transistor off and the circuit changes state, i.e., "flips." With a succeeding positive pulse, the input is routed to the other transistor and the circuit returns to its original state, i.e., "flops" back. Hence the name *flip-flop* for this circuit. The waveforms of the two collectors are shown in Fig. 9.31b. Note that the repetition frequency of the collector waveform is one-half of the input. Thus, the circuit can be considered to be a frequency divider. A cascade of these circuits counts down by a factor of 2 for each circuit.

## REFERENCES

C. L. Searle, A. R. Boothroyd, E. J. Angelo, Jr., P. E. Gray, and D. O. Pederson, "Elementary Circuit Properties of Transistors," SEEC, vol. 3, John Wiley & Sons, Inc., New York, 1964.

J. Millman and A. Taub, "Pulse, Digital, and Switching Waveforms," McGraw-Hill Book Company, New York, 1965, chaps. 9–10.

## PROBLEMS

**9.1**  For the single transistor circuit shown, design the bias circuit, i.e., find $R_B$ and $R_C$, assuming that a Ge transistor is used and given that

$$I_{CO} = 20 \ \mu A \qquad V_{CC} = +20 \text{ V}$$
$$\beta_0 = 50 \qquad I_C = 10 \text{ mA}$$
$$V_{CE} = +5 \text{ V}$$

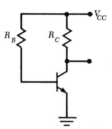

**Problem 9.1**

**9.2**  For a Ge transistor, design the bias circuit shown, i.e., for the values given below, determine values for $R_C$, $R_B$, and $R_E$.
(*a*) Assume that $V_{BE} = 0$.
(*b*) Assume that $V_{BE}$ is a constant equal to 0.3 V.
(*c*) Let $R_E = 0$, and redesign.

$$V_{CC} = 10 \text{ V} \qquad I_{CO} = 10 \ \mu A$$
$$I_C = 5 \text{ mA} \qquad \beta_0 = 50$$
$$V_{CE} = 3 \text{ V} \qquad V_E = 3 \text{ V}$$

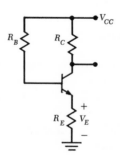

**Problem 9.2**

**9.3**   For the transistor circuit shown, assume that $V_{CC} = 20$ V, $\beta_0 = 100$, $I_{CO} = 4$ $\mu$A, and $V_{BE} = 0.3$ V. When $I_s = 0$, $V_{CE} = 8$ V; and when $V_C = 10.4$ V, $I_C = 2.4$ mA:

(a) Find $R_C$, $R_B$, and $R_E$.

(b) What value of $I_s$ will drive the transistor into saturation?

(c) What value of $I_s$ will drive the transistor into cutoff?

(d) What will be the value of $I_C$ at saturation?

(e) What will be the value of $I_C$ at cutoff?

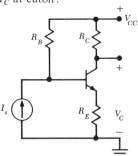

**Problem 9.3**

**9.4**   An *npn* transistor is used in a c-e configuration (see figure *a*).

(a) Given the $I_C V_{CE}$ characteristics shown in figure *b*, what is the quiescent (no-signal) operating point for $R_B = 250$ k$\Omega$, $R_C = 1$ k$\Omega$, and $V_{CC} = 10$ V, at a temperature of $25°$C? At this temperature, let $V_{BE} = 0.7$ V. (2N914 characteristics from Fairchild Semiconductor.)

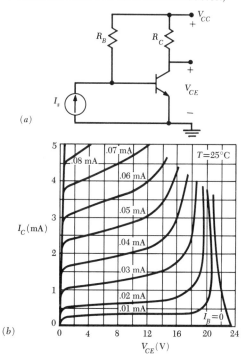

**Problem 9.4**

(b) What is the operating point at 100°C? Assume that $V_{BE}$ changes with temperature by $-2.3$ mV/°C.

(c) What is the operating point at $-55°C$?

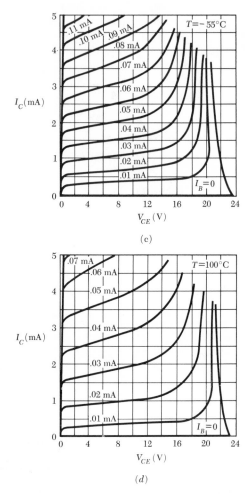

(c)

(d)

**9.5** For the transistor and operating point of Prob. 9.4, at 25°C:

(a) Determine the element values of the low-frequency circuit model shown. Obtain necessary information from $I_C V_{CE}$ characteristic.

(b) What is the voltage gain at "low" frequencies? Assume charge storage effects can be neglected.

(c) What is the current gain at "low" frequencies?

(d) What is the power gain at "low" frequencies?

(e) Let $i_s = I_1 \sin \omega t$, where $I_1 = 20 \ \mu A$. Determine the positive and negative peak values of output voltage and current.

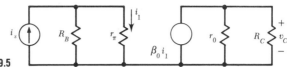

**Problem 9.5**

**9.6** (*a*) An alternate voltage-gain definition to (9.8) is the ratio $V_L/V_i$, where $V_i$ is the (phasor) input voltage of the transistor. For the circuit of Fig. 9.2c, establish an expression for this voltage gain at midband frequencies. For the values of the example in the text, what is the value of this gain?

(*b*) An alternate current-gain definition to (9.9c) can be made in terms of a Norton equivalent of the input source (the series $V_s$ and $R_s$ are replaced by the parallel $I_s$ and $R_s$, where $I_s = V_s/R_s$). Establish an expression for the new gain function $I_L/I_s$ at midband frequencies. What is the value of this gain for the values of the example in the text?

**9.7** (*a*) Develop an expression for the power gain of the single-stage amplifier of Fig. 9.2a at midband frequency, in terms of the power developed in $R_C \| R_L$ and in $r_i$.

(*b*) Under what condition is the maximum value of this power gain (9.10b) obtained?

**9.8** For the small-signal circuit model of a transistor amplifier shown, $R_s = 1$ k$\Omega$, $r_x = 40$ $\Omega$, $r_\pi = 220$ $\Omega$, $g_m = 1/6$ mho, and $R_L = 3$ k$\Omega$, determine (*a*) the voltage gain $V_L/V_s$, (*b*) the current gain $I_L/I_s$, and (*c*) the power gain.

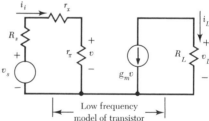

**Problem 9.8**

**9.9** For the circuit of Prob. 9.4, we introduce the $C_t$ circuit model of Fig. 8.12 and obtain the circuit below. Note that phasor voltage and currents are used. Let $\beta_0 = 70$, $I_C = 6$ mA, $C_t = 200$ pF, $r_x = 50$ $\Omega$, and $R_L = 500$ $\Omega$. A source resistance $R_s = 100$ $\Omega$ is added as shown. What is the magnitude of the current gain $I_L/I_s$ at low frequencies? At midband frequencies? At an input frequency of 1 MHz?

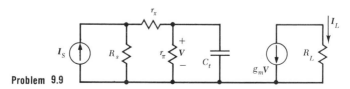

**Problem 9.9**

**9.10** For the circuit of Prob. 9.9, prove that the current gain as a function of the input frequency is

$$\frac{I_L}{I_s} = \frac{-a_{I0}}{1 + j(\omega/\omega_1)}$$

where

$$a_{I0} = \frac{g_m r_\pi R_s}{r_\pi + r_x + R_s}$$

and

$$\omega_1 = \frac{R_s + r_x + r_\pi}{C_t r_\pi (r_x + R_s)}$$

**9.11** In the circuit shown, the product of the magnitude of the current gain and the $-3$ dB bandedge frequency of the input sinusoid is found to be $3 \cdot 10^8$ Hz when a value of $R_s = 50\ \Omega$ is used. When $R_s$ is removed, the product of the current gain and bandedge frequency is $6 \cdot 10^8$ Hz. Removing $R_s$ also caused the low-frequency current gain to increase from 10 to 100.

(a) Find $r_x$, $r_\pi$, $C_t$, and $g_m$. (*Hint*: Find the current gain bandedge product as a function of $R_s$.)

(b) What is the change in the $-3$ dB bandwidth?

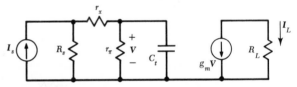

**Problem 9.11**

**9.12** Make a circuit analysis of Fig. 9.6 to obtain the voltage gain expressions (9.11).

**9.13** For the example corresponding to (9.13), make a plot of the upper bandedge frequency as (a) $R_L$ is varied from zero to infinity and for $R_s = 300\ \Omega$ and all other values remain the same and (b) $R_s$ is varied from zero to infinity for $R_L = 300\ \Omega$.

**9.14** If a sinusoidal voltage source is applied to the amplifier of Fig. 9.1b, what is the value of the lower $-3$ dB break frequency of the voltage gain function if $I_C = 3$ mA, $r = 300\ \Omega$, $R_C = 1$ k$\Omega$, $R_B = 100$ k$\Omega$, and $C_1 = C_2 = 1\ \mu$F?

**9.15** A resistance load $R_L$ is capacitively coupled to the collector of the transistor in the circuit of Prob. 9.4a. (See Fig. 9.1b, where a series $R_L C_2$ circuit is connected from collector to emitter.) For the values of Prob. 9.4a, and with $R_L = 200\ \Omega$ and $C_2 = 0.5\ \mu$F, what is the value of the lower $-3$ dB break frequency of the current gain function $I_L/I_s$?

**9.16** For a silicon transistor for which $I_{CO}$ is negligible, design the bias circuit shown for the following values:

$$V_{CC} = 20 \text{ V} \qquad V_{CE} = 8 \text{ V}$$
$$I_C = 4 \text{ mA} \qquad \beta_0 = 50$$
$$V_E = 4 \text{ V}$$

Assume that $V_{BE} = 0.7$ V for the Si transistor and that $I_D \simeq 10\, I_B$ for the voltage at $B$ to remain approximately constant.

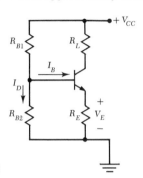

**Problem 9.16**

**9.17** The bias circuit of Prob. 9.16 is to be developed for a *pnp* Ge transistor. $V_{CC}$ now must be negative with respect to ground.

(a) Show actual flow direction of all currents and polarities of all voltages pertinent to the design.

(b) If $|V_{CC}| = 6$ V, $I_C = -2$ mA, $V_{CE} = 3$ V, and $V_E = -1$ V, and for $\beta_0 = 80$ and $I_{CO} = 1$ $\mu$A, obtain suitable values for the resistors.

**9.18** The change of the dc operating point of the bias circuit of Fig. 9.9 can be simply analyzed using the Thévenin equivalent of the input circuit, as in Fig. 9.11. Using the latter:

(a) Show that the input circuit equation is

$$V_{BB} = I_B R_B + V_{BE} + V_E$$

(b) Use the following to obtain an expression for $I_C$ in terms of $V_{BB}$, $V_{BE}$, and $\beta_0$ and the two resistances:

$$V_E = I_E R_E$$

$$I_C = -\frac{\beta_0}{\beta_0 + 1}\, I_E + I_{CO}$$

(c) Let $I_{CO} = 0$, and determine the change of $I_C$ with $\beta_0$ (i.e., $dI_C/d\beta_0$).

(d) Find the change of $V_{CE}$ for a change of $I_C$.

**9.19** Use the results of Prob. 9.18 to determine the change of the operating point of the design of Prob. 9.4 for a 10°C change in temperature.

**9.20**   For the circuit of Prob. 9.3, determine the change in operating point for a 10°C change in temperature. Compare with the results of Prob. 9.19.

**9.21**   Find the Thévenin and Norton equivalents for the output of the transistor-amplifier circuit model shown. When a circuit includes dependent sources, these sources are *not* reduced to zero when finding the impedances or admittances. Only independent sources are reduced to zero. Demonstrate this property by determining the Thévenin equivalent of the circuit shown if $g_m v$ is set equal to zero.

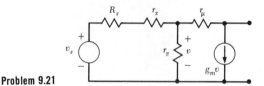

**Problem 9.21**

**9.22**   To illustrate the use of Norton's theorem, consider the circuit of Fig. 3.27. The resistance $R_3$ is taken as the load, and the "source" network is then as shown. To obtain the Norton-equivalent current source, the output terminals are shorted, as in figure *a*. Note that $C_2$ is shorted by the short-circuit load. Therefore, $C_2$ plays no part in the

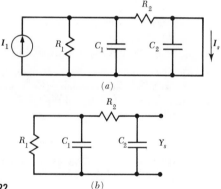

(a)

**Problem 9.22**          (b)

determination of $I_s$. The current $I_s$ is just that through $R_2$ in this condition. The Norton-equivalent admittance $Y_s$ is found by looking back into the network from the load terminals, with $I_1$ opened as shown in figure *b*. Show that the result is

$$Y_s = j\omega C_2 + \cfrac{1}{\cfrac{1}{G_2} + \cfrac{1}{G_1 + j\omega C_1}}$$

$$= \frac{G_1(G_1 + G_2) - \omega^2 C_1 C_2 + j\omega[(G_1 + G_2)C_2 + G_2 C_1]}{G_1 + G_2 + j\omega C_1}$$

For the complete circuit, including the load, we obtain the output voltages using Fig. 9.13, where we interpret $Y_L$ as $G_3$. Show that the result is

$$V_2 = \frac{I_s}{Y_s + G_3}$$

Using the above values of $I_s$ and $Y_s$, obtain an expression for the output voltage.

**9.23** For the circuit below, the quiescent (no-signal) operating point of $I_C = 10$ mA, $V_{CE} = 10$ V is set by the value of base current $I_B$ and the value of the collector supply voltage. Plot the dc load line on an ideal $I_C V_{CE}$ characteristic. If $n = 10$, plot the ac load line. For an input sinusoidal current source, estimate the maximum collector current and collector-emitter voltage excursions without clipping. What are the maximum excursions of the output current and output voltage? What is the maximum average output power in $R_L$ without clipping?

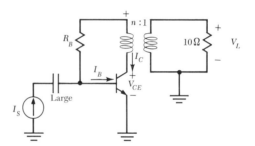

**Problem 9.23**

**9.24** The two-stage transistor amplifier shown in figure $a$ is used as a low-frequency amplifier.

(a) Determine the operating point of transistors $T_1$ and $T_2$; that is, determine $I_{C1}$, $V_{CE1}$ and $I_{C2}$, $V_{CE2}$ (neglect $V_{BE}$, $I_{CO}$).

(b) Assume the low-frequency circuit model for the transistor shown in figure $b$, and determine for each transistor the corresponding $g_m$ and $r_\pi$ (that is, $g_{m1}$, $r_{\pi1}$ and $g_{m2}$, $r_{\pi2}$).

(c) Draw the circuit model for the complete two-stage amplifier (neglecting $R_{B1}$, $R_{B2}$, $C_1$, $C_2$, and $C_3$).

(d) Assume that a sinusoidal voltage source $V_s$ with internal resistance $R_s$, as shown in figure $c$, is connected to the input terminals. Find the low-frequency voltage gain of the amplifier, $V_o/V_s$, in terms of $R_s$, $R_{C1}$, $R_{C2}$, $r_{\pi1}$, $r_{\pi2}$, $g_{m1}$, $g_{m2}$, $r_{x1}$, and $r_{x2}$.

(e) Assume $r_{x1} = r_{x2} = 50$ $\Omega$ and $R_s = 100$ $\Omega$. Find the numerical value of $V_o/V_s$.

**9.25** For the cascaded amplifier of Prob. 9.24, estimate the lower $-3$ dB bandedge frequency $\omega_l$ if $C_1 = C_2 = C_3 = 0.5$ $\mu$F, $R_s = 100$ $\Omega$, and if a load resistance $R_L = 100$ $\Omega$ is connected at the output from $C_3$ to ground.

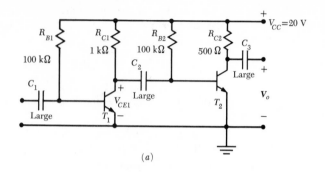

(a)

$$\beta_{01} = 50 \quad \beta_{02} = 70$$

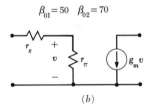

(b)

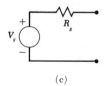

**Problem 9.24**                    (c)

**9.26**  What is the midfrequency current gain of the cascaded amplifier of Prob. 9.24 for a current-source input and a load resistance of 100 Ω?

**9.27**  The transistor circuit shown is used to obtain a high input impedance with almost unity voltage gain and low output impedance (for example, to couple a high-impedance source to a low-impedance load). Assume that $C$ can be considered a short circuit for the signal frequencies of interest.

(a) Replace the transistor by a small-signal circuit model for low frequencies and find the voltage gain $V_L/V_s$ as a function of $R_s$, $R_{B1}$, $R_{B2}$, $R_C$, $R_E$ and of the transistor parameters. Make simplifying assumptions as appropriate.

(b) If $R_s = 100$ kΩ, $R_E = 5$ kΩ, $R_{B1} = R_{B2} = 50$ kΩ, $R_C = 5$ kΩ, $r_\pi = 1$ kΩ, $r_x = 50$ Ω, $r_o = 25$ kΩ, and $\beta_0 = 50$, what is the magnitude of the voltage gain $V_L/V_S$?

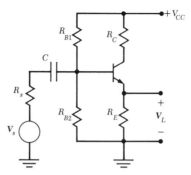

**Problem 9.27**

**9.28** (*a*) Given the $I_C V_{CE}$ characteristics shown in figure *a*, determine $R_B$ in figure *b* such that its dc operating point is at the edge of saturation. Show the graphical construction.

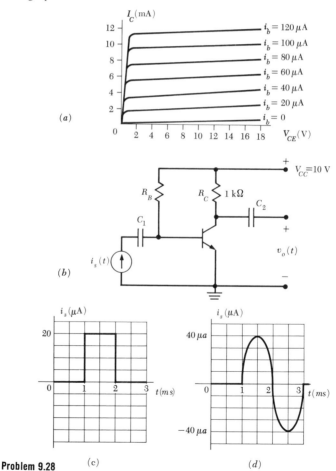

**Problem 9.28** (c) (d)

(b) The input current waveforms shown in figures c and d are applied. Sketch the shape and amplitude of the output-voltage waveforms. (Neglect all charge-storage effects in the transistor and coupling capacitors.)

**9.29** For the 2N914 transistor, the $I_C V_{CE}$ characteristics are given in Prob. 9.4; determine the value of $I_B$ and $R_B$ to saturate the transistor if $V_{CC} = 6$ V, $R_C = \frac{1}{2}$ kΩ, and $T = 25°C$. What value of $R_B$ should be chosen if the transistor is to remain saturated when $V_{CC}$ is varied $\pm 50$ percent. If $\beta_{ro} = 0.8$, what value of $R_B$ is needed to ensure saturation if $V_{CC}$ becomes negative?

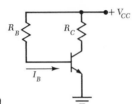

**Problem 9.29**

**9.30** In the circuit shown, the transistors are identical, $R_1 = R_2$, and $S1$ is a normally open switch. Each transistor *must be* either saturated or cut off.

(a) If $V_{C1} = 0.1$ V and $V_{C2} = 0.8$ V, which transistor is on?

(b) A dc voltage $V_1$ is now applied as shown. What must be the polarity of $V_1$ to turn the off transistor on, i.e., to cause a change of state?

(c) Which transistor will now be on when $V_1$ is removed?

(d) If $V_{C1} = 0.1$ V and $V_{C2} = 0.8$ V, what is the state of the circuit if switch $S1$ is closed? What is the state when switch $S1$ is reopened?

(e) If $V_{C1} = 0.1$ V and $V_{C2} = 0.8$ V, which transistor will be on if we close and reopen switch $S1$, and then apply a *positive* voltage $V_1$ (of sufficient magnitude)? Why?

(f) If $V_{C1} = 0.1$ V and $V_{C2} = 0.8$ V, which transistor will be on if we apply a *negative* voltage (of sufficient magnitude), and *then* close and reopen switch $S1$? Why?

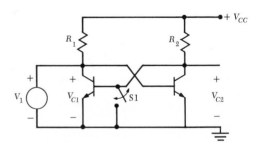

**Problem 9.30**

**9.31** The basic resistance-coupled bistable circuit of Fig. 9.31, repeated here, can be designed in a manner similar to that of the bias circuit of

Fig. 9.9. For a given value of $I_{CM}$ for the on transistor, say $T_2$, $R_C = V_{CC}/I_{CM}$. A base current is next chosen sufficient to saturate this transistor $[> -(1/\beta_0)I_{CM}]$. A current $I_2$ of comparable magnitude is chosen to flow through $R_{B2}$ to $V_{BB}(= -2$ V). With an estimate of $V_{BE}$ ($= 0.7$ V for a Si transistor),

$$R_{B2} = \frac{V_{BE} + V_{BB}}{I_2}$$

For $T_2$, $V_{CE} \simeq 0$, therefore for $T_1$, $V_{BE} \simeq -V_{BB}R_{B1}/(R_{B1} + R_{B2}) < 0$ and $T_1$ is off. Consequently, only the current $I_1 = I_B + I_2$ flows through both $R_C$ and $R_{B1}$:

$$R_C + R_{B1} = \frac{V_{CC} - V_{BE}}{I_1}$$

The other stable state is $T_1$ on, $T_2$ off. Use this procedure to design the circuit for $V_{CC} = 6$ V, $-V_{BB} = -2$ V, and $I_{CM} = 5$ mA. Let $\beta_0 = 50$.

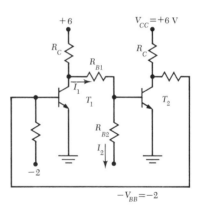

**Problem 9.31**

# chapter 10

# CHARGE CONTROL IN VACUUM

## 10.1 introduction

In studying devices that are used to achieve circuit functions, the last several chapters have stressed semiconducting devices because of their great present importance and because they demonstrate many fundamental physical phenomena typical of any electronic device utilized for amplification, switching, control, etc. Other types of solid-state devices are of importance, and vacuum devices are also. With respect to the latter, it should be remembered that electronic engineering grew from the ability to control charges in a vacuum. Therefore, if only for historical purposes, it would be worth looking at some of the fundamental processes in such devices, noting the similarities and differences with respect to semiconducting devices. In addition, vacuum devices are still used so that the study is of more than historical interest.

The largest number of vacuum devices manufactured a few years ago were space-charge-controlled *electron tubes* of the diode, triode, tetrode, or pentode type, used for oscillation, amplification, switching, and similar functions in radio and TV receivers, control systems, computers, and the like. It is for this class of functions that the vacuum devices have been largely replaced by the semiconductor devices in the low and moderate power ranges. Triodes and related tubes are still used in most transmitters, with the largest built to handle more than a megawatt of average signal power. Charge control of an electron stream by a grid structure is also an important function in microwave tubes and cathode-ray (display) devices. Thus an understanding of space-charge control remains fundamental.

328

*Electron optics* techniques (i.e., the shaping, focusing, and deflection of an electron beam) are also of continuing importance. Display devices, such as the cathode-ray tube of an oscilloscope, the picture tube of a TV set, or the storage tube widely used in data storage and display, are fundamental components of electronic systems. Camera tubes, photomultipliers, electron microscopes, and other special-purpose devices use many of the same techniques as the display devices.

All of the vacuum devices mentioned, together with the microwave devices of the following chapter, utilize the flow and control of electrons in vacuum. In order to study these devices, we thus need to bring in the fundamental aspects of electron flow, especially those aspects concerned with the mutual repulsion of individual electrons (space-charge effects). First, however, we study the mechanisms by which electron streams are obtained from solids. Most of the devices mentioned above utilize electrons which are obtained by heating an electrode (thermionic emission), although other processes of electron emission are important. Electron emission is considered in the following section.

## 10.2   electron emission from solids

In discussing the emission of electrons from solids, we are concerned mainly with metals since they have a large density of free electrons. At a finite temperature, $T > 0$, some of these electrons have sufficient energy to escape from the solid. We are concerned here with mechanisms for increasing this number. Figure 10.1a is an energy diagram for a metal showing the density of occupied states at temperature $T = 0°K$, as given earlier in Chap. 4.

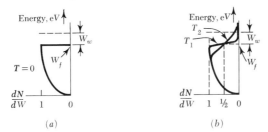

(a)                                         (b)

**FIGURE 10.1**   *Density of occupied energy states dN/dW for electrons in a metal emitter. (a) Degenerate case $T = 0$; (b) curves for finite temperature $T_2 \gg T_1 > 0$. $W_w$ = work function. $W_f$ = Fermi energy level.*

Figure 10.1b shows the density of occupied states for two higher temperatures: $T_1$ may be considered as room temperature, say $300°K$, and $T_2$ a temperature much above room temperature. From (4.10) the high-energy portion of this distribution approaches a Maxwell-Boltzmann distribution

$$\frac{dN}{dW} \sim e^{-W/kT} \tag{10.1}$$

**WORK FUNCTION**    Electrons may be removed from the metal in a variety of ways, but all require that a certain minimum energy be given an electron in order to free it from the metal. This energy, measured with respect to the Fermi level, is called the *work function*, $W_w$, and is illustrated in Fig. 10.1*a* and *b*. Assuming the electron free from its parent atom, and neglecting complications of surface phenomena, one can understand this energy by recognizing that the removal of the electron from the surface of the solid leaves a net positive charge. The attraction between the electron and this "image" charge produces a force which must be overcome if the electron is to escape. The work function is the integral of this image force from the surface to a large distance away from the surface. The effective barrier occurs over a few atomic distances, but is pictured in Fig. 10.2 as an abrupt step.

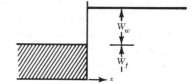

**FIGURE 10.2**  *Potential energy of electrons versus distance x from a metal surface.*

This barrier is seen to be analogous to that of the *pn* junction in that removed charges build up the potential, but here there is only electron transfer and not holes. When a junction is formed between two different metals, a potential barrier also exists between the metals, which is equal to the difference between the work functions of the two materials. This potential difference is the *contact potential* referred to in Sec. 5.4.

The above picture is clearly an idealized one since the electron starts not from the plane of the surface but from within the crystal. The actual structure of the solid is thus important. A more complete model of the solid shows that the work function is a function of lattice spacing. It is also very sensitive to purity of the surface. Table 10.1 gives some values of work functions for several materials.

**TABLE 10.1    *Properties of Thermionic Emitters*†**

| Type of emitter | Thermionic work function, eV | Operating temperature, °K | Maximum usable dc emission, A/cm² | Approximate life, hr |
|---|---|---|---|---|
| Tungsten | 4.5 | 2600 | 0.5 | 10,000 |
| Tantalum | 4.1 | 2400 | 0.5 | 10,000 |
| Thoriated tungsten | 2.6 | 2000 | 3.0 | 5000 |
| Philips dispenser (barium-tungsten) | 2.1 | 1200 | 1.3 | 8000 |
| Oxide cathode | 1.2 | 1100 | 0.5 | 3000 |

†From various sources; lifetime values very approximate.

**THERMIONIC EMISSION**  Figure 10.1*b* shows that at any finite temperature some electrons have enough energy to surmount the potential barrier which we have called the work function, so that such high-energy electrons can become free (i.e., are emitted) from the metal. At room temperature $T_1$, the number of emitted electrons is so small as to be undetectable. As temperature is increased, however, the number of electrons with the required minimum energy increases rapidly because of the Boltzmann relation (10.1). Thus useful electron emission can occur. The energy necessary to surmount the work-function barrier is supplied as thermal energy and the resultant emission is called *thermionic emission*. The emitted current density is expected to include the Boltzmann factor in a manner analogous to that for the *pn* junction of Chap. 5. The equation for current density $J$ is

$$J = A_0 T^2 e^{-V_w/V_T} \qquad (10.2a)$$

where $T$ is absolute temperature, $A_0$ is a constant of the material,[1] $V_w$ is the work function in volts, and $V_T$ is the thermal energy in volts, as used earlier:

$$V_T = \frac{kT}{q} \qquad (10.2b)$$

Equation (10.2a) is known as Richardson's equation or the Richardson-Dushman equation.[2]

The $T^2$ factor in (10.2a) is dominated by the exponential factor in the equation. This is similar to the situation for the density of carriers in a semiconductor as given in Sec. 4.5. A logarithmic plot is consequently useful in studying thermionic emitters. From (10.2a)

$$\ln \frac{J}{T^2} = \ln A_0 - \frac{V_w}{V_T} = \ln A_0 - \frac{qV_w}{kT} \qquad (10.3)$$

A plot of this equation, as in Fig. 10.3, results in a straight line with a

**FIGURE 10.3**  *Thermionic emission from a hot cathode as a function of cathode temperature.*

negative slope $qV_w/k$ when plotted versus $1/T$. The intercept with the vertical axis gives $\ln A_0$.

---

[1] Idealized analysis yields a value for $A_0$ of 120 A/cm² (°K)², a value which is approximated by pure metals.

[2] Richardson had originally proposed a term $T^{1/2}$, but quantum-mechanical considerations led to $T^2$. It is difficult to show the difference experimentally.

Tungsten is the most common pure metal used as a practical thermionic emitter. As shown in Table 10.1, its work function is about 4.5 V. Tungsten's melting point is about 3700°K, and operation at a temperature around 2500°K gives useful current densities. Current densities around 0.5 A/cm² are obtainable from tungsten with a reasonable length of life. There are metals with lower work functions than tungsten. But the metal must not melt, or vaporize, too rapidly at the temperature required for the desired emission density. Tantalum and molybdenum are used but not as widely as tungsten.

As noted earlier the value of $V_w$ is markedly affected by surface conditions. It has been found that the work function of a metal is reduced if a monolayer of a suitable material is adsorbed on the metal surface. Thoriated tungsten emitters make use of this effect by introducing thorium oxide into tungsten metal. Heating of the metal produces a surface layer of thorium atoms on the tungsten. Because the ionization potential of thorium, about 4.0 V, is lower than the 4.5 V work function of tungsten, the thorium atoms lose valence electrons to the tungsten. The thorium ions form a dipole layer (positive on the thorium side) which reduces the potential barrier at the metal surface. The resulting work function is reduced to about 2.6 V so that this emitter gives useful current densities at temperatures around 2000°K.

Experiments show that oxide-coated cathodes have even lower work functions, of the order of 1.1 to 1.5 V. Such emitters consist of nickel with a surface coating of a mixture of barium, strontium, and calcium oxides. They give adequate electron emission at a temperature of about 1100°K. Oxide coating is, however, quite vulnerable to bombardment by the heavy positive ions.[1] Because of this bombardment, one usually restricts the use of such oxide emitters to collector-emitter potentials of less than 1000 V unless special focusing measures are introduced to prevent the ions from striking the emitter.

The high temperatures required for pure metals and for thoriated tungsten are usually obtained by passing a current directly through a wire or filament

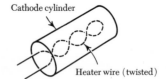

Cathode cylinder

Heater wire (twisted)

**FIGURE 10.4**   *Indirectly heated cathode.*

of the material, producing a filamentary emitter. Oxide-coated emitters are frequently heated by a heater filament separated from the emitting surface.

---

[1] As the vacuum is not really perfect, there are always some positive ions present which under the influence of the $\vec{E}$ field are accelerated to the cathode. The ion impact damages the oxide surface.

This process is illustrated for a cylinderical structure in Fig. 10.4. An ac voltage, which can be obtained from an ac supply via a small transformer, is supplied to the heater filament. If the thermal heat capacity of the cathode cylinder is high enough, variations in temperature caused by the ac heating of the filament are smoothed out at the emitting surface, resulting in nearly constant electron emission. The heater is often twisted, as shown in the figure, to minimize inductive coupling of the ac heater current to other portions of the circuit.

**PHOTOELECTRIC EMISSION**    The energy for the removal of electrons from metals can be supplied by light, in which case the emission is called *photoelectric emission*. When light falls on the surface of a solid, a photon can give energy to an electron in the solid in the amount $hf$, where $f$ is the frequency of light and $h$ is Planck's constant equal to $6.63 \cdot 10^{-34}$ J/s. If we assume that this energy is greater than the work function, the electron escapes from the metal with energy

$$W = hf - qV_w \qquad \text{joules} \qquad (10.4)$$

The above is Einstein's photoelectric equation. We see that the energy of emission of the electrons depends upon the frequency of the light. The current density of the emitted electrons depends upon the intensity of light striking the surface and upon the *quantum efficiency*. Quantum efficiency is the probability of emitting one electron for each quantum of light. Photoelectric emission is considered further in Chap. 12.

**SECONDARY EMISSION**    Energetic electrons striking a surface transmit energy to the solid through collisions. Electrons originally in the solid which are directed toward the surface can escape the solid if the energy imparted to them by the collisions is larger than or equal to $V_w$. Such electrons are called *secondary electrons*. The electrons striking the surface of the solid from outside are called the *primary electrons*. If the energy of the primary electron is larger than $V_w$, more than one secondary electron may be liberated. The number of secondary electrons produced for each primary electron is called the *yield* and is a function of the energy of the primary electron. The yield cannot be increased without limit by using primary electrons of higher energy because they simply penetrate deeper into the atomic structure. Secondary electrons inside the solid will be reabsorbed and will be lost for the secondary emission. The yield has, therefore, a maximum, as shown in Fig. 10.5. Yields as high as 50 are obtained from special composite surfaces.

**HIGH-FIELD EMISSION**    When a strong electric field (with an intensity of the order of $10^7$ V/cm) is applied to the surface of a solid at room temperature, appreciable electron emission may occur because the potential barrier at the surface of the solid is lowered in value and confined to a smaller region of space. When the barrier is very thin, (about 100 Å), electrons can penetrate

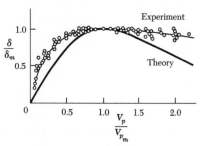

**FIGURE 10.5** *Normalized secondary emission yield versus normalized energy of primary electrons, composite plot for several metals.* $\delta_m$ *is maximum yield for each metal;* $V_{pm}$ *is voltage for* $\delta_m$. *(From L. V. Azaroff and J. J. Brophy, "Electronic Processes in Materials," McGraw-Hill Book Company, New York, 1963.)*

the barrier by "tunneling" through it.[1] Quite large emitted current densities can consequently result. The current density for metals has been given by Fowler and Nordheim as

$$J = A_f E^2 e^{-B_f/E} \qquad A/cm^2 \qquad (10.5)$$

where $E$ is the magnitude of the field in volts per centimeter normal to the surface and

$$A_f = \frac{6.2 \cdot 10^{-6}}{V_B}\left(\frac{V_f}{V_w}\right)^{1/2} \qquad A/V^2$$

$$B_f = 6.8 \cdot 10^7 V_w^{3/2} \qquad V/cm$$

In order to visualize the effect of the field on the potential barrier, consider Fig. 10.6 which shows the effect of the electric field at the surface on the potential energy diagram. If the field is assumed constant, the curve of

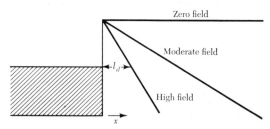

**FIGURE 10.6** *Potential energy barrier at idealized metal surface as electric field is applied.*

potential energy versus distance is linear as in Fig. 10.6. High-energy electrons in the solid, i.e., those high in the conduction band, can tunnel through the distance $l_d$, as illustrated in the figure. This distance decreases as the field increases, as shown in the figure.

[1] In quantum mechanics there is a finite probability of a particle surmounting a potential barrier even if the energy of the particle is insufficient from the point of view of classical mechanics. The probability increases rapidly as the thickness of the barrier decreases, and hence the name "tunneling."

The field at the surface is a strong function of the geometrical configuration and is much higher at sharp points. Field emitters which are used in X-ray tubes and electron microscopes may have radii of curvature as low as a few hundred angstroms. Field emission may occur in any high-voltage device, around sharp edges and points, where it may be an undesired effect.

## 10.3    the vacuum diode; child's law

The vacuum diode is a two-electrode device as sketched in Fig. 10.7a. (The heater, described in Sec. 10.2, may require additional terminals but is not

(a)                                    (b)

**FIGURE 10.7**    (a) *Planar diode;* (b) *symbol for diode shown with applied dc voltage.*

essential to the behavior discussed here.) The symbol for the device, shown with an applied voltage, is given in Fig. 10.7b. Electrons flow from the emitter, which is a *thermionic cathode* for this device, to the positively biased collector which is called the *anode* or *plate*. The first such device was built by A. Fleming in 1904, although T.A. Edison's experimental arrangement which led to the discovery of thermionic emission (the Edison effect) in 1883 might be considered to be such a diode.

**THE PHYSICAL BASIS FOR SPACE-CHARGE LIMITATION OF CURRENT**    For the development of this section we assume that the two electrodes are parallel planes in a vacuum, that a fixed voltage $V$ is applied between the cathode and the anode (plate), and that all effects are one-dimensional. With negligible electron emission (low cathode temperature) the electric field between electrodes is just the constant value $V/d$, where $d$ is the spacing between planes as shown in Fig. 10.7a. The potential curve versus distance away

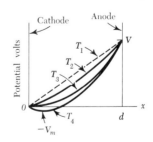

**FIGURE 10.8**    *Potential distribution versus distance between electrodes for several cathode temperatures.* $T_4 > T_3 > T_2 > T_1$.

from the cathode is linear, as shown by the dashed line in Fig. 10.8. As temperature is increased, electrons are emitted and a negative space charge appears in the region between cathode and anode. This charge lowers the potential, as shown by the curve labeled $T_2$. For a still higher temperature, $T_3$, the space charge caused by electron emission is sufficient to lower the electric field at the cathode to zero. No additional current can flow for this given anode-cathode voltage since a higher space charge would depress the current further, as shown by the curve labeled $T_4$. The resulting negative gradient at the cathode would then inhibit electron emission, restoring matters to the curve with zero gradient at the cathode. The reasoning above assumes that the electrons are emitted from the cathode surface with zero velocity. Emitted electrons actually have a distribution of emitted velocities as indicated by the energy diagram of Fig. 10.1b. Therefore a potential minimum, $-V_m$, occurs in front of the cathode, as in the curve labeled $T_4$. The value of $V_m$ is of the order of the average emission energy, which is about 0.1 V. For this case, as well as for the idealized case of zero emission velocity, only a limited maximum current can flow for a given voltage $V$ because of the negative charge within the space. This condition of operation is called *space-charge limitation of current*.

For space-charge-limited operation, the current changes as the voltage $V$ changes. A higher value of $V$ produces a higher field at the cathode in the absence of space charge, and this requires more space charge to depress the potential enough to produce the described balance. The nature of the current-voltage characteristic can easily be determined if the small thermal velocities of emission are neglected. For this case, the electric field from the negative space charge must just cancel the applied field $V/d$ at the cathode surface. From Gauss' law, the field from the charge is proportional to the total charge within the space. The charge $Q$ is the current density $J$ multiplied by the time of travel $\tau$ across the diode. The time $\tau$ is in turn proportional to spacing $d$ and inversely proportional to some average velocity. Finally, from (4.6b), the velocity is proportional to $V^{1/2}$. Thus

$$Q = J\tau = J\frac{d}{v_{av}} = K\frac{Jd}{\sqrt{V}} \tag{10.6a}$$

where $K$ is a constant. The electric field produced by this space charge is then

$$E = \frac{K_1 Jd}{\sqrt{V}} \tag{10.6b}$$

where $K_1$ is a new constant. If (10.6b) is equated to the applied field in the absence of space charge, $V/d$,

$$J = K_2 \frac{V^{3/2}}{d^2} \tag{10.6c}$$

Thus current density is seen to be proportional to the $\frac{3}{2}$ power of anode potential $V$. This important law was derived by C. D. Child for ions in 1913 and by I. Langmuir for electrons in 1914. It is consequently known as *Child's law*, or the *Child-Langmuir law*. It is derived more completely below.

**DERIVATION OF CHILD'S LAW**   For the derivation of Child's law, we continue to assume one-dimensional flow and to neglect the velocities of electron emission. The potential distribution within the diode $V(x) = V_x$ is given by Poisson's equation[1]

$$\frac{d^2 V_x}{dx^2} = -\frac{\rho}{\varepsilon_0} \tag{10.7a}$$

where $\rho$ is charge density and $\varepsilon_0$ is permittivity of free space, equal to $(1/36\pi) \, 10^{-9}$ F/m in MKS units.[2] Charge density is given by current density divided by velocity and the velocity at $x$ is given in terms of the potential $V_x$ by the usual expression for a static problem. Thus

$$\rho = -\frac{J}{v_x} = -\frac{J}{\sqrt{\dfrac{2q}{m} V_x}} \tag{10.7b}$$

The negative sign is introduced in (10.7b) in order to obtain the current density $J$ as a positive number. Introduction of (10.7b) in (10.7a) gives

$$\frac{d^2 V_x}{dx^2} = \left(\frac{m}{2q}\right)^{1/2} \frac{J}{\varepsilon_0} V_x^{-1/2} \tag{10.7c}$$

It should be noted that current density in the dc case must be independent of $x$, since continuity requires that $J$ be a constant for our one-dimensional model. We set the conditions that $V_x = 0$ at the cathode, $x = 0$. Also, by the argument for space-charge limitation given above, $dV_x/dx = 0$ at $x = 0$. The equation is integrated by substituting $y = dV_x/dx$ so that $d^2 V_x/dx^2$ is $dy/dx$ (Prob. 10.1). The result, with these conditions substituted, is

$$V_x = \left(\frac{m}{2q}\right)^{1/3} \left(\frac{9J}{4\varepsilon_0}\right)^{2/3} x^{4/3} \tag{10.7d}$$

This result may also be checked by differentiation and substitution in (10.7c). From the result, we see that the potential curve is a 4/3 power of distance for the space-charge-limited case with zero emission velocity. Thus the curve labeled $T_3$ in Fig. 10.8 should be of this form.

To obtain the current density which flows with a given applied voltage, the anode condition, $V_x = V$ at $x = d$, is substituted in (10.7d):

---

[1] $V(x) = V_x$ is used instead of the $\psi(x)$ notation of Chap. 5. Note that $V_x$ does not represent the $x$ component of a vector.

[2] As noted in Chap. 4, we utilize the MKS system when the force equation is included in the development in order to avoid inclusion of a conversion factor in this equation.

$$V = \left(\frac{m}{2q}\right)^{1/3} \left(\frac{9J}{4\varepsilon_0}\right)^{2/3} d^{4/3} \qquad (10.8a)$$

The solution for $J$ yields

$$J = \frac{4\varepsilon_0}{9} \left(\frac{2q}{m}\right)^{1/2} \frac{V^{3/2}}{d^2} \qquad (10.8b)$$

Substitution of numerical values for $\varepsilon_0$ and $q/m$ gives

$$J = 2.33 \cdot 10^{-6} \frac{V^{3/2}}{d^2} \qquad (10.8c)$$

In this equation current density is in amperes per square meter if $d$ is in meters, in amperes per square centimeter if $d$ is in centimeters, etc. For a numerical value, a voltage of 25 V across a spacing of 1 cm produces a space-charge-limited current of

$$J = 2.33 \cdot 10^{-6} \frac{(25)^{3/2}}{(1)^2} = 2.33 \cdot 10^{-6} \cdot 125 = 0.291 \cdot 10^{-3} \text{ A/cm}^2$$

This current is 0.291 mA/cm$^2$. If the diode spacing is decreased to 1 mm, current density goes up by a factor of 100, yielding 29.1 mA/cm$^2$. If voltage is now increased to 100 V, current density increases by a factor $(100/25)^{3/2}$ $= (4)^{3/2} = 8$, and becomes 233 mA/cm$^2$.

The derivation given above is for the planar diode, but a physical argument as used in arriving at (10.6c) leads to the conclusion that space-charge-limited current in diodes of any shape, neglecting initial velocities, is proportional to the $\frac{3}{2}$ power of voltage. That is

$$I = K_3 V^{3/2} \qquad (10.9)$$

where the constant $K_3$ must be obtained by analysis of the specific configurations, or from experiment.

**DIODE CHARACTERISTIC AND APPLICATIONS**    The $IV$ characteristic of an idealized diode following the Child-Langmuir law is shown in Fig. 10.9a. Current is zero in such a diode for $V < 0$ since the cathode is assumed to be the only emitting electrode, and emitted electrons are assumed to have zero velocity. The characteristic of an actual diode departs from this ideal because of a number of practical factors, such as nonuniformities of emission, positive ions within the space-charge region, and anode emission. Of the fundamental assumptions made in the derivation, the neglect of initial thermal velocities becomes important for low-voltage operation. The nonzero thermal velocities produce a small but finite current when the collector voltage is negative, $V = -V_r$. Because of the Boltzmann distribution, (10.1), there are always some electrons with emission energies greater than $V_r$. These high-energy electrons have enough energy to over-come a retarding field and reach the collector. The region of low and

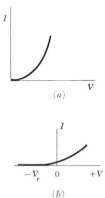

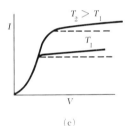

**FIGURE 10.9**   (a) *IV characteristic of a vacuum diode following Child's law;* (b) *IV characteristic on expanded scale;* (c) *IV characteristic showing saturation.*

negative collector potential is shown expanded in Fig. 10.9*b*. In contrast to the semiconducting diodes, note that the current for the vacuum diode is in the same direction for reverse bias as for forward bias (Prob. 10.2).

For large anode-cathode voltages, the current density predicted by (10.8*c*) may be larger than the current that is actually available from the cathode for the given temperature. This leads to a saturation of current as indicated by the horizontal dashed line in Fig. 10.9*c*. In actual diodes, the current continues to increase slightly with voltage because of a com-bination of field and thermal effects acting to increase emission (Schottky effect). Notice in Fig. 10.9*c* that use of a higher temperature, $T_2$, raises the value of this "saturation" effect, as expected. Operation in the saturated region is known as *temperature-limited operation.*

Since the vacuum diode provides larger currents for positive voltage than for negative voltage, it resembles the semiconductor diode (although the *IV* equation is different) and could be used for the same purposes: rectification, clipping, slicing, clamping, and logic operations. The non-linear characteristic of the diode has also been used in mixing, modulation, demodulation, and other functions described in Chap. 2 and illustrated in Sec. 3.3. Vacuum diodes have been used for all such purposes, but semi-conductor diodes are now generally preferable and the principle of operation is largely given to introduce the interesting matter of space-charge control of current. Similarly the following section is presented primarily as a base for small-signal analysis of the triode and pentode described in Secs. 10.4 and 10.6.

**SMALL-SIGNAL CONDUCTANCE OF THE DIODE**   If the diode is biased by a dc anode-to-cathode voltage, $V_{DD}$, and if a smaller signal voltage is placed in series, the ac current is given approximately by the slope of the $IV$ characteristic at $V_{DD}$, as illustrated in Fig. 10.10. This is exactly as in the small-signal

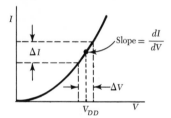

**FIGURE 10.10**   *Slope of diode characteristic used for variational quantities.*

analysis of semiconductor diodes and transistors given previously. The slope of the characteristic is called the *small-signal incremental conductance*. For a diode obeying Child's law, (10.9), this conductance is

$$g_d = \frac{dI}{dV} = \frac{d}{dV}(K_3 V^{3/2}) = \tfrac{3}{2} K_3 V^{1/2} = \tfrac{3}{2} \frac{I}{V} \qquad (10.10)$$

For a diode of 1 mm spacing and 1 cm$^2$ area operated at 25 V, the current is $0.291 \cdot 10^{-3}$ A from the earlier numerical example. The diode con-ductance $g_d$ is then $1.74 \cdot 10^{-5}$ mho $= 17.4$ $\mu$mho. This analysis is useful in the study of the other space-charge-controlled devices which follow.

## 10.4   the triode

The vacuum triode is a three-electrode, electronic vacuum device (electron tube) formed by introducing an open electrode, called a *grid*, between the cathode and the anode. The grid electrode may be a mesh, a helix, or a series of parallel wires. It controls current by means of a potential applied between it and the cathode. Because of the open nature of the grid, control is achieved while permitting most of the current to pass through to the anode. Amplification is possible with the triode as it was for the transistor. De Forest built the first such device, which he called an *audion*, in 1906.

The triode is shown symbolically in Fig. 10.11 with dc potentials applied between grid and cathode and between anode and cathode. Because the anode of a triode is also usually called the plate, we use the latter term in the remainder of this chapter. Normal active operation is obtained with the grid biased negatively and the plate positive with respect to

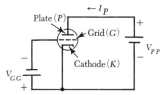

**FIGURE 10.11** *Symbol of vacuum triode shown with dc sources (biases) applied.*

the cathode. Figure 10.12*a* is a sketch of a section through a planar triode which has a grid of parallel wires all at the same potential. With the grid negative and the plate positive, the curve of potential versus distance from the cathode to the plate for a section through a grid wire (as *AA* of Fig. 10.12*a*) is shown by the solid curve of Fig. 10.12*b*. A section midway

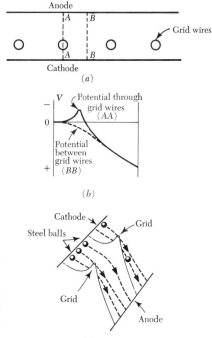

**FIGURE 10.12** (a) *Section through planar triode with parallel-wire grid;* (b) *two-dimensional potential distribution for triode of* (a)*;* (c) *rubber membrane model with steel balls representing electron flow in triode*

between grid wires (as *BB* of Fig. 10.12*a*) yields the dashed potential curve of Fig. 10.12*b*. Positive potential is plotted downward in the curves for easy comparison with the three-dimensional analog sketched in Fig. 10.12*c*. This analog is one in which potential is analogous to the vertical displacement of a stretched rubber membrane above some fixed reference.

The reference for modeling the triode is the cathode potential. Rods which represent the grid wires push the membrane to a height proportional to $-V_{GK}$ at the rods, while a line representing the plate is held down to a level proportional to $-V_{PK}$. The height of the membrane at any point is then approximately proportional to the potential of that point. The analog of Fig. 10.12c can also be used to approximate the motion of electrons if small balls are introduced, as shown, and allowed to roll down the potential hill. This analog provides moderately accurate quantitative results, but it is even more useful for qualitative visualization of the different potential profiles and the electron paths.

A further study of Fig. 10.12 shows that a given change in grid voltage is more effective in controlling current from the cathode region than the same change in plate voltage because of the closer proximity of the grid to the cathode. The important matter, actually, is the shielding of the plate by the grid with most of the field lines from the plate ending on the grid instead of on the cathode. Figure 10.12b also shows that although the potential curves versus distance vary greatly in the immediate vicinity of the grid, all potential curves are almost coincident near the cathode and near the plate. Of particular interest is the region near the cathode which is effective in controlling current by means of the space-charge mechanism discussed in Sec. 10.3. As with the diode, the space-charge-limited current is that which produces a charge in the space which in turn produces a field at the cathode equal and opposite to the applied field in the absence of space charge. This assumes ample emission at the cathode and negligible emission velocities, as in the diode. The triode current, however, depends upon both the voltage between grid and cathode and that between plate and cathode.

We may obtain ideal current-voltage characteristics of the triode by considering the region near the cathode as an equivalent diode and applying Child's law, (10.8c),

$$J = 2.33 \cdot 10^{-6} \frac{V_{\text{eq}}^{3/2}}{d_{\text{eq}}^2} \tag{10.11a}$$

where $V_{\text{eq}}$ and $d_{\text{eq}}$ are equivalent voltage and distance parameters. The equivalent voltage is some linear combination of the grid and plate voltages. It is reasonable to expect that the grid-to-cathode voltage enters directly, while the plate-to-cathode voltage is modified by a multiplier arising from the shielding effect:

$$V_{\text{eq}} = V_{GK} + \frac{V_{PK}}{\mu_0} \tag{10.11b}$$

The quantity $\mu_0$, which is called the *electrostatic amplification factor*, is the ratio of effectiveness of grid to plate voltage. Values for practical triodes range from 2 to 200. For reasonably high values of $\mu_0$, which result because of the close spacing of grid wires, the cathode and grid electrodes act as a diode when $V_{eq} > 0$. The equivalent spacing for normal operation is approximately the cathode-grid spacing, $d_{GK}$. Consequently, for an area $A$, the cathode current from (10.11$a$) and (10.11$b$) is

$$I_K \simeq 2.33 \cdot 10^{-6} \frac{A}{d_{GK}^2} \left( V_{GK} + \frac{V_{PK}}{\mu_0} \right)^{3/2} \quad \text{ampere} \quad (10.12)$$

If the grid is sufficiently negative, negligible current flows to the grid and (10.12) corresponds to the plate current $I_P$.

As a numerical example, if $A = 1$ cm$^2$, $d_{GK} = 0.5$ mm, $V_{GK} = -1$ V, $V_{PK} = 200$ V, and $\mu_0 = 20$, then

$$I_P = \frac{2.33 \cdot 10^{-6} \cdot 1}{0.25 \cdot 10^{-2}} \left( -1 + \frac{200}{20} \right)^{3/2} = \frac{2.33 \cdot 10^{-6} \cdot 27}{0.25 \cdot 10^{-2}}$$

$$= 0.0252 \text{ A} = 25.2 \text{ mA}$$

**CHARACTERISTIC CURVES OF THE TRIODE**   From (10.12), a plot of $I_P$ versus $V_{PK}$ with $V_{GK}$ as a parameter yields the set of curves[1] shown in Fig. 10.13. In the idealized model, each curve is of the same form, but the curves are displaced

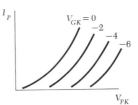

**FIGURE 10.13**  *Plate characteristics of idealized triode.*

from one another by the values of grid bias. The idealized curves also show a sharp cutoff, yielding zero current for $V_{GK} = -V_{PK}/\mu_0$. The $IV$ characteristics for practical triodes differ from the idealized ones for several reasons. Finite emission velocities and the variation of electric field along the cathode surface are two of the important departures from the model described. A set of characteristics for a typical triode is shown in Fig. 10.14.

For a triode with load resistance $R_L$, as shown in Fig. 10.15, the load line and operating point may be found in the same manner as for transistors. If $V_{PP}$ is the supply voltage, the actual anode voltage is

$$V_{PK} = V_{PP} - I_P R_L \quad (10.13)$$

---

[1] This set is known as the *plate family*. Other methods of plotting this function of two variables are of course possible. The *grid family*, which is plotted with $I_P$ as a function of $V_{GK}$, with $V_{PK}$ a parameter, is also useful.

This relation is readily plotted by finding the intercepts $V_{PP}$ and $V_{PP}/R_L$, as shown in Fig. 10.16. The operating point is found by the intersection of this load line and the bias voltage, $V_{GK} = V_{GG}$. Thus if $V_{GG} = -2$ V,

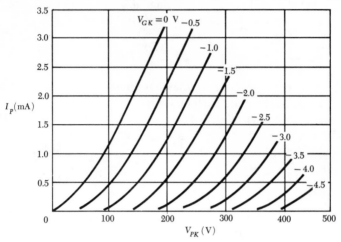

**FIGURE 10.14** *Plate characteristics for a typical triode.*

the operating point is $A$ of Fig. 10.16. If a sinusoidal signal voltage is introduce in the grid circuit,

$$v_s = 2 \sin \omega t \qquad \text{volts}$$

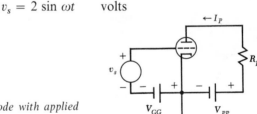

**FIGURE 10.15** *Circuit for triode with applied sinusoidal signal.*

the instantaneous grid voltage changes with time from $-2 + (-2) = -4$ to $-2 + 2 = 0$. The operation is on the load line between $B$ and $C$ as shown in Fig. 10.16.

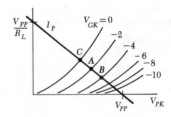

**FIGURE 10.16** *Plate characteristics with load line for circuit of Fig. 10.15.*

## 10.5  small-signal parameters and circuit models of the triode

If the signal variations for a triode are small compared with dc values at the operating point, the slopes of the characteristic are useful for calculating the behavior of signals. The small-signal circuit models result, as was also the case for transistors. We could develop these circuits in a manner completely parallel to that used in Chap. 8. The development to be given is essentially the same as in Chap. 8, but utilizes the partial derivative notation.

In general the plate current $I_P$ is a function of both $V_{GK}$ and $V_{PK}$:

$$I_P = f(V_{GK}, V_{PK}) \qquad (10.14a)$$

The total differential of $I_P$ is given by

$$dI_P = \frac{\partial I_P}{\partial V_{GK}} dV_{GK} + \frac{\partial I_P}{\partial V_{PK}} dV_{PK} \qquad (10.14b)$$

The differential changes may be taken as signals, $dI_P = i_p$, $dV_{GK} = v_g$, and $dV_{PK} = v_p$. The first coefficient of (10.14b) can be defined as the transconductance, $g_m$:

$$g_m = \frac{\partial I_P}{\partial V_{GK}} \simeq \left. \frac{\Delta I_P}{\Delta V_{GK}} \right|_{\Delta V_{PK} = 0} \qquad (10.15a)$$

The second coefficient is the output or plate conductance $g_p$:

$$g_p = \frac{1}{r_p} = \frac{\partial I_P}{\partial V_{PK}} \simeq \left. \frac{\Delta I_P}{\Delta V_{PK}} \right|_{\Delta V_{GK} = 0} \qquad (10.15b)$$

Then (10.14b) may be written

$$i_p = g_m v_g + g_p v_p = g_m v_g + \frac{v_p}{r_p} \qquad (10.16)$$

The reciprocal of $g_p$ is called the *plate resistance* $r_p$ and is more commonly used than $g_p$. It is clear from (10.15) that the parameters $g_m$ and $g_p$ are the slopes of the $IV$ characteristics about the operating point (Prob. 10.3).

A small-signal circuit model may be derived from (10.16) by interpreting the equation as a Kirchhoff current relation. The first term on the right represents a dependent current source. This source is dependent upon $v_g$ and is shown between the nodes $P$ and $K$ in Fig. 10.17. Note that $v_g$ is defined positive as shown between the nodes $G$ and $K$. The second term of (10.16) is a current proportional to $v_p$ and is represented by resistance $r_p$ connected between the nodes $P$ and $K$ of the figure. A load resistance

$R_L$ is added, as shown, for completeness (bias and coupling elements are neglected). Note that the grid-to-cathode node pair is considered as an open

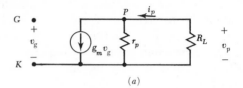

(a)

**FIGURE 10.17**  (a) *Small-signal circuit model for triode amplifier using dependent current source;* (b) *circuit model using dependent voltage source.*

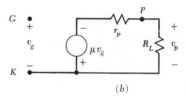

(b)

circuit. A leakage resistance $r_g$ can be added, if necessary, to model grid current (see Prob. 10.8).

The output signal voltage $v_L = v_p$ is found from Kirchhoff's current law for the output circuit:

$$-\frac{v_p}{R_L} = g_m v_g + \frac{v_p}{r_p} \tag{10.17}$$

Solving for $v_p$, we obtain the voltage-gain function $a_V$:

$$a_V = \frac{v_p}{v_g} = \frac{-g_m}{1/r_p + 1/R_L}$$

or

$$a_V = -g_m R_L \frac{r_p}{r_p + R_L} \tag{10.18}$$

As a numerical example, if $g_m = 10^{-3}$ mho and $R_L = r_p = 20$ kΩ, $a_V = 10$.

An alternate circuit model utilizes a dependent voltage source, and introduces the important tube parameter called the *amplification factor*, $\mu$. If a Thévenin equivalent is taken of $g_m v_g$, and $r_p$ in Fig. 10.17a, we obtain the equivalent circuit shown in Fig. 10.17b. The Thévenin equivalent resistance is just $r_p$ itself, as shown in Sec. 9.6. The Thévenin-equivalent voltage is written as $\mu v_g$, where

$$\mu = \frac{g_m}{g_p} = g_m r_p \tag{10.19a}$$

The polarity of the dependent voltage source follows from the sense of the dependent current source of Fig. 10.17a, and is shown in Fig. 10.17b. The parameter $\mu$, from (10.19a) and (10.14b), is also the ratio of plate-voltage change to grid-voltage change to maintain $I_P$ constant:

$$\mu = -\frac{\partial V_{PK}}{\partial V_{GK}} \simeq -\frac{\Delta V_{PK}}{\Delta V_{GK}}\bigg|_{\Delta I_p = 0} \qquad (10.19b)$$

As we shall see below, it is also related to the electrostatic amplification factor $\mu_0$ defined earlier. If (10.19a) is used in (10.18), the voltage amplification for this model can be written as

$$a_V = \frac{v_p}{v_g} = -\frac{\mu R_L}{r_p + R_L} \qquad (10.20)$$

Note that $a_V$ approaches $\mu$ for $R_L \gg r_p$, so that $\mu$ is sometimes described as the *open-circuit voltage gain* of the triode.

The parameters of the circuit model are usually obtained from measurements of the device. It is helpful, however, to obtain the values of the parameters from the idealized triode equation (10.12). Let us rewrite (10.12) with the constant multiplier as $K$:

$$I_P = K\left(V_{GK} + \frac{V_{PK}}{\mu_0}\right)^{3/2} \qquad (10.21)$$

Then
$$g_m = \frac{\partial I_P}{\partial V_{GK}} = \frac{3}{2}K\left(V_{GK} + \frac{V_{PK}}{\mu_0}\right)^{1/2} = \frac{3}{2}\frac{I_P}{V_{GK} + V_{PK}/\mu_0} \qquad (10.22a)$$

$$g_p = \frac{\partial I_P}{\partial V_{PK}} = \frac{3}{2}\frac{K}{\mu_0}\left(V_{GK} + \frac{V_{PK}}{\mu_0}\right)^{1/2} = \frac{g_m}{\mu_0} \qquad (10.22b)$$

$$\mu = \frac{g_m}{g_p} = \mu_0 \qquad (10.22c)$$

These expressions show the ideal dependence on the operating point. Note that in this ideal, $\mu$ defined by (10.19b) is equal to the electrostatic amplification factor $\mu_0$ and is independent of the operating point. In an actual triode, $\mu$ varies with the operating point.

**CAPACITIVE ELEMENTS**    For all but low-frequency applications, capacitive elements must be added to the circuit models of Fig. 10.17. These exist between all three electrodes because of the finite size and spacing of the metallic electrodes. The circuit model of the triode with these capacitances is shown in Fig. 10.18a. The capacitances $C_{gk}$ and $C_{gp}$ are usually of the order of a few picofarads. $C_{pk}$ is smaller because of the shielding effect of the grid between plate and cathode. Even with lead effects it is typically a fraction of a picofarad. Neglecting lead effects, $C_{pk}$ is equal to $C_{gk}/\mu_0$.

The most useful connection of the triode is the *common-cathode* connection with the input signal applied between grid and cathode, and the load connected between plate and cathode.[1] For this connection, as seen in Fig. 10.18$a$, the grid-to-cathode capacitance $C_{gp}$ introduces feedback from the

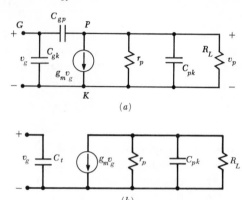

**FIGURE 10.18**  (a) *Circuit model including interelectrode capacitances;* (b) *simplified model of* (a).

output to the input comparable to that from $C_\mu$ in the transistor. Under some conditions this feedback can produce undesired oscillations, but the major effect in the usual operating range is an additional capacitive current introduced into the input circuit. If the load is a pure resistance $R_L$ as shown in Fig. 10.18$a$, the main effect of $C_{gp}$ can be included as an equivalent capacitance $C_{\text{equiv}}$ connected in parallel with $C_{gk}$:

$$C_{\text{equiv}} = C_{gp}(1 + g_m R_L) \qquad (10.23a)$$

The total capacitance is labeled $C_t$, as for the comparable effect in the transistor.

$$C_t = C_{gk} + C_{\text{equiv}} = C_{gk} + C_{gp}(1 + g_m R_L) \qquad (10.23b)$$

The capacitance arising from $C_{\text{equiv}}$ is usually much greater than $C_{gk}$ since $g_m R_L$ is greater than unity in order to produce voltage gain. The reduced circuit model utilizing $C_t$ is shown in Fig. 10.18$b$. Clearly, from either Fig. 10.18$a$ or $b$, we expect the gain versus frequency performance of the common-cathode triode to be similar to that of the common-emitter transistor.

To expand on this similarity, as well as to bring out the difference, we

[1] The *common-cathode* (grounded cathode) connection is useful because it has both voltage and current gain and thus has a high value of power gain. As with the transistor, other connections are possible and are useful under certain circumstances. The *common-grid* (grounded grid) connection has a relatively low input impedance, approximately $1/g_m$, with high output impedance. It is useful at high frequencies because the coupling between the input and the output is small through the capacitance $C_{pk}$. The *common-plate* (cathode follower) connection has current gain but not voltage gain and is useful for coupling between a high input impedance and a low output impedance.

consider a typical amplifier utilizing a single triode in the common-cathode connection as shown in Fig. 10.19a. In this circuit, the correct grid-cathode bias voltage is obtained by introducing a cathode resistor $R_K$. The dc cathode

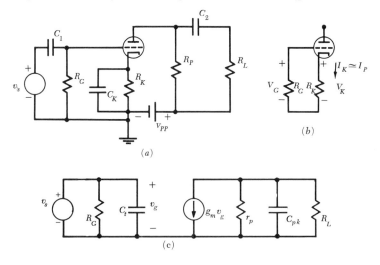

(a)

(b)

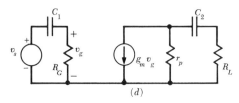

(c)

(d)

**FIGURE 10.19**   (a) *Triode amplifier circuit with self bias;* (b) *voltage relations in the biasing resistor;* (c) *circuit model using $C_t$ approximation;* (d) *circuit model for low frequencies.*

current, which is approximately the plate current, flows through this resistor and develops dc voltage $V_K$, as shown in Fig. 10.19b. The grid current is returned to ground through an external resistor $R_G$. Since this current is very small, $V_G \simeq 0$, $V_{GK} = -V_K = -I_P R_K$, and a "self-bias" arrangement is obtained. The resistor $R_K$ is paralleled with a large capacitor $C_K$ which bypasses $R_K$ for signals of frequency components high enough so that

$$\omega C_K \gg \frac{1}{R_K} \| g_m$$

This is similar to the condition on the transistor bias circuit of Sec. 9.5.

The signal in Fig. 10.19a is introduced to the grid by an input coupling capacitor $C_1$ to achieve ac coupling only. For simplicity, we assume that the source resistance is much smaller than $R_G$ and can be neglected. The load resistance $R_L$ is also shown ac coupled to the plate through capacitor $C_2$. The plate bias resistor $R_P$ is introduced but is usually large in comparison with $R_L$. $R_P$ is consequently neglected in the small signal circuit model.

In the midfrequency range of operation, the effects of the capacitances of the device and of the circuit are negligible, and (10.18) provides the voltage gain. The power gain is

$$G_p = \frac{\frac{1}{2}|V_p|^2/R_L}{\frac{1}{2}|V_g|^2/R_G} = \frac{R_G}{R_L}\left(\frac{g_m R_L r_p}{r_p + R_L}\right)^2 \tag{10.24}$$

For $R_G = 1\ M\Omega$, $R_L = 20\ k\Omega$, and a voltage gain of 10 as in the earlier numerical example, power gain is 5000, or about 37 dB.

For the upper bandedge of the gain function for the amplifier, the circuit model is that of Fig. 10.19c, where the $C_t$ approximation of Fig. 10.18b is used. Since the voltage source $v_s$ appears directly across $C_t$ with the approximations we have taken, this element does not affect the frequency response, however. The shunting effect of capacitance $C_{pk}$ across the load provides the limit for the upper frequency response. The gain function from a simple circuit analysis of Fig. 10.19c is

$$a_V = \frac{-g_m}{1/r_p + 1/R_L + j\omega C_{pk}} \tag{10.25a}$$

This function gives a lowpass response with a break frequency ($-3$ dB bandedge) of

$$\omega_u = \frac{R_L + r_p}{C_{pk} R_L r_p} \tag{10.25b}$$

Above $\omega_u$, the magnitude of (10.25a) falls off at the rate of 6 dB per octave or 20 dB per decade. Thus the gain response is of the same type as that of a transistor amplifier.

For very low frequencies, the circuit model of the amplifier stage becomes that shown in Fig. 10.19d, if $C_{gk}$ is sufficiently small to be neglected in relation to $C_1$. The coupling capacitors $C_1$ and $C_2$ are the limiting elements at low frequencies and the transmission response of both the input and output sections is the highpass response studied earlier (Secs. 3.9 and 9.2).

## 10.6   tetrodes and pentodes

Additional electrodes may be introduced into a space-charge-controlled vacuum device in order to modify its electrical characteristics from those of the triode. As an example, if a second grid is introduced between the control grid and plate, the resulting four-electrode device is called a *tetrode*. The additional grid, called a *screen grid*, provides electrical shielding between the control grid and the plate so that the plate resistance $r_p$ and the amplification factor $\mu$ are increased. This increase arises because the plate voltage is less effective in producing a field at the cathode when there is screening by the extra grid. Moreover, the plate-grid capacitance $C_{gp}$ is decreased by the shielding so that there is less coupling effect from this capacitance between output and input in the common-cathode connection.

The screen grid of the tetrode is operated at a positive dc potential. Secondary electrons from the plate (see Sec. 10.2) may be drawn to this screen when the plate voltage is less than the screen voltage. Irregularities in the low-voltage portion of the $IV$ characteristics may result and, if these are undesirable, the effects of the secondary electrons may be eliminated in one of two ways. In one common arrangement the screen-grid

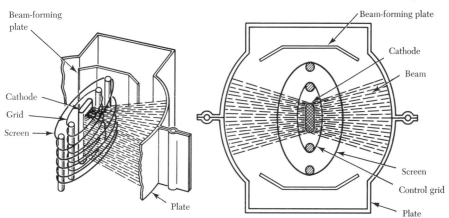

**FIGURE 10.20** *Constructional features of a beam tetrode. (From F. E. Terman, "Electronic and Radio Engineering," McGraw-Hill Book Company, New York, 1955.)*

wires are aligned behind the control-grid wires, and the streams of electrons are focused in such a way that a high electron density builds up near the plate. This negative space charge repels any possible secondary elec-

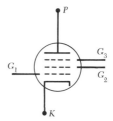

**FIGURE 10.21** *Representation for pentode.*

trons and minimizes their escape from the plate to the screen. This *beam tetrode* is illustrated in Fig. 10.20. A second method of eliminating the harmful effect of secondaries from the plate utilizes a third grid, called a *suppressor grid*, in front of the plate. The resulting five-electrode device is called a *pentode* and is shown schematically in Fig. 10.21. The suppressor

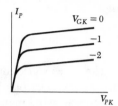

**FIGURE 10.22**   *Pentode or beam tetrode plate characteristics.*

grid of the pentode is operated at a voltage negative with respect to the plate. For simplicity, the suppressor grid is usually at cathode potential.

Typical *IV* characteristics for either a pentode or beam tetrode are shown in Fig. 10.22. Notice that over much of the range of operation the plate current is nearly independent of the plate-to-cathode voltage because of the screening effect of the extra grid or grids. A simple amplifier stage using a pentode is shown in Fig. 10.23. The suppressor grid is directly

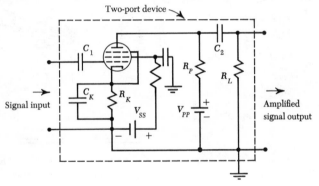

**FIGURE 10.23**   *Actual pentode RC amplifier stage.*

connected to the cathode so that it has no signal voltage between it and the cathode. The dc supply for the screen grid is bypassed by a large capacitance so that its potential does not vary with the signal. Therefore,

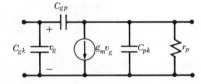

**FIGURE 10.24**   *Circuit model for pentode.*

the only terminals of importance for the signal are the cathode, the control grid, and the plate. We again have a three-electrode device for ac so that the three parameters defined for the triode—amplification factor, plate resistance, and transconductance—may be utilized for the pentode also. The small-signal circuit model is also of the same form as for the triode and is repeated in Fig. 10.24.

The plate resistance $r_p$ of the pentode is very high because of the small

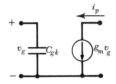

**FIGURE 10.25**   *Simplified circuit model for pentode.*

slope of the $IV$ characteristics in the useful range. Thus $r_p$ may often be assumed infinite and removed from the circuit model. The feedback capacitance $C_{gp}$ is often sufficiently small to be neglected also so that the very simple circuit model of Fig. 10.25 is obtained. The incremental plate current from this model has the form

$$i_p = g_m v_g \tag{10.26}$$

When the idealizations leading to (10.26) are not justified, the more complete model of Fig. 10.24 is used. Some typical values for a pentode are $g_m = 5 \cdot 10^{-3}$ mho, $r_p = 700$ kΩ, $C_{gk} = 4$ pF, $C_{pk} = 2$ pF, and $C_{gp} = 0.005$ pF.

## 10.7   electron-beam display devices

In a cathode-ray tube for an oscilloscope or TV receiver, a controlled electron stream is used to produce light by striking a material called a phosphor, as is explained in more detail in Sec. 12.5. The source of the electrons is called the "electron gun," which consists of a thermionic cathode and control and focusing electrodes as shown in Fig. 10.26.

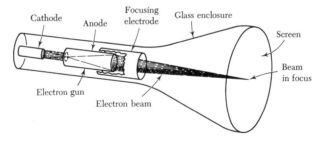

**FIGURE 10.26**   *Schematic view of electrodes and beam focusing in a cathode-ray tube.*

The stream may be controlled in intensity by a grid as in the space-charge-controlled devices studied in the previous sections. The electrons are focused into a fine beam by electric or magnetic fields and are then deflected to a desired position on the screen by either electric or magnetic fields.

The processes of focusing and deflection are discussed in following sections. We note here the usefulness of the transconductance parameter in describing the current control of the beam. If the voltage on the control electrode is varied by an increment $dV_{GK}$, the beam current varies by $dI$ and we define

$$g_m = \frac{dI}{dV_{GK}} \tag{10.27}$$

as in the triode. The control electrode may have the form of a grid parallel to a planar cathode as in Fig. 10.27a. Therefore, the transconductance is comparable to that of a triode of similar configuration. Some control electrodes are simply conducting cylinders lying outside the path of the beam, as in Fig. 10.27b. For such configurations the net applied field,

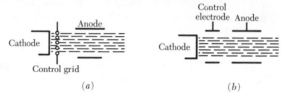

(a)                         (b)

**FIGURE 10.27** (a) *Gun with control of current by a grid;* (b) *gun with control by a cylindrical electrode.*

and hence current flow, varies across the cathode and transconductance is usually lower than can be obtained with a grid. However, the input capacitance is also lower, which is important if the beam current is to be controlled rapidly. For a TV picture tube, for example, the electron beam current controls the brightness of the image and changes are required up to the 4 MHz rate for which picture information is transmitted.

## 10.8 electron-beam focusing

The electron beam of a cathode-ray device tends to spread out because of transverse components of the emission velocity, fringing fields in the electrodes near the cathode, and the space-charge repulsion effect of the electrons upon one another. Counteracting forces in the form of focusing fields are required in order to have a well-defined beam and a reasonably sharp picture on the screen of the cathode-ray device.

**BEAM FOCUSING BY ELECTRIC FIELDS**   The focusing of an electron beam with an electric field can be understood by considering the motion of a single electron which moves through a region. We assume, as in Fig. 10.28, that the electron enters the region of interest with a velocity $\overrightarrow{v}_1$ making an angle of $\theta_1$ to be defined. As shown, the electrostatic potential at the left of the region is $V_1$ and that at the right is $V_2$. Because of the potential difference, an electric field also exists which deflects the electron. From (4.1) and (4.2) we know that the electrons are accelerated in a direction opposite to that of the field vector $\vec{E}$, or we can use the relation between

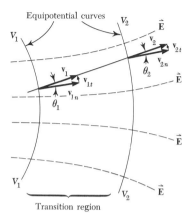

**FIGURE 10.28**  *Electron "refraction" by changes in potential.*

Transition region

potential and velocity given by (4.5) or (4.6b). The electric field lines are perpendicular to the electrostatic potential surfaces, which are represented on the figure as "equipotential curves." These curves are the intersections of the equipotential surfaces with the paper. For the problem at hand, axial symmetry of the electric field is assumed, and the field is shown in two-dimensional coordinates. The equipotential surfaces, then, become curves which are intersections of the surfaces with the paper.

The change of electron direction in the electric field leads to a relation which is similar to Snell's law of optics. We obtain this by decomposing the velocity vector $\vec{v}_1$ into two components, $v_{1n}$ which is normal to the potential $V_1$ curve, and $v_{1t}$ which is tangential to the curve. Acceleration of the electrons occurs only perpendicular to the potential curve. Therefore, only the $v_{1n}$ component of velocity is influenced and $v_{1t}$ remains unchanged. From Fig. 10.28

$$v_{1t} = v_1 \sin \theta_1 \tag{10.28a}$$

Similarly for $\theta_2$ in Fig. 10.28

$$v_{2t} = v_2 \sin \theta_2 \tag{10.28b}$$

By the above argument, $v_{1t} = v_{2t}$. If we also relate velocity to potential by (4.6b), which assumes electrons emitted at zero potential, we obtain

$$\sqrt{V_1} \sin \theta_1 = \sqrt{V_2} \sin \theta_2 \tag{10.29a}$$

This is the same form as used in Snell's law in optics

$$n \sin \alpha = n' \sin \alpha' \tag{10.29b}$$

where $n$ and $n'$ are the refractive indices of the media on both sides of a boundary as in Fig. 10.29, $\alpha$ is the angle of the incident ray with respect to the normal to the boundary, and $\alpha'$ is the angle of the refracted ray.

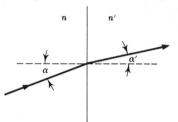

**FIGURE 10.29**  *Refraction of a light beam at the boundary of two dissimilar media.*

The analogy between an optical ray passing from one medium into another with different refractive indices, and the path of an electron when going from one region of potential $V_1$ to another region of $V_2$ has led to the name "electron optics." Effects as obtained with optical lenses have their analogs in special field configurations.

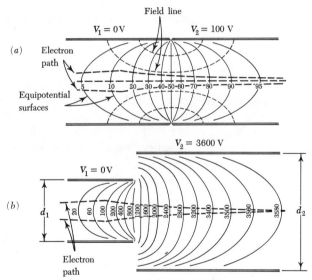

**FIGURE 10.30**  (a) *Equipotential curves for coaxial cylinders of equal diameter. (After V. K. Zworykin and G. A. Morton, "Television," John Wiley & Sons, Inc., New York, 1940.)* (b) *Equipotentials for coaxial cylinders of different diameter. (After I. G. Maloff and D. W. Epstein, "Electron Optics in Television," McGraw-Hill Book Company, New York, 1938.)*

Figure 10.30 shows two different arrangements of coaxial cylinders to achieve focusing. The electron beam passes along their axis. One of the cylinders is at potential $V_2$ and the other is at potential zero.[1] The potential

[1] In practical applications, one usually uses for the left-hand cylinder a nonzero potential above the cathode potential of the electron gun; we assume zero potential for simplicity.

difference between the two cylinders is therefore $V_2$, and an electric field exists. Instead of showing the field lines, we show in Fig. 10.30 the potential lines, which have been obtained experimentally.[1] Using the relation (10.29a), we could graphically find the path followed by an electron entering the electric field at a small angle from the normal of the potential lines. Such paths of electrons are shown in Fig. 10.30; clearly, the electron is focused toward the axis. By proper design, the focal point may be made to fall where the beam hits the screen.

**THE PIERCE GUN** When the defocusing forces in an electron beam arise primarily from space-charge fields, the Pierce gun is frequently used. This type of gun has special electrode shapes outside the beam region which are formed to counteract the outward space-charge forces. J. R. Pierce recognized that an analytic solution is possible for a two-dimensional beam of the type shown in Fig. 10.31. With this solution, it is possible to

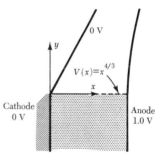

**FIGURE 10.31** *Pierce gun for two-dimensional (strip) beam.*

produce a potential at the beam edge which matches the Child's law potential (10.7d) of the beam and which also has a zero transverse component of field. The electrode at cathode potential must be a conducting plane at angle 67.5°, as shown in the figure. The anode electrode has the form, in polar coordinates,

$$\left(\frac{r}{d}\right)^{4/3} = \frac{1}{\cos{(4\theta/3)}} \qquad (10.30)$$

The corresponding forms of electrodes for Pierce guns of axial symmetry are obtained by numerical computation, or from electrolytic tank analogs. Typical electrode shapes for such a gun are shown in Fig. 10.32.

**BEAM FOCUSING IN MAGNETIC FIELDS** Constant axially symmetric magnetic fields can also be used to focus the beam. A distinction is made between a long coil and a short coil for use in producing such fields. In this section only the latter is presented.

[1] Electrolytic tanks are very useful for obtaining potential distributions between electrodes of any shape through an analog simulation.

We assume that an electron beam with axial velocity $v_0$ emanates from an electron gun and that random radial velocities (perpendicular to the beam axis) for different electrons are present. These radial velocities,

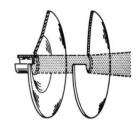

**FIGURE 10.32**    *An axially symmetrical Pierce gun. (From J. R. Pierce, "Theory and Design of Electron Beams," D. Van Nostrand Company, Inc., Princeton, N.J., 1954.)*

although much smaller than the axial velocity $v_0$, can defocus the beam as the axial distance increases. Figure 10.33 shows a view of some of the radial velocities in a plane perpendicular to the beam axis at the exit of the electron gun. If an axial magnetic field is introduced, these radial

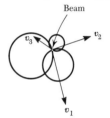

**FIGURE 10.33**    *Paths of electrons having different radial velocities in a beam.*

velocities and the axial $\vec{B}$ field produce a circular motion for the electrons, as discussed in Sec. 4.10. The translatory motion along the beam axis, caused by the initial axial velocity $v_0$, is superimposed on the circular motion resulting in a helical motion.

Because of the axial symmetry it is convenient to use cylindrical coordinates for analysis (see Fig. 10.34). The beam axis is taken as the $z$ direction,

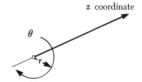

**FIGURE 10.34**    *Cylindrical coordinates r, θ, and z.*

the radius is $r$, and the azimuth angle is $\theta$ (taken as positive in the clockwise direction). It is now convenient to compare the motion of an electron in a beam with a ray of light as for electrostatic focusing. We need take into account only so-called "paraxial" rays, that is, rays that are close to the axis, forming only a small angle with it. This is in accord with an assumption of a slightly defocused beam. The path of paraxial rays, neglecting any electric field, is represented by the following equations:

$$\frac{d^2r}{dz^2} = -\frac{qB_z^2}{8mV} r \qquad (10.31a)$$

$$\frac{d\theta}{dt} = \frac{q}{2m} B_z \qquad (10.31b)$$

where $B_z$ is the component of the $\vec{B}$ field at the axis, and $V$ is the accelerating voltage used in the electron gun to produce the beam velocity $v_0$ in the axial direction. (For derivation, see references at end of chapter.)

A solution of (10.31a) and (10.31b) gives the path of a paraxial ray but requires knowledge of the variation of $B_z$ with distance $z$. We can, however, obtain a qualitative picture of the path. For this purpose let us consider the short coil of Fig. 10.35. When an electron enters the $\vec{B}$ field, the $\vec{B}$ vector is toward the beam axis; a force out of the paper appears at

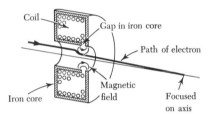

**FIGURE 10.35** *Path of electron focused by a magnetic field.*

the electron, and it moves in a circle out of the paper. As $B_z$ becomes stronger, this motion continues but the radius of the circle becomes smaller. This means that the electron moves in a helical path out of the paper and closer to the beam axis. Once the electron passes the midplane of the gap in the coil, the $\vec{B}$ vector is outward, away from the beam axis, and the force on the electron moving to the right is into the paper. The helical motion moves the electron still closer to the beam axis. When the electron is out of the $\vec{B}$ field, to the right, it retains a net inward radial velocity and is focused at some point on the axis, as shown in Fig. 10.35.

Because of the helical motion, the plane of motion of an individual electron will be rotated by angle $\theta$ when traveling through the $\vec{B}$ field. This angle can be obtained by using (10.31b) and integrating between two points, one to the left at $z_1$ and one to the right of the $\vec{B}$ field at $z_2$. Corresponding times are $t_1$ and $t_2$, respectively. We obtain

$$\theta = -\frac{q}{2m} \int_{t_1}^{t_2} B_z \, dt = -\frac{q}{2mv_0} \int_{z_1}^{z_2} B_z \, dz \qquad (10.32)$$

where $v_0$ is the axial velocity of the beam produced by the electron gun. As the $\vec{B}$ field is produced by a dc current $I$ in the coil of $N$ turns of wire, the integral of magnetic field over the region where it is significant is equal to the ampere-turn product $NI$. The angle from (10.32) is then

$$\theta = -\frac{\mu q}{2mv_0} NI = -0.187 \frac{NI}{V^{1/2}} \quad \text{rad} \qquad (10.33)$$

where $V$ is the accelerating voltage used in the electron gun to produce a velocity $v_0$ and where $\mu$ is the magnetic permeability (see inside covers).

## 10.9  electron-beam deflection

It has been noted that display tubes, such as those used in cathode-ray oscilloscopes or in TV receivers, require means of steering the beam so that it is deflected in any desired manner. This control can be achieved either by electric fields or by magnetic fields.

**BEAM DEFLECTION BY $\vec{E}$ FIELDS**  As an example, let us consider the cathode-ray oscilloscope. The electron beam originates in an electron gun, i.e., it starts from a thermionic cathode and is properly focused by one of the means described in the last section. In an electric-field deflection scheme, the beam then passes between a pair of plates as shown in Fig. 10.36. Let us

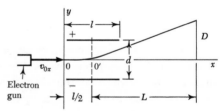

**FIGURE 10.36**  *Beam deflection by an electric field.*

assume that a voltage is applied between the two plates. The resulting electric field is directed vertically downward and causes an acceleration $a_y$ vertically upward. Electrons in the beam which enter this electric field follow a path which is the sum of the motion along the $x$ axis with constant velocity $v_{0x}$ and the motion in the $y$ direction. The latter is

$$v_y = \frac{dy}{dt} = a_y t \qquad (10.34)$$

Integration of (10.34) gives

$$y = \tfrac{1}{2} a_y t^2 + C \qquad (10.35)$$

The integration constant $C$ is zero if we assume the electrons to be at $y = 0$ at time $t = 0$. We assume also that the electric field $E_y$ exists only between the deflecting plates. If the length of the plates in the $x$ direction is $l$, the time needed by the electrons to pass through is

$$t_t = \frac{l}{v_{0x}} \tag{10.36}$$

The path of the electrons between the plates is a parabolic one, as shown in Fig. 10.36. To obtain an expression for the path we label the coordinates of the electron beam as it leaves the electric deflecting field:

$$x_1 = l \quad \text{and} \quad y_1 = \tfrac{1}{2} a_y \left( \frac{l}{v_{0x}} \right)^2 \tag{10.37}$$

In the space between the edge of the deflecting plates and the screen, the electrons follow a straight line, the equation of which is

$$\frac{y - y_1}{x - x_1} = \frac{v_y}{v_{0x}} \tag{10.38}$$

Substituting the values for $x_1$ and $y_1$ from (10.37) and for $v_y$ from (10.34), we obtain

$$y - \tfrac{1}{2} a_y \left( \frac{l}{v_{0x}} \right)^2 = a_y \frac{l}{v_{0x}^2} (x - l) \tag{10.39}$$

Rearrangement of terms gives

$$y = a_y \frac{l}{v_{0x}^2} \left( x - \frac{l}{2} \right) \tag{10.40}$$

Note that for $x = l/2$, $y = 0$. This means that we can draw the straight line which represents the path of electrons outside of the deflecting field by starting at the midpoint of the deflecting plates on the $x$ axis. The slope

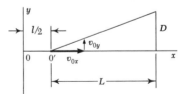

**FIGURE 10.37**   *Origin for calculation of beam deflection.*

of the path is given by the ratio of the velocities in the $y$ and $x$ directions. The total deflection at the screen is found as follows. Let $L$ be the length from point $0'$ of Fig. 10.37 to the screen of the tube and let $D$ be the deflection from the $x$ axis. $D$ is given by the point on the straight line at $x = L + l/2$. Then

$$\frac{D}{L} = \frac{v_y}{v_{0x}} \tag{10.41}$$

or
$$D = \frac{v_y}{v_{0x}} L = \frac{a_y}{v_{0x}^2} L \tag{10.42}$$

We now assume that the accelerating voltage used at the electron gun is $V_a$, the deflecting voltage $V_d$, and the distance between the deflecting plates $d$. We obtain

$$a_y = \frac{q}{m} \frac{V_d}{d} \quad \text{and} \quad v_{0x}^2 = \frac{2q}{m} V_a \tag{10.43}$$

Substitution in (10.42) gives

$$D = \frac{q}{m} \frac{V_d}{d} lL \frac{m}{2qV_a} = \frac{lL}{2d} \frac{V_d}{V_a} \tag{10.44}$$

From this, a *deflection sensitivity* of the beam-display tube can be defined as

$$\frac{D}{V_d} = \frac{lL}{2d} \frac{1}{V_a} \tag{10.45}$$

This is an important figure of merit which characterizes the beam-display tube. If a large value of the deflection sensitivity is wanted, increasing $L$ or decreasing $V_a$ is useful. However, it is not possible to increase $L$ to very large values, for then the tube becomes bulky. On the other hand, $V_a$ cannot be reduced to very low values, because this would decrease $v_{0x}$. The luminosity of the spot on the tube screen depends on the energy of electrons when arriving at the screen; therefore, the decrease of $v_{0x}$ reduces the luminosity.

It is possible to use low values of $V_a$ to yield a high value of deflection sensitivity provided we use *postacceleration* of the electrons in the space

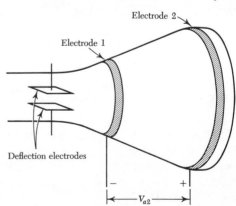

**FIGURE 10.38**  *Post acceleration of beam after deflection.*

between the deflecting plates and the screen. This can be done by using an extra potential $V_{a2}$ between two new electrodes 1 and 2 (see Fig. 10.38). Electrode 2, usually a conducting ring inside the glass enclosure of the tube is placed close to the screen. A lower limit is placed upon $V_a$, however, by the necessity of keeping the transit time through the plates, $t_t$ of (10.36), smaller than the period of the highest frequency component to be deflected.

To this point, we have considered only one set of deflection plates for the deflection of the beam. Usually a second set is necessary, positioned so thats its $\vec{E}$ field is perpendicular to that of the first set of deflection plates. The second set of plates deflects the electron beam along the horizontal axis. By using appropriate voltages on the deflection plates, we can show patterns in $xy$ coordinates on the screen. In an oscilloscope, the signal to be observed is usually applied to the set of plates producing vertical deflection. The other set has a voltage which has a waveform that increases linearly with time for a period, then drops to zero and repeats periodically, i.e., a sawtooth wave. This situation is illustrated in Fig. 10.39. The wave-

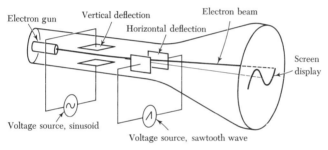

**FIGURE 10.39** *Beam deflection horizontally and vertically, as in the display of a sinusoidal voltage wave on an oscilloscope.*

form applied to the vertical plates is displayed on the screen as a function of time. In a TV tube, both sets of plates have deflections related to time and the intensity of the beam is modulated to convey the information concerning brightness.

**BEAM DEFLECTION BY $\vec{B}$ FIELDS** To study magnetic deflection, we assume that an electron beam leaves an electron gun with a velocity $v_0$ and is exposed to a magnetic field, which is directed into the paper as shown in Fig. 10.40. From (4.34b), it is clear that the electrons of the beam move in a circular path of radius.

$$ r = \frac{mv_0}{qB} \quad \text{meters} \tag{10.46} $$

Again, the $\vec{B}$ field extends only over a limited distance $l$ along the beam axis, as shown in the figure. The screen is assumed to be at a distance $L$ from the midplane of the $B$ field, which establishes point $0'$ at a distance $l/2$. The deflection $D$ at the screen is related to the angle $\theta$, here assumed

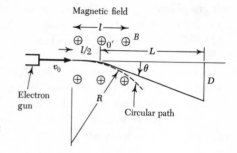

**FIGURE 10.40** *Beam deflection by a magnetic field ($\vec{B}$ vector into paper).*

to be small, which is formed by the straight line through $0'$. We obtain

$$D = L \tan \theta \simeq L\theta \simeq \frac{Ll}{r} \tag{10.47}$$

where we have used $\tan \theta \simeq \theta$ for small $\theta$. The value of $r$ from (10.46) may be substituted in (10.47). Then

$$D = \frac{Ll}{mv_0} qB = \frac{LlB}{V_a^{1/2}} \left(\frac{q}{2m}\right)^{1/2} \tag{10.48}$$

where $V_a$ is the acceleration voltage used at the electron gun. The deflection sensitivity for magnetic deflection can be defined as

$$\frac{D}{B} = \frac{Ll}{V_a^{1/2}} \left(\frac{q}{2m}\right)^{1/2} \tag{10.49}$$

As in the case of electric deflection one may use a second magnetic field, perpendicular to the first one, and deflect the beam again so that an $xy$ pattern appears at the screen.

### REFERENCES

W. W. Harman, "Fundamentals of Electronic Motion" McGraw-Hilll Book Company, New York, 1953.

J. Millman, "Vacuum Tube and Semiconductor Electronics," McGraw-Hill Book Company, New York, 1958.

J. R. Pierce, "Theory and Design of Electron Beams," 2d ed., D. Van Nostrand Company, Inc., Princeton, N.J., 1954.

R. L. Sproull, "Modern Physics," 2d ed., John Wiley & Sons, Inc., New York, 1963, chap. 12.

### PROBLEMS

**10.1** Complete the steps sketched in Sec. 10.3 for solution of the differential equation (10.7c) for voltage in the presence of space charge.

Substitute $y = dV_x/dx$ as suggested, with the boundary conditions $V_x = 0$ and $dV_x/dx = 0$ at $x = 0$.

**10.2** Explain why reverse bias for a vacuum diode yields the same direction of current as forward bias, whereas the sign of current reverses with bias in a semiconducting junction diode.

**10.3** For the output $I_P V_{PK}$ characteristic of the 12AU7A triode shown in figure $a$, estimate the values of $g_m$, $r_p$, and $\mu$ from these curves about the operating point $V_{PK} = 250$ V and $V_{GK} = -8$ V. Show your construction on the curves of figure $a$. Compare your results with the values obtained from figure $b$.

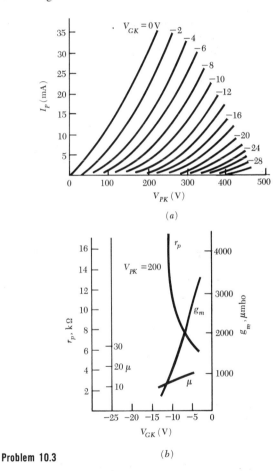

(a)

(b)

**Problem 10.3**

**10.4** The parameters of a given triode are $r_p = 8$ kΩ and $\mu = 50$. (a) Show a circuit model using a dependent voltage source. (b) If $R_L = 10$ kΩ and if an input signal (sinusoid) of 3 V peak is applied, find the magnitudes of $I_p$ and $V_p$. (c) Show a circuit model with a dependent current source. Does it give the same value of $V_p$?

**10.5**   For a vacuum triode at a quiescent point, $V_{PK} = 250$ V, $I_p = 8$ mA, and $V_{GK} = -8$ V, the values of the parameters are $r_p = 10$ k$\Omega$ and $\mu = 20$.

(a) To what value must $V_{GK}$ be changed to obtain a plate current of 12 mA if $V_{PK}$ is constant at 250 V?

(b) To what value must the voltage $V_{PK}$ be changed if the current $I_p$ is to be brought back to its original value of 8 mA? Assume that the grid voltage $V_{GK}$ obtained in part a is kept constant.

**10.6**   A triode is used in a circuit, as shown, and has $I_p V_{PK}$ characteristics as in Fig. 10.14. Assume an operating point at $V_{PK} = 250$ V and $V_{GK} = -2$ V.

(a) What plate supply voltage $V_{PP}$ is needed if the plate bias resistance $R_P$ is 10 k$\Omega$?

(b) Show the load line for $R_P = 10$ k$\Omega$.

(c) If a sinusoidal signal having a peak value of 2 V is applied in series in the grid circuit, what are the maximum and minimum values of $i_p$?

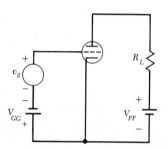

**Problem 10.6**

**10.7**   A triode with the $I_P V_{PK}$ characteristics as in Fig. 10.14 is operated with a supply voltage of $V_{PP} = 400$ V and a load resistance of 200 k$\Omega$.

(a) What is the maximum output signal swing which can be obtained without clipping (assume you are free to choose any operating point)?

(b) If the input signal is a sinusoid, how would the maximum positive change in plate current, $I_{P,max} - I_{Po}$, compare with the change for the negative signal half cycle $I_{Po} - I_{P,min}$, where $I_{Po}$ is the value at the operating point?

(c) How would you choose the operating point so that the largest possible sinusoidal signal could be handled without appreciable distortion?

**10.8**   A triode has the following parameter values at a specified operating point:

$$g_m = 10^{-3} \text{ mhos} \qquad r_p = 10 \text{ k}\Omega \qquad r_g = 10 \text{ M}\Omega$$

$$C_{gk} = 4 \text{ pF} \qquad C_{gp} = 2 \text{ pF} \qquad C_{pk} \text{ negligible}$$

where $r_g$ is the leakage resistance from grid to cathode.

    (a) What is the value of $f_t$ for this device? From Chap. 8, $f_t = f_{o\ dB}$ of the short-circuit current gain function.

    (b) If the triode is used with a resistance load of $R_L = 50$ k$\Omega$, what is the value of $C_t$?

    (c) If the source resistance presented to the input of the triode is 1 k$\Omega$, what is the value of the mid-band voltage gain if $R_L = 50$ k$\Omega$? What is the value of the upper $-3$ dB bandedge of the voltage gain function?

**10.9** A vacuum pentode with $I_P V_{PK}$ characteristics as shown is operated at a quiescent point $V_{PK} = 200$ V, $V_{G2} = 150$ V, and $V_{G1} = -2.5$ V.

    (a) Find the plate resistance $r_p$.

    (b) Find the transconductance $g_m$.

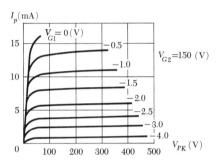

**Problem 10.9**

**10.10** A pentode with $I_P V_{PK}$ characteristics, as shown in Prob. 10.9, is biased with a plate resistor $R_P = 25$ k$\Omega$ and a supply voltage $V_{PP} = 400$ V.

    (a) Show the dc load line.

    (b) If you were free to choose the operating point, where would you put it so that the largest possible sinusoidal signal swing could be handled?

    (c) What is the maximum and minimum value of $I_P$ under the conditions of part b?

    (d) Compare the changes in $I_P$ for the positive and negative signal half cycle. Would you expect a distorted output signal?

**10.11** Assume that a pentode with $I_P V_{PK}$ characteristics, as shown in Prob. 10.9, is used with a plate resistor $R_P$ of 25 k$\Omega$ and $V_{PP} = 400$ V. The input signal is a positive pulse.

    (a) What operating point should be chosen so that the largest possible pulse height could be handled.

    (b) What grid bias voltage is needed?

    (c) What is the value of $I_P$ when a pulse with maximum height is applied?

    (d) What is the current $I_P$ with no pulse present?

**10.12**  Show the circuit model for a pentode with $g_m = 3500$ $\mu$mho and $r_p = 1.2$ M$\Omega$. If a sinusoidal signal of 1 V peak value is applied and if the load resistance is 10 k$\Omega$, what is the magnitude of the output signal? Can you neglect some resistances in your circuit model?

**10.13**  Small-signal measurements made with a pentode at a particular operating point provide the following data:

$$f_t = 100 \text{ MHz} \qquad g_m = 5 \cdot 10^{-3} \text{ mhos} \qquad r_p \gg R_L$$

$$C_{\text{out}} = 3 \text{ pF with input ac shorted}$$

What are the element values of the circuit model of the pentode if $C_{pk}$ is neglected?

**10.14**  For the pentode of Prob. 10.13, used as a single-stage amplifier, what are the values of the mid-band voltage gain and $-3$ dB bandedge of the voltage gain function if $R_s = 1$ k$\Omega$ and $R_L = 10$ k$\Omega$?

**10.15**  For simplicity, we consider that the small-signal circuit model for a pentode with $r_p \gg R_L$ is as shown. Find the power gain, i.e., ratio of the ac load power and the input power, for a sinusoidal input signal at a frequency of $10^6$ Hz. The parameters of the circuit are:

$$r_g = 10^6 \text{ } \Omega \qquad\qquad R_L = 10^4 \text{ } \Omega$$

$$C_{gk} = 10 \cdot 10^{-12} \text{ F} \qquad g_m = 5 \cdot 10^{-3} \text{ mho}$$

$$C_{pk} = 5 \cdot 10^{-12} \text{ F}$$

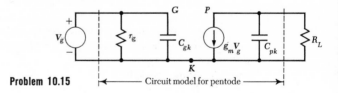

**Problem 10.15**    $\longleftarrow$ Circuit model for pentode $\longrightarrow$

**10.16**  Assume that a transistor operated at $I_C = 5$ mA has the same values of $f_t$ and $C_{\text{out}} = C_{ob}$ as the pentode of Prob. 10.13.

(a) Compare the circuit models of the two devices if we neglect $r_x$ for the transistor.

(b) Which device is better suited to amplify high frequencies if the same source and load resistances are to be used?

**10.17**  Utilizing (10.30), plot the form of the focusing electrode in the Pierce gun from $r = 0$ to $r = 2d$.

**10.18**  Illustrate the focusing properties of Fig. 10.30a by sketching the path of an electron starting from the left with a direction parallel with the axis and at a radius half that of the cylinders. Utilize the relation (10.29a) and, for simplicity, use only every other equipotential curve.

**10.19**  Repeat Prob. 10.18, utilizing the configuration of Fig. 10.30b.

**10.20**  For Fig. 10.30a and b, explain physically the reason for the focusing action by studying the direction of the electric field for different portions of the electron path. Note that there are two possible effects—radial position and different velocity on the two sides. Is one of these more important than the other?

**10.21**  Consider "long-coil" magnetic focusing in which a constant axial magnetic field extends over the entire region of an electron beam. An electron gun introduces electrons into the region with a constant axial velocity $v_0$ but with different radial velocities. Describe the path of the electrons and show that all electrons return to their initial radial positions at a distance

$$z = v_0 \frac{2\pi m}{qB}$$

**10.22**  One of the frequency limits of a cathode-ray deflection system is set by the transit time through the deflection plates. Assuming that this transit time should be kept to 0.1 cycle or less, what is the upper frequency limit of an electrostatic deflection system with plates 1 cm long if electrons enter with velocities corresponding to 1000 eV? What is the deflection sensitivity if $L = 10$ cm and the distance between plates is 2 mm? What factor or factors can be changed if frequency response is to be doubled without changing the deflection sensitivity?

**10.23**  A magnetic deflection system is substituted for the electrostatic deflection system of Prob. 10.22. Assuming the same dimensions and same entrance velocity, what magnetic field is required to give a deflection equal to that resulting from 1 V applied to the deflection plates of Prob. 10.22?

# chapter 11

# MICROWAVE DEVICES

## 11.1 introduction

The microwave frequency range extends from about 1 GHz to 300 GHz. Corresponding free-space wavelengths are 30 cm to 1 mm. Circuits and devices tend to be different in this frequency range from those at lower frequencies. The differences may be only of degree, but are often more fundamental. The circuits used are usually hollow pipes or cavities best analyzed from field theory, although concepts of impedance, bandwidth, etc., remain useful. For our purposes, we will consider microwave circuit elements as impedances with a certain frequency response.

Microwave devices utilize a variety of solid-state phenomena or use the interaction of charges with fields in a vacuum. Examples of semiconducting microwave devices include transistors and diodes designed for this frequency range where the principles are similar to those discussed in earlier chapters except for concentration on techniques to raise the upper range of operating frequency. Other devices use different effects in semiconductors. For example, the *tunnel diode*, invented by L. Esaki in 1958, utilizes a quantum tunneling similar to that for field emission discussed in Sec. 10.2 and is useful for high-speed switching and microwave oscillation. *Varactor diodes* utilize the change in space-charge capacitance under negative bias conditions as discussed in Sec. 6.3, and are useful for parametric amplification at microwave frequencies.[1]

[1] Parametric amplification comes from the time variation of a reactance in a circuit. The energy for amplification of the signal comes from the ac source or "pump" which produces changes in the reactance. The special usefulness of this type of amplifier arises because of its low-noise capability.

Acoustic-wave amplifiers utilize a traveling-wave interaction between acoustic waves and drift electrons in a solid such as cadmium sulfide. Microwave oscillations in bulk cadmium sulfide discovered by J. Gunn in 1963 (the Gunn effect) show much promise for microwave applications in the future, as do the transit-time oscillations in avalanche diodes (Read diodes) proposed in 1958.

Thus a number of important solid-state microwave devices are currently in use, and there will undoubtedly be more in the future. The understanding of most of these requires more depth in solid-state physics, or of specialized circuitry, than is appropriate to an introductory text. This is especially true since the art is changing so rapidly. Thus our concentration here will be on the basic processes important in several microwave vacuum devices (klystrons, traveling-wave tubes, etc.). Many of these principles, especially transit-time effects and traveling-wave interactions, are basic to the operation of all the solid-state devices mentioned.

Microwave vacuum devices are still widely utilized. We saw in Chap. 1 the use of the traveling-wave tube in modern systems such as the communication satellites. The tubes provide gain over a wide bandwidth with good efficiency and proven reliability. Thus application of these and related microwave devices are likely to remain important for some time to come.

## 11.2 motion of charges in high-frequency fields

Before beginning the study of specific devices, it is well to note some matters concerning the motion of electrons in time-varying fields. We have considered time-varying fields in earlier chapters, but it was usually assumed that variations were slow enough so that operation is *quasi-static*; that is, it was assumed that at any instant of time the action of the time-varying field or potential on a charge is the same as that of a static field having the same instantaneous value. As we shall see, this assumption is valid only if the transit time of the charge over the region of interest is a small part of a period of the highest frequency of interest. Transit-time effects were seen in Chap. 8 to set an upper frequency limit on transistor performance.

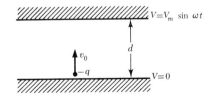

**FIGURE 11.1** *Electron entering region of ac fields with velocity $v_0$.*

Transit-time effects are important for nearly all microwave devices.

Consider an electron entering with velocity $\overrightarrow{v_0}$ a region between parallel planes as in Fig. 11.1. A voltage, $V_m \sin \omega t$, is applied between the plates, with a separation $d$, producing a corresponding ac field in the region. The time-varying electric fields generate magnetic fields, according to Maxwell's equations, but the effect of the latter is unimportant for many problems and will be neglected here. The electric field of the region is

$$E_x = -\frac{V_m}{d} \sin \omega t \qquad (11.1)$$

The force equation for an electron of charge $(-q)$ is then

$$m\frac{dv_x}{dt} = -q\left(-\frac{V_m}{d}\right) \sin \omega t$$

or
$$\frac{d^2 x}{dt^2} = \frac{qV_m}{md} \sin \omega t \qquad (11.2)$$

Integration of this yields

$$\frac{dx}{dt} = v_x = -\frac{qV_m}{m\omega d} \cos \omega t + C_1 \qquad (11.3a)$$

A second integration yields

$$x = \frac{qV_m}{m\omega^2 d} \sin \omega t + C_1 t + C_2 \qquad (11.3b)$$

If we apply initial conditions, $x = 0$, and $v_x = v_0$ at an entering time, $t = t_0$,

$$C_1 = v_0 + \frac{qV_m}{m\omega d} \cos \omega t_0 \qquad (11.4a)$$

$$C_2 = \frac{qV_m}{m\omega^2 d} (\sin \omega t_0 - \omega t_0 \cos \omega t_0) - v_0 t_0 \qquad (11.4b)$$

Let us also define

$$M = \frac{qV_m}{m\omega v_0 d} \qquad (11.5)$$

Then (11.3a) and (11.3b) may be written

$$v_x = v_0[1 + M(\cos \omega t_0 - \cos \omega t)] \qquad (11.6a)$$

$$x = v_0[(t - t_0) + M(t - t_0)\cos \omega t_0 - \frac{M}{\omega}(\sin \omega t - \sin \omega t_0)] \qquad (11.6b)$$

The quantity $\omega t$ appearing in the above is the *transit angle* in radians, equal to $2\pi t/T$, where $T$ is the period. Plots of $v_x$ versus $\omega t$ and of $x$ versus $\omega t$ are shown in Figs. 11.2a and 11.2b, respectively, for $M = 0.5$ and for two values of entering time, $\omega t_0 = 0$ and $\omega t_0 = \pi/2$. The numerical values are chosen only to show the effects of time-varying fields on charge motion. Inspection of the figures shows that velocity varies sinusoidally about an

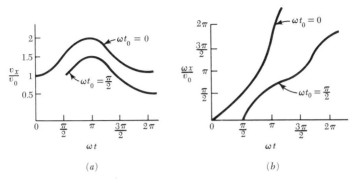

**FIGURE 11.2** (a) *Curve of $v_x/v_0$ versus $\omega t$ for $qV_m/m\omega v_0 d = 0.5$ and two values of entering time in Fig. 11.1; (b) corresponding distance curves, $\omega x/v_0$ versus $\omega t$.*

average value $v_0(1 + M \cos \omega t_0)$. The distance versus time curves have corresponding variations about the average slope.

It is especially important to note that the velocity at any instant in a time-varying problem is not given by the value of potential at that point and at that instant, as it is for static fields. The acceleration has come from an integration of the time-varying forces over the path. To stress this point, let us consider an electron entering $x = 0$ at $t_0 = 0$ and with zero velocity in the above problem. From (11.6a) and (11.5),

$$v_x = \frac{qV_m}{m\omega d}(1 - \cos \omega t) \qquad (11.7a)$$

Suppose it takes a half cycle, $\omega t = \pi$, for the electrons to arrive at $x = d$. From (11.7a) they arrive with velocity $2qV_m/m\omega d$, but the potential

$$V = V_m \sin \omega t \qquad (11.7b)$$

is zero at that time. The result is not surprising since electrons have been accelerated over the full half cycle. Thus the example stresses the inapplicability of the local, instantaneous potential for determining velocity in the general time-varying case.

If the transit time between the plates is small enough, the energy relation for static fields remains useful. Returning to (11.6a), let

$$t = t_0 + \tau \qquad (11.8a)$$

where $\tau$ is the transit time between the plates. If $\omega \tau \ll 1$, $\cos \omega t = \cos \omega(t_0 + \tau) = \cos \omega t_0 \cos \omega \tau - \sin \omega t_0 \sin \omega \tau \simeq \cos \omega t_0 - \omega \tau \sin \omega t_0$. Therefore, from (11.6a) and (11.5),

$$v_x \simeq v_0 + \frac{qV_m}{m\omega d}\omega\tau \sin \omega t_0 \qquad (11.8b)$$

If we square both sides of the equation and neglect the term in $(\omega\tau)^2$, we obtain

$$v_x^2 \simeq v_0^2 + \frac{2qV_m v_0}{m\omega d}\omega\tau \sin \omega t_0 \qquad (11.8c)$$

Letting $\tau = d/v_0$, where $d$ is the distance between the plates, we find the kinetic energy of an electron at the plane $x = d$

$$\tfrac{1}{2} mv_x^2 \simeq \tfrac{1}{2} mv_0^2 + qV_m \sin \omega t_0 \qquad (11.8d)$$

From this expression, it is seen that when $\omega\tau$ is small, the field is substantially constant throughout the transit of the charge, and the energy added is given by the instantaneous potential, as in statics. As noted earlier, $\omega\tau$ is not small for many important microwave devices.

## 11.3   microwave triodes

Space-charge-controlled tubes of the type discussed in the preceding chapter have been used in the lower parts of the microwave frequency range, although there are serious difficulties in obtaining high-frequency performance. There are circuit difficulties, arising from the lead inductance and internal capacitances of the device which may produce filter effects and internal feedback. Other difficulties arise from transit-time effects which affect the interaction between fields and electrons, as discussed in Sec. 11.2. The transit-time problems are enhanced because the cathode-grid region is inherently a low-velocity region. Recall that the charge is controlled at the cathode where electrons are emitted with small thermal velocities.

Circuit effects are minimized by designing the tube to fit as an integral member of a closed resonant cavity of the type used at microwave frequencies. An example of this is shown in Fig. 11.3. Lead inductances are thus small, and the interelectrode capacitances are little more than those inherent in the active portion of the electrodes. Operation is nearly always in the common-grid (grounded-grid) connection with the input applied between grid and cathode, and the output taken between anode (plate) and grid.[1] In this circuit the small capacitance $C_{pk}$ is the unavoidable feedback capacitance between output and input.

Transit-time effects are minimized by making the interelectrode spacings very small. As an example, consider the 416 class of triodes developed by the Bell Telephone Laboratories and the Western Electric Company for

[1] See footnote on page 348.

use in the TD-2 microwave relay system operating at 4 GHz. For such triodes the grid wire has a diameter of the order of $10^{-3}$ mm and the spacing between the grid wires is $10^{-2}$ mm. The distance between grid and anode is about 0.3 mm. The cathode-grid spacing, about $10^{-2}$ mm, is

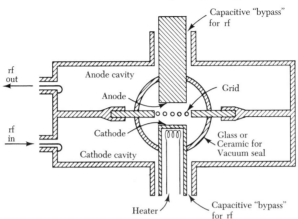

**FIGURE 11.3** *Schematic of parallel-plane microwave triode with cavity-resonator circuits in common-grid connection.*

extremely small because of the low electron velocities in this region. It is clear that the fabrication of such tubes requires extreme skill and care, but we also see why extension to the higher microwave frequencies is difficult and seldom competitive with other methods of interaction.

The circuit model for small-signal operation of a microwave triode is similar to that of Sec. 10.5 for a lower frequency triode except that all tube parameters are a function of frequency and the transit time. Thus the input admittance is a function of $\omega\tau_{kg}$, where $\tau_{kg}$ is the transit time between cathode and grid. The transconductance parameter $g_m$ is replaced by a transadmittance $y_m$ in which the phase shift between current induced in the output and controlling grid-cathode voltage is related to the total transit time across the tube.

In the initial design consideration for this typical stage it is useful to begin with the low-frequency power gain of the common-grid connection. The circuit model is shown in Fig. 11.4 for a high-$\mu$ tube. The input conductance is seen to be $g_m$, and the signal power input is

$$P_i = v_s^2 g_m \tag{11.9}$$

If $r_p \gg R_L$, where $R_L$ is the effective load resistance between the grid and the anode presented by the output resonant cavity, the output ac current is approximately

$$i_p = -g_m v_{kg} = -g_m v_s \tag{11.10}$$

The output power in $R_L$ is

$$P_o = R_L i_p^2 = R_L g_m^2 v_s^2 \tag{11.11}$$

The power gain is then

$$G_p = \frac{P_o}{P_i} = \frac{R_L g_m^2 v_s^2}{g_m v_s^2} = g_m R_L \tag{11.12}$$

The $g_m$ of a microwave triode with small spacings may be as high as $10^{-2}$ mho. With a load resistance of 10 k$\Omega$, a power gain of 100 (20 dB) is attained. The degree of impedance matching of the actual source and load to the cavities, the circuit effects, and the transit-time modifications of the basic

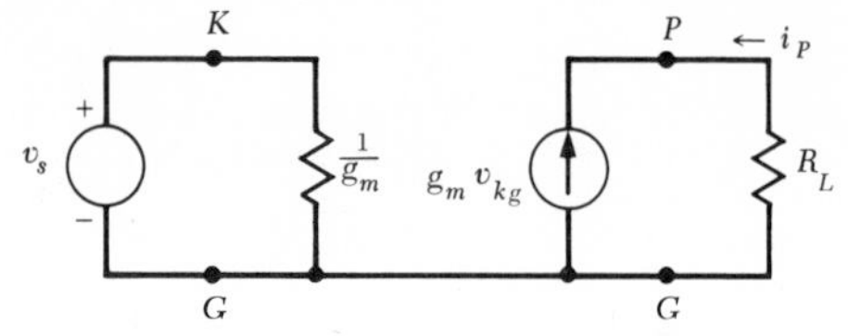

FIGURE 11.4  *Circuit model for common-grid high-$\mu$ triode. All reactances are assumed tuned out.*

tube parameters all affect the result. However, the above value of the power gain is of the correct order of magnitude for practical microwave triodes.

Space-charge control by a grid or by a nonintercepting control electrode is also used in some beam-type microwave tubes (klystrons and traveling-wave tubes) for specialized systems such as frequency-compression radar. Charge control at microwaves is thus important in a broader sense, as it was seen to be for display devices in Chap. 10.

## 11.4  the klystron

The klystron is a microwave tube in which velocity control of the electron beam is used, rather than intensity control as in the triode.[1] In the klystron the microwave input signal causes velocity variations of the electron beam. By a drifting action, the velocity variations are converted to current variations which may induce a microwave signal in the output circuit. Thus the transit time of the electron beam is utilized rather than minimized as it is in space-charge control. This operation is in contrast to that of the triode, where the input signal causes current variations of the electron beam by direct application of an electric field at the cathode region, which is a region of low beam velocity. In the klystron the input signal is impressed on a part of the beam having a high velocity. Therefore the transit-time limitations which are present in a klystron are less serious than in the triode.

---

[1] The klystron was developed by R. Varian and S. Varian in 1939 following publication of the velocity-variation concept by O. Heil and A. A. Heil in 1934.

**TWO-CAVITY KLYSTRON**   The essentials of a simple two-cavity klystron are shown in Fig. 11.5. The input and output circuits are of the cavity type, as in the case of the microwave triode. Each of the cavities has a gap through which the electron beam passes. This gap behaves much as the region between planes analyzed in Sec. 11.2. At the input cavity an $\vec{E}$ field is produced across the gap $g_1$ by the microwave input signal. This impresses on the electron beam of constant dc velocity a time-varying velocity component at the microwave frequency. That is, the beam now contains both a dc and time-varying component of velocity. The beam enters a field-free region, called a *drift region*, where fast electrons catch up with slower ones, producing a *bunching* of electrons. This results in a time variation of current. Although the resulting current waveform is not sinusoidal, the output cavity is tuned to the fundamental microwave frequency and is able to extract the fundamental component. With proper design of cavities, beam current, velocity, and drift length, it is possible to obtain more power at the output cavity than was put into the first cavity so that a net power gain results.

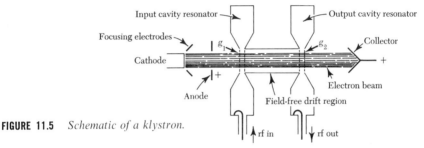

**FIGURE 11.5**   *Schematic of a klystron.*

**PRINCIPLES OF KLYSTRON BUNCHING** The principles of klystron action are also present to a considerable extent in other microwave tubes, such as the traveling-wave tube. We will now analyze the klystron action of a simplified model. We assume that the electron beam emanates from an electron gun with a constant velocity $v_0$ due to a dc accelerating voltage $V_0$ in the electron gun of the tube. At the input gap $g_1$ of the first cavity we apply a microwave sinusoidal signal $V_1 \sin \omega t$ and assume that the transit time through the gap is a small fraction of the period of the microwave signal. The gap may be analyzed as the region between planes studied in Sec. 11.2. The exit velocity of the beam when leaving the gap $g_1$ is then found from (11.8d) to be

$$v_x \simeq \sqrt{\frac{2q}{m}}(V_0 + V_1 \sin \omega t_0)^{1/2} \qquad (11.13)$$

where $t_0$ is the time when the beam passes through the gap $g_1$. When the gap voltage $V_1$, is small compared with the accelerating voltage $V_0$, a binomial expansion can be used and only the first term retained. This yields

$$v_x \simeq \sqrt{\frac{2q}{m} V_0} \left(1 + \frac{V_1}{2V_0} \sin \omega t_0\right) = v_0\left(1 + \frac{V_1}{2V_0} \sin \omega t_0\right) \quad (11.14)$$

It is helpful now to draw a distance versus time plot for the electrons passing through the drift region. Because the drift region is field free, the velocities of the individual electrons in this region do not change; therefore, the distance traveled $x$ versus time $t$ is a linear relation. Figure 11.6

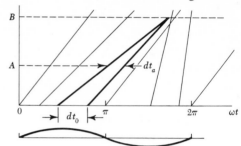

**FIGURE 11.6**  *Distance versus time plot for klystron electron motion.*

shows such a plot with lines for electrons leaving at various parts of the cycle. The reference sinusoid is shown below the axis of time. The slopes of the lines correspond to the various electron velocities. From Fig. 11.6 we see that electrons which enter the drift region when the gap voltage is zero have just the average velocity $v_0$. Those which enter with velocities above the average tend to catch up with other electrons having lower velocities. Similarly, electrons entering the drift region with below-average velocity are gradually overtaken by those having larger velocity. The net effect is a bunching. For a transverse plane in the drift region, such as $A$ in Fig. 11.6, the bunching is relatively small and the resulting time variation of the current is almost sinusoidal. However, at a plane such as $B$, where fast electrons begin to pass slow ones, the current waveform with time may be very complicated and rich in harmonics. The arrival time at a given reference plane $x$ is

$$t_a = t_0 + \frac{x}{v} \simeq t_0 + \frac{x}{v_0}\left(1 - \frac{V_1}{2V_0} \sin \omega t_0\right) \quad (11.15)$$

We now estimate the waveform of the current for this ideal model. The two heavy lines in Fig. 11.6 represent electrons which leave the input gap at times $t_0$ and $(t_0 + dt_0)$. During the incremental time interval $dt_0$ between entrance of the two electrons under consideration, a charge $I_0\, dt_0$ crosses $x = 0$, where $I_0$ is the entering dc current. Because of continuity requirements, the total charge is conserved between the two reference electrons, at least up to the time of crossover of the two lines. The charge must then be the same at corresponding arrival times $t_a$ and $t_a + dt_a$ in order to preserve continuity of charge. Thus for charge equality we have the relation

$$I_a \, dt_a = I_0 \, dt_0 \tag{11.16a}$$

From this, we obtain

$$I_a = I_0 \frac{dt_0}{dt_a} \tag{11.16b}$$

If the ratio, $dt_0/dt_a$, is obtained from (11.15), the current $I_a$ is

$$I_a = I_0 \frac{1}{1 - (\theta V_1/2V_0) \cos \omega t_0} \tag{11.17}$$

where $\theta$ is the phase delay for an electron of average velocity:

$$\theta = \frac{\omega x}{v_0} \tag{11.18}$$

For small values of $\theta V_1/(2V_0)$ we again use a binomial series expansion, retaining only the first term. We then obtain the sinusoidal form

$$I_a \simeq I_0 \left( 1 + \frac{\theta V_1}{2V_0} \cos \omega t_0 \right) \simeq I_0 \left[ 1 + \frac{\theta V_1}{2V_0} \cos (\omega t_a - \theta) \right] \tag{11.19}$$

If $\theta V_1/(2V_0)$ is large, we use both (11.15) and (11.17) to plot the current versus $t_a$. Waveshapes for several values of $\theta V_1/(2V_0)$ are shown in Fig. 11.7. From these waveforms, the high-harmonic content is immediately

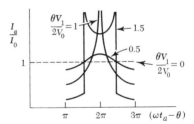

**FIGURE 11.7** *Current waveshapes in an idealized klystron.*

apparent. Consequently, the klystron can be used not only as an amplifier, but also as a harmonic generator if the output cavity is chosen for a harmonic frequency.

An actual input gap as in Fig. 11.5 introduces a loss because of finite transit-time loading. In addition, there are also losses present in the input circuit (cavity). The losses reduce the power gain, which can nevertheless be very high. There are other factors which make the actual tube deviate from the ideal model. Prominent among these is the repulsion caused in the space charge, notably when bunching begins. These effects may cause alternate bunching and debunching of charge, resulting in "space-charge waves." These are especially important in high-density beams and interact with circuit waves to provide the useful gain in a traveling-wave tube.

**REFLEX KLYSTRON**   A klystron becomes an oscillator if its amplified output is fed back into the input, as shown in Fig. 11.8. However, a much simpler possibility for obtaining the feedback exists by using a single cavity only.

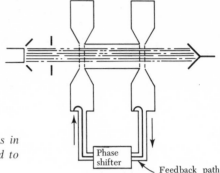

**FIGURE 11.8**   *Two-cavity klystron, as in Fig. 11.5, with feedback path added to produce an oscillator.*

This is the reflex klystron shown in Fig. 11.9. The electron beam is emitted with a constant velocity from the electron gun and passes through the gap, where it experiences velocity control, as in the case of the klystron. Now the beam enters a retarding field set up between a repeller and the anode of the electron gun. This field is produced by applying a negative potential

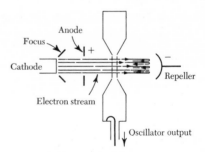

**FIGURE 11.9**   *Schematic of a reflex klystron.*

to the repeller and a positive potential to the anode. As a result of the retarding field, the motion of the electrons is reversed and the electrons return to the gap. Thus the beam passes through the gap twice. The slow electrons in the beam return to the gap earlier than fast ones. Because of the difference of time in the repeller regions, the retarding field converts the velocity variations to current variations. Provided that the electrons return to the gap in the proper phase, oscillation occurs. The proper phase relation can be obtained for a given tube by adjusting the repeller voltage. Over limited ranges, useful electronic tuning can be obtained by variation of the repeller voltage. The extent of tuning depends on the bandwidth of the cavity, but is usually less than 1 percent of the center frequency.

## 11.5   traveling-wave tubes

The traveling-wave tube (TWT) also utilizes the principle of velocity variation of an electron beam by a high-frequency signal. Again, a bunching of the electrons occurs as explained in the last section for the klystron. The difference is that the interaction between the signal wave and the electron beam occurs over the entire active length of the tube. In other words the modulation, bunching, and power coupling are distributed, rather than localized in a resonant circuit as is the case with the klystron. The distributed circuits may have much greater bandwidths than the resonant circuits used with klystrons or microwave triodes. The TWT may have very large bandwidths (values from 30 to 100 percent or more of the center frequency of the passband). Therefore it is important where wideband microwave communications are needed. This is one of the reasons a TWT is used in the communication satellites as discussed in Chap. 1.

The TWT uses an electron beam which emanates from the electron gun (often a Pierce gun as studied in Sec. 10.8) at a certain axial velocity $v_b$, as shown in Fig. 11.10$a$ and $b$. The beam passes through an interaction region of length $L$ and is ultimately collected at an electrode, called the

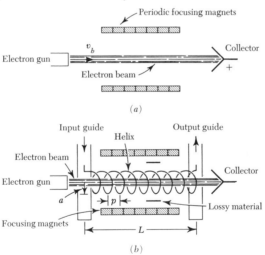

**FIGURE 11.10**   *Traveling-wave tube.* (a) *Electron beam and focusing device;* (b) *helix slow wave structure in 0-type TWT.*

*collector.* The collector is at a positive potential with respect to the cathode of the electron gun. Periodic focusing magnets are used along the interaction region. Most often these are lightweight ferrite magnets. Their magnetic field keeps the beam focused along the length $L$ as explained in Sec. 10.8.

The electron beam travels with an axial velocity $v_b$ much slower than the velocity of light. The idea of the TWT is to have a continuous inter-action between the beam and an electromagnetic wave. We thus need a mechanism for slowing the wave down to approximate synchronism with velocity $v_b$. Such a mechanism is the slow-wave circuit which can be obtained by using a helix which is coaxial with the beam, as shown in Fig. 11.10$b$. To a fair degree of approximation the signal wave follows the conductor of the helix approximately at the velocity of light $c$. However, the net progress of this signal wave or circuit wave along the axis is much slower. The net velocity, which corresponds to a phase velocity $v_p$, is

$$v_p \simeq c \frac{p}{2\pi a} \tag{11.20}$$

where $a$ is the radius of the helix and $p$ is its pitch. This expression holds surprisingly well in the range of use. It shows to this approximation that the phase velocity $v_p$ of the helix is independent of frequency. Therefore, proper interaction between the wave and electron beam is accomplished. (The helix is not the only slow-wave circuit that could be used. Special periodic circuits are useful also. Such periodic circuits generally have a narrower bandwidth than the helix.)

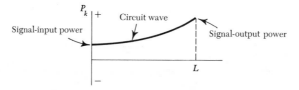

**FIGURE 11.11**   *Kinetic power flow $P_k$ of the signal wave in a TWT.*

An input signal from a waveguide is launched on the slow-wave structure with a special coupler. We now have a circuit wave traveling along the beam axis with the phase velocity $v_p$. It interacts with the electrons of the beam, which are traveling at approximately the same velocity $v_b \simeq v_p$ and which become velocity modulated and bunched. This produces "space-charge waves." In effect the electrons in the beam are slowed down and yield energy, while the circuit wave gains the equivalent energy. When the electron beam leaves the region of interaction, it has less power than on entrance because of transfer of power to the circuit wave. Figure 11.11 illustrates the power growth of the signal wave. Because the circuit wave gains power from the beam, amplification takes place. The output signal wave is obtained by the use of another coupler.

There is a tendency toward oscillation in the TWT because of reflections within the tube or at the output coupler. To prevent this oscillation, an attenuating material is placed in or near the slow-wave circuit to decrease any such reflected feedback. This attenuator is usually a film of resistive material placed in close proximity to the helix, as shown in Fig. 11.10b. It extends only over a small fraction of the tube region L.

Pierce[1] has shown that the power gain of an idealized traveling-wave tube can be written

$$G_p = A + BCN \quad \text{dB} \tag{11.21a}$$

where $A$ is a negative number representing loss in coupling to the amplified wave and is about $-9$ dB in the idealized model; $B$ is a constant equal to 47.3 dB in the model, but lower for actual tubes; $N$ is the number of wavelengths in the circuit,

$$N = \frac{l}{v_p} \tag{11.21b}$$

and $C$ is a gain parameter related to dc current $I_0$, beam voltage $V_0$, and impedance of the circuit $K$,

$$C = \left(\frac{KI_0}{4V_0}\right)^{1/3} \tag{11.21c}$$

Gain parameters are typically in the range 0.01 to 0.1, the latter for high-power tubes.

A gain of 30 dB with a frequency range of 2:1 in a length of 6 in. represents good design for a medium-power traveling-wave tube. Power output from such a tube might be 100 W with an efficiency of 30 percent.

## 11.6  crossed-field devices

An important class of microwave devices utilizes electron interaction in crossed electric and magnetic fields, i.e., fields which are perpendicular to one another. Energy exchange between charges and the fields in such devices is by way of the potential energy of the field which is transverse to the electron motion. Therefore the amplification process is different from the process in klystrons or traveling-wave tubes where the energy for amplification comes from the kinetic energy of the beam. Crossed-field interactions also occur in solids, the most elementary example being the Hall effect described in Sec. 4.10. Further, crossed-field motion is important in a variety of nonmicrowave devices, such as mass spectrographs and high-speed photomultipliers. In this section, this basic process is studied briefly and we begin by considering charge motion in crossed fields.

---

[1] J. R. Pierce, "Traveling-Wave Tubes," D. Van Nostrand Company, Inc., Princeton, N.J., 1950.

**CHARGE MOTION IN CROSSED ELECTRIC AND MAGNETIC FIELDS**    Figure 11.12 shows a dc electric field $\vec{E}$ in the $-x$ direction of a rectangular coordinate system, with dc magnetic field $\vec{B}$ in the $-y$ direction. The two fields are thus at right

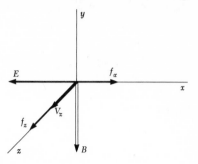

**FIGURE 11.12**   *Electron in crossed $\vec{E}$ and $\vec{B}$ fields.*

angles, or "crossed." The force equation for an electron of charge $-q$ is

$$\vec{f} = -q[\vec{E} + (\vec{v} \times \vec{B})] \qquad (11.22a)$$

One interesting and important special case is that in which the electron moves in the $z$ direction with an exact balance of the electric and magnetic forces. That is, if velocity is $v_z$ in the $z$ direction only, the force is

$$f_x = -q(E_x - v_z B_y) \qquad (11.22b)$$

This force is zero if

$$v_z = \frac{E_x}{B_y} \qquad (11.23)$$

For constant fields $E_x$ and $B_y$, the constant velocity $v_z$ given by (11.23) eliminates all force and the electron moves in a straight line as shown in Fig. 11.13.

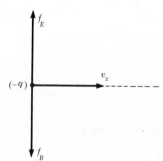

**FIGURE 11.13**   *Balance of electric and magnetic forces when $v_z = E/B$.*

Let us next consider the motion when the electron enters the region of fields at some origin $x = 0$, $z = 0$ at time $t = 0$ with given initial velocity. This situation is shown in Fig. 11.14. Any motion in the $x$ direction produces a force in the $z$ direction because of the magnetic field, and vice versa, as shown in Fig. 11.15. There is no force and hence no motion in the $y$ direction. The force equations for the $x$ and $z$ directions are

$$f_x = m\frac{dv_x}{dt} = -q(E_x - v_z B_y) \tag{11.24a}$$

$$f_z = m\frac{dv_z}{dt} = -q(v_x B_y) \tag{11.24b}$$

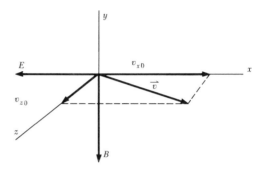

FIGURE 11.14 *Electron with initial velocities $v_{x0}$ and $v_{z0}$ entering crossed fields.*

Let us make use of the cyclotron angular frequency, as defined in (4.35),

$$\omega_c = \frac{qB}{m} \tag{11.25}$$

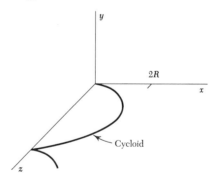

FIGURE 11.15 *Cycloidal path of electron in crossed fields.*

We also let $E_x = -E$ and $B_y = -B$. Equations (11.24a) and (11.24b) may then be written

$$\frac{d^2x}{dt^2} = \frac{q}{m}E - \omega_c\frac{dz}{dt} \tag{11.26a}$$

$$\frac{d^2z}{dt^2} = \omega_c\frac{dx}{dt} \tag{11.26b}$$

An integration of the two equations with respect to time yields

$$\frac{dx}{dt} = \frac{qE}{m}t - \omega_c z + C_1 \qquad (11.27a)$$

$$\frac{dz}{dt} = \omega_c x + C_2 \qquad (11.27b)$$

The initial conditions $v_x = v_{x0}$, $v_z = v_{z0}$, $x = 0$, $z = 0$ at $t = 0$ allow us to identify $C_1 = v_{x0}$ and $C_2 = v_{z0}$. For simplicity we carry on the remaining steps for zero initial velocity, $v_{x0} = 0$ and $v_{z0} = 0$. Substitution of (11.27a) in (11.26b) gives

$$\frac{d^2 z}{dt^2} = \frac{\omega_c qE}{m}t - \omega_c^2 z \qquad (11.28)$$

The first term on the right may be removed by the transformation

$$z = z' + ut \qquad (11.29a)$$

where

$$u = \frac{qE}{m\omega_c} = \frac{E}{B} \qquad (11.29b)$$

Then (11.28) becomes

$$\frac{d^2 z'}{dt^2} = -\omega_c^2 z' \qquad (11.30)$$

This equation has solutions of sinusoidal form

$$z' = R \sin \omega_c t + S \cos \omega_c t \qquad (11.31)$$

The initial condition on the variable $z'$, by (11.29a), is that $z' = 0$ when $z = 0$, $t = 0$, and therefore $S = 0$ in (11.31). The initial derivative $dz'/dt$ is $-u$ when $z = 0$, $t = 0$, and from (11.31) it is $\omega_c R$. Hence we identify

$$R = -\frac{u}{\omega_c} = -\frac{E}{\omega_c B} \qquad (11.32)$$

The equation for $z$, using (11.29a), (11.29b), (11.31), and (11.32), is then

$$z = -R(\omega_c t - \sin \omega_c t) \qquad (11.33)$$

Substitution in (11.27b), with $C_2 = 0$, gives $x$:

$$x = R(1 - \cos \omega_c t) \qquad (11.34)$$

The equations (11.33) and (11.34) can be recognized as the parametric equations for a cycloid, as sketched in Fig. 11.15. Such a curve is generated by a point on a circle of radius $R$ as the circle rolls along the $z$ axis with velocity $u$. For this case $u$ and $R$ are given by (11.29b) and (11.32), respectively.

If the initial velocities $v_{x0}$ and $v_{z0}$ are retained, the equations for $x$ and $z$ are easily extended to give

$$x = \left(\frac{v_{z0}}{\omega_c} - \frac{E}{B\omega_c}\right)\cos\omega_c t - \frac{v_{x0}}{\omega_c}\sin\omega_c t + \frac{E}{B\omega_c} + \frac{v_{z0}}{\omega_x} \qquad (11.35a)$$

$$z = \frac{v_{x0}}{\omega_c}\cos\omega_c t + \left(\frac{v_{z0}}{\omega_c} - \frac{E}{B\omega_c}\right)\sin\omega_c t + \frac{E}{B}t - \frac{v_{x0}}{\omega_c} \qquad (11.35b)$$

Curves for these more general equations are epicycloids or hypocycloids, depending on the values of $v_{x0}$ and $v_{z0}$.

**CROSSED-FIELD AMPLIFIERS AND OSCILLATORS**  We now look at the simple model of a crossed-field microwave amplifier pictured in Fig. 11.16. Like a traveling-

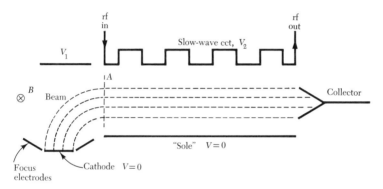

**FIGURE 11.16**  *Crossed-field traveling wave amplifier. The sole is the lower electrode in the interaction region.*

wave tube, the crossed-field amplifier has a region in which electrons interact with a slow wave, as well as a mechanism for injecting electrons into that region. The injection region and the mechanism of interaction both differ from those of the TWT. Electrons are emitted from a thermionic cathode in the form of a sheet. A magnetic field is applied parallel with the cathode, and an electric field—normal to the cathode and to the magnetic field—arises from a potential $V_1$ on an anode. The electrons begin to move vertically and are then given longitudinal forces by the magnetic fields. The path of the electron approximates the cycloidal path of Fig. 11.15 up to a plane $A$, which is the beginning of the interaction region. At that point the value of transverse electric field has a different value, but the constant $\vec{B}$ field into the paper is maintained. The dc electric and magnetic forces in this region are made to cancel. The relation is approximately (11.23), modified slightly to account for the space-charge fields of the beam. The beam then continues in a straight line toward the collector in the absence of ac fields.

For interaction between the electron beam and a signal, the upper electrode is in the form of a slow-wave circuit as shown in Fig. 11.16. The wave on the circuit is arranged to be in approximate synchronism

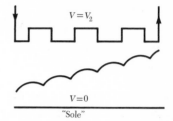

**FIGURE 11.17** *Path of an electron showing drop in potential energy when reacting with rf field.*

with the velocity of electrons. This relationship is as in the traveling-wave tube of Sec. 11.5, but here the interaction is with the potential energy of the transverse field instead of with the kinetic energy of the beam as

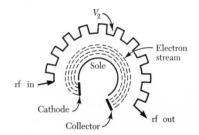

**FIGURE 11.18** *Crossed-field amplifier of circular form.*

in the TWT. Details of the interaction require a knowledge of the ac fields, but ac energy is taken from the electrons by the circuit wave. The electrons must move nearer the top electrode and utilize the energy of the transverse electric field as shown in Fig. 11.17. The axial component of

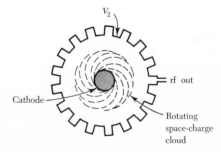

**FIGURE 11.19** *Crossed-field oscillator of circular form (magnetron).*

electron velocity is affected little and so the electrons can remain in synchronism with the wave over a wider range of signal levels than in the TWT. The efficiency of converting dc energy to signal energy is correspondingly higher in the crossed-field tube than in the TWT.

The crossed-field amplifier may be constructed in circular form, as shown in Fig. 11.18, for compactness. Centripetal forces, together with the electric, magnetic, and space-charge forces, must then be taken into account, but the principles of operation are as described. If the electrons are not collected but are allowed to continue around the circle as in Fig. 11.19, they provide feedback and can produce oscillations. The classical magnetron oscillator, used as the pulsed source in many microwave radar systems, is essentially such a device. The general class of crossed-field devices is thus frequently known as *magnetron-type* or *M-type* devices.

### REFERENCES

W. W. Harman, "Fundamentals of Electronic Motion," McGraw-Hill Book Company, New York, 1953.

M. Chodorow and C. Susskind, "Fundamentals of Microwave Electronics," McGraw-Hill Book Company, New York, 1964.

### PROBLEMS

**11.1**  Show that the time of flight (transit time) for an electron between parallel planes of spacing $d$ with potential $V_0$ between them is

$$\tau = \frac{2d}{v_0}$$

when
$$v_0 = \sqrt{\frac{2q}{m}V_0}$$

The electron leaves the first plane with zero velocity and space-charge effects are negligible.

**11.2**  Repeat Prob. 11.1 for a planar diode with space-charge limitation according to Child's law. Show that transit time is then

$$\tau = \frac{3d}{v_0}$$

**11.3**  Utilizing the results of Probs. 11.1 and 11.2, find the approximate transit times between cathode and grid and between grid and plate of a vacuum triode. The potential of the equivalent grid plane is 1 V, and the plate-cathode potential is 200 V. Spacings are $d_{gk} = 0.1$ mm and $d_{gp} = 0.5$ mm.

**11.4**  A microwave triode connected in the common-grid connection has $g_m = 6 \cdot 10^{-3}$ mho and a resistive load of $10^4\ \Omega$. $r_p$ may be neglected. If $C_{pk} = 0.01$ pF, calculate the capacitive current through it at 3 GHz in comparison with input and load currents. (*Hint*: Utilize the circuit model of the figure and calculate first the approximate $V_L$, assuming $C_{pk}$ is negligible.)

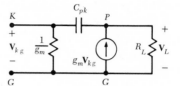

**Problem 11.4**

**11.5** The lead inductances of electronic tubes may be important in some circuits in addition to the interelectrode capacitances. For the common-cathode connection of a triode, the inductance of the cathode lead internal to the tube is indicated in the figure. Explain how this causes a coupling between output and input.

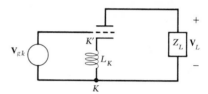

**Problem 11.5**

**11.6** (a) Plot curves of distance versus time, such as those of Fig. 11.6, for an ideal klystron with beam voltage $V_0 = 100$ V and a voltage across the input gap $V_1 = 10 \sin \omega t$. Plot curves for every $1/12$ period of the sinusoid.

(b) At what distance do electrons begin to pass those which started earlier?

(c) For a distance 80 percent of that calculated in part b, plot a rough curve of current in the beam as a function of time, using the expression

$$I = I_0 \frac{dt_o}{dt} \simeq I_0 \frac{\Delta t_o}{\Delta t}$$

**11.7** A two-cavity klystron is formed into an oscillator by feeding output back into the input through a phase-shifting 2-port, as shown in the figure. The dc beam voltage is 1 kV, drift distance is 0.5 cm, and frequency is 1 GHz. Assuming that both input and output gaps appear as pure resistances, what phase shift should the external network supply for oscillation? (*Hint*: The feedback signal must be in phase with the original input.)

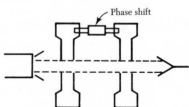

**Problem 11.7**

**11.8** Assume that the retarding field in a reflex klystron is $E_x = E_0$. (a) If electrons leave the gap with velocity $v_0 + v_1 \sin \omega t_0$, where $t_0$ is the time of passing through the gap, find the equations of motion in the retarding region. (b) Plot distance versus time curves for $v_0 = \sqrt{(2q/m)}100$, $v_1 = 0.1v_0$, and $E_0 = 500$ V/cm. Explain how this diagram shows the bunching action of the retarding field.

**11.9** A traveling-wave tube has a helix of pitch equal to 2 mm and a radius of 1 cm. Find the helix voltage with respect to the cathode in order for electrons to be in synchronism with the wave in the helix. Use the simple law for propagation along the helix, which is mentioned in the text.

**11.10** The helix impedance $K$ of (11.21c) for a particular traveling-wave tube is 30 $\Omega$. Helix voltage is 200 V and beam current is 10 mA. What length is required by the simple formula for the tube to produce a gain of 30 dB?

**11.11** An $\vec{E}$ field of $10^4$ V/m and a $\vec{B}$ field of 1 mWb/m$^2$ are parallel to each other and in the same direction. The fields are uniform and constant. 100 eV electrons enter the fields at an angle of 45°, as shown in the figure. A vertical plane at $x = 0.02$ m is hit by the electrons.

(a) At what point do the electrons hit the vertical plane?

(b) What is the electron velocity when arriving at the plane?

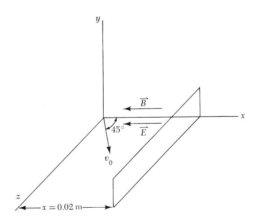

**Problem 11.11**

**11.12** Repeat Prob. 11.11 under the assumption that the direction of the $\vec{E}$ field is reversed.

**11.13** Electrons are injected with an initial velocity $v_{y0}$ parallel to the $y$ axis, as shown in the figure. A $\vec{B}$ field is parallel to the $x$ axis and an $\vec{E}$ field is parallel to the $xz$ plane and has components $E_x$ and $E_z$; $E_y = 0$. Both the $\vec{B}$ and the $\vec{E}$ fields are uniform and constant.

(a) If the electrons should remain in the $xy$ plane, what value of $v_{y0}$ is to be used?

(b) Using the assumptions under part a, what is the path of the electrons. Show the x and y coordinates as functions of time.

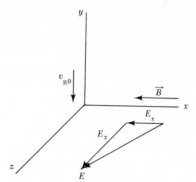

**Problem 11.13**

**11.14** The essential dc electrodes of a simple crossed-field amplifier are shown in the figure. Trace the path of an electron emitted at $x = 0$, $z = 0$, with zero velocity. $V_0 = 200$ V, $d = 1$ cm, $B = 0.01$ Wb/m², $l = 2$ cm, and $L = 10$ cm. What velocity should the wave on the slow-wave circuit have for approximate synchronism with the $x$ component of electron velocity?

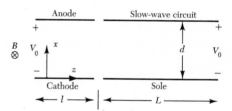

**Problem 11.14**

**11.15** The electron gun in the figure is designed to inject electrons into the interaction region with parallel flow only, as explained in the text. Assuming that electrons leave the cathode with zero velocity, they enter the interaction region at the top of a cycloid and then enter a region of interaction in field $E_x$, where electric and magnetic forces balance.

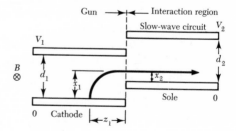

**Problem 11.15**

(a) Show that the following conditions satisfy the requirements for this flow:

$$x_1 = 2x_2 \qquad z_1 = \pi x_2 \qquad \frac{V_2}{d_2} = \frac{2V_1}{d_1}$$

Note that the potential is the same on the two sides as the beam enters the interaction region.

(b) What is the minimum allowed value of $\vec{B}$?

# chapter 12

# PHOTON-INTERACTION DEVICES

## 12.1  energy quantization and the photon

The electronic components used as examples in this book have largely been those with electrical inputs and outputs. That is, control has been by means of electric or magnetic fields acting on free charges in space or in solids. In this chapter we look briefly at devices in which the inputs, outputs, or both are light waves or other electromagnetic waves of such a high frequency that the quantum nature of the energy must be considered. Some of the devices, such as phototubes, are old in principle. Other devices, such as the semiconducting photoconductors, are newer but can be understood from simple extensions of the models for charge flow in solids studied in preceding chapters. To broaden the picture we shall consider some newer devices such as the laser. Although these devices are still in rapid development, they establish a very basic principle and will certainly have a great impact on electronic systems of the future.

The principles and devices to be discussed in this chapter can be considered as examples from the field of *quantum electronics*. This term legitimately stresses that the understanding of many modern devices requires quantum physics rather than classical physics. It seems certain that still more quantum principles will be applied, so the picture to be given in this chapter is not that of a completed field but rather a progress report on a new and rapidly changing one. It is fitting that we close the book on this open-ended note, for such change has been the characteristic of electronics and electrical engineering since the subject began.

The examples to be described fall broadly into two categories—those with absorption of photons (i.e., having photon inputs) and those with emission of photons (having photon outputs). Examples of each will be discussed and also of the optoelectronic devices which use photons for coupling between two parts of a circuit.

Radiant energy occurs in quantized form, each *photon* having an amount of energy proportional to frequency:

$$W = hf \quad \text{joules} \tag{12.1}$$

where $h$ is Planck's constant ($6.625 \cdot 10^{-34}$ J-s) and $f$ is frequency in hertz. Thus, at 60 Hz the energy per photon is about $4 \cdot 10^{-32}$ J, so that a 100-W lamp would have about $25 \cdot 10^{32}$ photons passing through each second. In such a case we are no more concerned with the "granularity" of the energy than we are with the molecular nature of fluid flow when we water our lawn with a garden hose emitting perhaps $10^{25}$ molecules per second. Even at 100 GHz a microwatt of power represents nearly $2 \cdot 10^{16}$ photons per second, and here also quantum effects generally reduce to classical effects, although for some purposes we may have to look at the individual atomic or molecular process and apply quantum laws. At still higher frequencies (in the infrared, visible, or ultraviolet) the need to use quantum laws is more common.

At this point it is convenient to introduce different units of measure. We have frequently used the electron volt for energy ($1.60 \cdot 10^{-19}$ J). Radiation may also be characterized by its wavelength $\lambda$ instead of by its frequency $f$, where $\lambda = c/f$ ($c$ = velocity of light, $2.998 \cdot 10^8$ m/s). Optical wavelengths are measured either in microns or angstroms, where

$$1 \text{ micron } (1 \ \mu) = 10^{-6} \text{ m} = 10^{-4} \text{ cm}$$
$$1 \text{ angstrom } (1 \text{ Å}) = 10^{-10} \text{ m} = 10^{-8} \text{ cm} \tag{12.2}$$

In these units, (12.1) may be written

$$W = \frac{1.24}{\lambda_\mu} = \frac{12,400}{\lambda_{\text{Å}}} \text{ eV} \tag{12.3}$$

Visible light corresponds to the range of about 0.39 to $0.75\mu$, or 3900 to 7500 Å, yielding quanta with energies from 1.65 to 3.2 eV. X rays have wavelengths of a few angstroms, and therefore energies of a few tens of kilovolts. The upper limit of the microwave range of frequencies with wavelength of about 1 mm or $10^3\mu$ yields energy per photon of 1.24 mV. Transitions between energy levels in atoms are typically of the order of volts, so radiated (or absorbed) photons in atomic processes are in the visible region or nearby. As a confirmation of this, consider the richness of atomic spectral lines in the visible range. Molecular vibrations or rotations usually have energies of a fraction of a volt and thus yield radiations in the infrared or even microwave range of frequencies as seen by (12.3). A quantum of energy in the microwave range (say $\lambda = 1$ cm $= 10^4 \mu$) is 0.124 meV and thus is normally masked by statistical fluctuations of the thermal energy $kT$, which we have seen to be about 26 meV at room temperature. Thus for clear observation of quantum effects in the microwave range, very low temperature operation may be required. As noted above, radiation and absorption of photons arise in the change between quantum states of different energy levels. Thus, (12.1) is more properly written

$$hf = W_2 - W_1 \qquad \text{joules} \qquad (12.4)$$

The sign of (12.4) is defined such that $hf$ is positive when the particle falls from energy level $W_2$ to a lower energy, $W_1$, and energy is radiated. Conversely, energy is absorbed when the sign of (12.4) is negative, representing an electron which goes from a lower to a higher energy level in the atom.

## 12.2   photoelectric emission and phototubes

In Chaps. 10 and 11, we considered vacuum devices most of which employ electrons emitted from thermionic cathodes. As shown in Sec. 10.2, electrons can leave a metal provided they gain an amount of energy equal to the work function $W_w$ of the material. For thermionic cathodes this energy is supplied in the form of heat. The required energy can be supplied in other forms, and here we consider emission resulting from photon energy. Such photoelectric emission was introduced briefly in Sec. 10.2. Reasoning from the preceding section, we expect monochromatic light of frequency $f$ to produce emitted electrons with an energy equal to the energy of the photon less the work-function energy required for the electron to escape from the metal, as illustrated in Fig. 12.1. Thus the emitted kinetic energy is

$$^1/_2 \, mv^2 = hf - W_w \qquad (12.5)$$

This equation, met earlier as (10.4), is known as Einstein's equation and was developed in 1905 from M. Planck's then newly formulated quantum theory. Photoelectric emission was known before, together with (12.5),

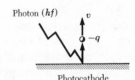

Photon ($hf$)

$-q$

Photocathode

**FIGURE 12.1**   *Electron emitted by impinging photon.*

in empirical terms. It was in fact quite a bothersome law before quantum postulates were made. By analogy with thermionic emission where the average energy of emission depends on the temperature, and therefore on the amount of heat supplied, one might expect the average energy of photoelectric electrons to increase with the amount of light supplied. But in quantum terms the light flux affects the number of electrons emitted and not the energy per electron. A large light flux (of a given wavelength) signifies a larger number of photons impinging on the metal surface. If each photon liberates one electron, we say that we have a *quantum efficiency of unity*. If the probability of electron emission by a photon is $\eta$, the quantum efficiency is $\eta$. For a given quantum efficiency, the emitted photoelectric current is directly proportional to the light flux. The fact that Einstein could explain these two aspects of photoelectric emission from quantum principles did much to speed the acceptance of that theory in its early stage of development.

The simplest conception of a practical device is that of a diode with a *photocathode*. As shown in Fig. 12.2, the emissive surface is usually large

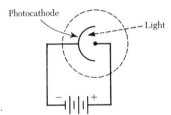

Photocathode

Light

**FIGURE 12.2**  *Photodiode.*

to capture the maximum amount of light, and the anode is small to give a negligible shadow on the cathode. With applied dc voltage of the polarity shown, light impinging on the tube causes current to flow. Thus, the device acts as a light-energy to electric-energy transducer. The tube may be a vacuum device or may be filled with gas. In the latter case the gas becomes ionized and reduces the voltage drop in the tube to a value approximately equal to the ionization potential of the gas (for example, 21.5 V for neon).[1] The student is familiar with some applications of phototubes; for example, in automatic doors and many industrial control processes. In many applications these tubes are being replaced by semiconducting photodevices. Nonetheless, important applications of phototubes remain.

**PHOTOMULTIPLIERS**    The most sensitive phototubes utilize multiplication of the emitted photocurrent through secondary emission, a process also discussed in Sec. 10.2. The principle is diagramed in Fig. 12.3*a*. Light impinges on the photocathode, and the emitted electrons are then directed by electron-focusing techniques to an auxiliary electrode called a *dynode*. The dynode

---

[1]When an atom is ionized, the electron is removed from the influence of the atom and becomes free. In a gas discharge, the free electrons may be accelerated, ionizing other atoms in a cascade process. Thus the current increases rapidly until it is limited by the external resistance, and the voltage drop across the tube is just the value needed to maintain ionization.

may be silver oxide on silver which yields eight to ten secondary electrons for every primary electron striking it. This multiplied current is then focused toward another dynode, and so on, until the multiplied current is finally

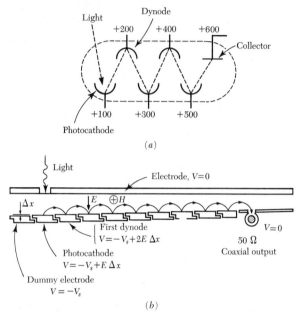

*(a)*

*(b)*

**FIGURE 12.3** (a) *Photomultiplier using electrostatic focusing;* (b) *fast-response photomultiplier using crossed electric and magnetic fields.* [*From R. C. Miller and N. C. Wittwer, "Secondary Emission Amplification at Microwave Frequencies," IEEE Journal of Quantum Electronics,* **QE-1**, *49-59 (1965)*].

collected. When a large number of dynodes is used, the final electron stream to the collector can be several million times larger than the initial photo-current. These devices are among the most sensitive photon detectors known and are developed with a variety of photoemissive surfaces for different ranges of wavelength. Photomultipliers are used in astronomy, in scientific research, and for various sensitive control devices.

Figure 12.3*b* shows an alternate configuration which uses crossed electric and magnetic fields to direct the electrons from one dynode to another. Electron motion is as described in Sec. 11.6. The response of this configuration is very fast. Figure 12.4 shows the spectral response of several photomultipliers.

## 12.3 photoconductivity in semiconductors

When a photon strikes a semiconductor, ionization can occur and valence electrons may be freed to produce free electrons and holes. There are a number of important resulting effects, sometimes classified separately as photogalvanic, photovoltaic, etc., but generally grouped together as *photoconductivity*.

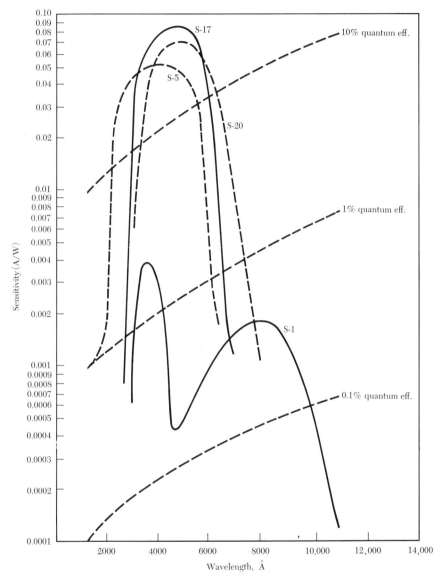

**FIGURE 12.4** *Spectral response of selected photoemissive devices (from ITT Laboratories data).* S-1: Ag-0-Cs *with visible light transmitting glass window;* S-5: Cs-Sb *with UV transmitting glass;* S-17: Cs-Sb *with visible transmitting glass;* S-20: Sb-K-Na-Cs *with visible transmitting glass.*

The energy equation to be satisfied is (12.4). Thus, to raise an electron from the valence band to the conduction band in silicon or germanium, where the band gap is of the order of a volt, light in the micron-wavelength range will be required by (12.3). This is in the near infrared range (i.e., wavelengths longer than but near the visible range). For certain doped materials, lower energies may be sufficient to raise the electrons from the donor level into the conduction band or from the valence band into an acceptor level with longer infrared wavelengths.

For a bulk material, the presence of conduction electrons controlled by light clearly gives us the possibility of a *photoconductor*.[1] In a photoconductor, a voltage is applied to the semiconductor by ohmic contacts, as shown in Fig. 12.5, and the resistance to current flow is controlled by the amount of light falling on the material.[2]

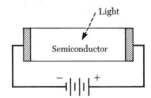

**FIGURE 12.5**   *Photoconductor.*

It would appear that the maximum current possible from the photoconductor would be that corresponding to one electron-hole pair generated per photon (quantum efficiency of unity). However, the currents may be greater than this because of a multiplication mechanism. The multiplication is accomplished by "trapping" of one class of carriers, say holes, by impurities or crystal defects for a finite time. This produces a fixed positive charge within the semiconductor. In order to maintain overall charge neutrality of the material additional electrons must be supplied by the attached electrodes during the lifetime of the traps. The multiplication ratio depends on the transit time across the material, the average time between trapping sites, and the average lifetime in a trapped state. A long trap lifetime gives a high multiplication ratio but also increases the response time and thus limits applications to low-frequency devices.

[1] In order for the photo effect to be more than a surface effect, the semiconductor material must also be reasonably transparent to the radiation of interest. For a review of photoconductivity, see A. Rose, "Concepts in Photoconductivity and Allied Problems," John Wiley & Sons, Inc., New York, 1963.

[2] An interesting use of photoconductivity apart from electronic control is in the xerography process of duplication. In one such process the duplicating paper is coated with a zinc oxide photoconductor and is charged by a corona discharge. Light from the material to be duplicated increases the conductivity and thus discharges the photoconductor in the lighted portion. The dark portions remain charged and thus attract a pigmented resin powder. The powder may be fixed in position by heat, yielding a duplicate of the original page.

## 12.4   junction photoconductive devices: photodiodes, phototransistors, and solar cells

The simplest of the *pn* junction photoconductive devices, other than the bulk devices, is the *photodiode*. A diode with impinging light is illustrated in Fig. 12.6. Assume that the diode is reverse biased so that without light we have only the small saturation current already studied. This is called the *dark current* of the photodiode. With light applied, particularly to a region near the junction, additional charge carriers are generated near the junction as discussed in Sec. 12.3. For example, on the *n* side, photons with energy

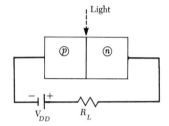

**FIGURE 12.6**   *Photodiode with impinging light.*

greater than the energy gap generate electron-hole pairs. On a percentage basis, the minority carriers (holes) increase the most since under thermal equilibrium $p_n \ll n_n$. If the generation is within the recombination distance (diffusion length) $L_h$ of the junction, the holes can flow to the potential hill and be collected, i.e., fall down the hill and drift into the *p* side. The electrons remain in the *n* region and eventually recombine with holes there. The net effect, however, is a current flow across the junction proportional to the light flux which generates the minority carriers.

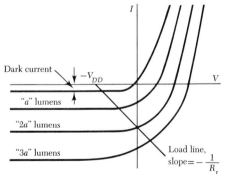

**FIGURE 12.7**   *Photodiode IV characteristics with load line (exaggerated sketch).*

To obtain the form of the *IV* characteristics of the photodiode, we start with the mathematical model of the *pn* junction, (5.22c),

$$I = I_s(e^{V/V_T} - 1) \tag{12.6}$$

where $I_s$ is the saturation current. To this we add the current produced by photons. Since the current is produced by a drift of holes from the $n$ side to the $p$ side and of electrons in the opposite direction, we add a photon-produced current of $-I_L$ to the forward current. $I_L$ is a positive number which increases with the intensity of light. The total current is then

$$I = -I_L + I_s(e^{V/V_T} - 1) \tag{12.7}$$

With no light flux, $I_L = 0$ and we have the usual diode characteristic shown by the curve labeled "dark current" in Fig. 12.7. With increasing light flux, the curve is displaced by $-I_L$ as in the curve for "$a$" lumens in Fig. 12.7. Curves for "$2a$" and "$3a$" lumens are also sketched to indicate the effect of increasing light flux.

In a reverse-biased photodiode, with voltage $-V_{DD}$ as in Fig. 12.6, the load line is given by

$$I = -\frac{V_{DD} + V}{R_L} \tag{12.8}$$

This load line is shown in Fig. 12.7. For the special case of the short-circuited diode, $R_L = 0$, $V = 0$ so that the short-circuit current is just that generated by the light

$$I_{sc} = -I_L \tag{12.9}$$

For the special case of an open-circuited diode, $R_L = \infty$, $I = 0$ and the open-circuit voltage is

$$V_o = V_T \ln \left( \frac{I_L}{I_s} + 1 \right) \tag{12.10}$$

For large values of light flux the first term in the parentheses of (12.10) is dominant and the open-circuit voltage is essentially a logarithmic function of light flux. For $I_L/I_s << 1$, we can expand the ln function in (12.10) and retain only the first term

$$\ln (1 + x) = x - \frac{x^2}{2} + \frac{x^3}{3} + \cdots \simeq x \tag{12.11}$$

For low values of illumination, the open-circuit voltage is thus nearly proportional to the light flux:

$$V_o \simeq \frac{V_T I_L}{I_s} \tag{12.12}$$

The generation of photocurrent can be used to determine the location of a junction. Figure 12.8a illustrates the use of a fine light beam scanned along the side of the junction. The curve of current versus position of the Fig. 12.8b, defines the junction of the specimen.

**SOLAR CELLS**    The solar cell is a photodiode with zero applied bias, i.e., without a dc source of power. Its purpose is to produce electrical energy

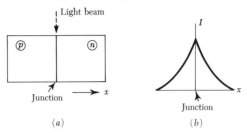

**FIGURE 12.8**    (a) *Light beam scanning junction region;* (b) *current versus x.*

from incident light as in photographic exposure meters. Efficient modern versions are practicable for power production from solar energy in remote locations, as in telephone line amplifiers in the desert. The major present use is in space where solar cells supply power to satellites and space vehicles used for interplanetary missions.

The *IV* equations of the ideal solar cell are those given above. Since there is no bias, $V_{DD} = 0$, and the load line defined by (12.8) is given by

$$I = -\frac{V}{R_L} \tag{12.13}$$

Operation is then in the fourth quadrant of Fig. 12.7. This area is shown separately in Fig. 12.9 and is usually the only portion of the characteristic

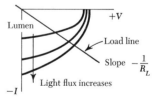

**FIGURE 12.9**    *IV characteristics of a solar cell with the load line for an external load $R_L$.*

that is supplied for practical solar cells. Actual solar cells have characteristics which differ in detail from those given by the simple mathematical model, as is the case for diodes and transistors.

Notice that power is given to $R_L$ even though no external voltage is applied. The voltage across $R_L$ is given by the value of light flux and the load line as shown in Fig. 12.9. The energy to $R_L$ comes from the photon energy in the light.

Practical solar cells use silicon (Si), gallium arsenide (GaAs), or cadmium sulfide (CdS) for the semiconductor, although those for photographic purposes have used copper oxide on copper or selenium on various metals. Figure 12.10 shows a typical solar cell of silicon. The base is usually *n* type with about a micron thickness of $p$-type material diffused into it. The solar radiation passes through the thin $p$ layer, which therefore must be transparent. Rectangular cells have typical dimensions of 1 cm by 2 cm. Conversion

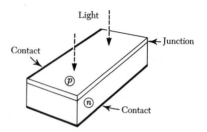

Light

Contact

Junction

$p$

$n$

Contact

**FIGURE 12.10**   *Typical solar cell.*

efficiencies are typically 9 to 14 percent but may be higher. Voltages are usually a fraction of a volt, so large installations use many cells in a series-parallel combination. The Telstar satellite mentioned in Chap. 1, for example, used 3600 solar cells, consisting of 50 groups in parallel, each group having 72 cells in series. This arrangement delivered a maximum power of 14 W and a maximum voltage of 29.5 V[1] (that is, each cell is rated at a voltage of $29.5/72 = 0.41$ V and a current of $14/(29.5 \times 50)$A $= 10$ mA).

**PHOTOTRANSISTORS**   Light falling near the collector junction of an *npn* or a *pnp* device generates excess carriers in a fashion analogous to that for the photodiode. The inherent gain of the *c-e* transistor connection provides an increased output current (Prob. 12.9). Terminals may be provided for only the collector and emitter regions or for all three regions. When terminals to all three regions are brought out, such a device is called a phototransistor. Characteristics of a phototransistor are shown in Fig. 12.11.

## 12.5   spontaneous emission of radiation

We have discussed in the preceding sections devices which absorb photons. Now we consider several devices which emit photons. A number of these devices are old and utilize the *spontaneous emission* occurring when an electron falls from an excited or ionized state to one of lower energy level. Many gas-discharge devices utilize such emission. For example, electrons in atoms of the gas may be excited to higher energy levels by sufficiently high dc voltages, say from level 1 to level 2 of Fig. 12.12*a*. The return of the electrons to their original energy level is called a *transition* and is accompanied by the emission of photons of corresponding energy. The frequency is given by (12.4). If the gas has only one dominant transition,

[1]A detailed description of these solar cells is given in the *Bell System Technical Journal*, **XLII**: 1765 (July, 1963).

the light is of a very characteristic color, but if it has a number of transitions of comparable probability or if there is a mixture of gases, the emitted light contains a number of frequencies which are called *spectral lines.* All excited

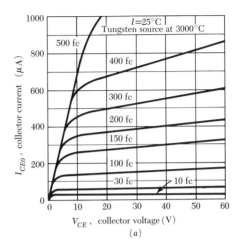

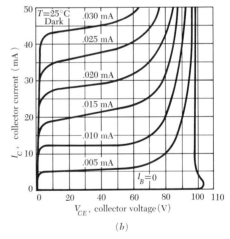

**FIGURE 12.11** *Characteristics of 2N986 planar phototransistor. (a) Collector current $I_{CEO}$ versus collector voltage with $I_B = 0$ and with incident light in footcandles (fc); (b) collector characteristics with no incident light. (From Fairchild Semiconductor.)*

energy levels have finite "lifetimes" with exponential decay from the excited state, as we will see in detail below. That is, given an initial population of electrons in an excited state, only $1/e$ of these remain in the state at a time equal to the lifetime.

The fluorescent material of a TV screen or cathode-ray tube is another example of emission of photons after atoms have been excited to a higher energy state. Here the excitation is by the kinetic energy of an incident electron beam which scans the screen. As noted above, there is a finite

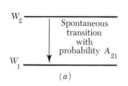

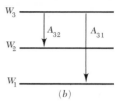

**FIGURE 12.12** (a) *Two-level system showing probability of spontaneous transition from 2 to 1*; (b) *three-level system showing the spontaneous transitions from level 3.*

lifetime for electrons in an excited state of the atom, during which time most fall back and release their energy as light. When this lifetime is long enough to be observed visually, the materials are called *phosphors*. Phosphors are chosen for a particular application depending on the decay time as well as on the color and intensity of light for a given current and velocity of the scanning beam. Characteristics of some standard phosphors are given in Appendix D.

Still another example of spontaneous emission related to the devices of concern here is the recombination radiation in a semiconductor. When electrons and holes recombine, the electron drops from the conduction band to the valence band, and there may be emission of a photon of corresponding energy. This phenomenon is observable, although for many energy gaps the emission occurs in the infrared range and so requires infrared sensors for observation of this type of emission. This radiation is of importance in the injection laser to be discussed later, and in photon coupling of semiconducting circuits, which is presented in the next section. For a forward-biased diode the recombination radiation is localized near the junction because the injected minority carriers lie principally within a diffusion length on either side of the junction.

Not all of the recombinations in the semiconductors result in light emission. In many cases, the recombination process occurs in a sequence of stages, for instance when a hole is first trapped by an imperfection, and then later recombines with an electron. In some of these processes, most of the energy is released in the form of thermal energy and contributes to the vibration of the crystal lattice.

**LIFETIME OF A STATE WITH SPONTANEOUS EMISSION**   If there are two levels of concern in a particular radiative emission process, as sketched in Fig. 12.12a, a *transition probability* $A_{21}$ may be defined as the probability for an excited electron to fall spontaneously from state 2 to state 1. If there are then $n_2$ atoms in state 2 at a given instant, the number of transitions per unit time is the product of $n_2$ and $A_{21}$.

$$r_{21} = A_{21}n_2 \tag{12.14}$$

This rate represents a time rate of decrease of the number in state 2,

$$\frac{dn_2}{dt} = -A_{21}n_2 \tag{12.15}$$

This quantity is also the time rate of increase of the number in state 1. The solution of (12.15) is an exponential form which we have seen many times earlier.

$$n_2 = n_{20}e^{-A_{21}t} + N_2 = n_{20}e^{-t/\tau_{21}} + N_2 \tag{12.16a}$$

where $N_2$ is the equilibrium or steady-state population of state 2. The "lifetime" of the excited electrons is defined as $\tau_{21}$ for this two-level problem and is seen to be the reciprocal of the transition probability.

$$\tau_{21} = \frac{1}{A_{21}} \tag{12.16b}$$

For a three-level system, as sketched in Fig. 12.12b, the total rate of decrease in state 3 is the sum of rates to levels 2 and 1:

$$\frac{dn_3}{dt} = -A_{31}n_3 - A_{32}n_3 = -\frac{n_3}{\tau_3} \tag{12.17}$$

where $\tau_3$ is the net lifetime in state 3 given by

$$\frac{1}{\tau_3} = A_{31} + A_{32} \tag{12.18}$$

The extension to a greater number of levels is evident.

A state which has no "allowed" transitions to lower states is called a *metastable state*. The lifetime of such a state is not infinite but is finite because of (1) collisions between atoms, (2) collision of an atom with the boundaries of a container, or (3) weak radiation processes. Lifetimes of allowed transitions are typically of the order of $10^{-8}$ s. "Forbidden" transitions may have lifetimes of seconds or longer, as noted in the example of phosphors discussed above.

**INCOHERENCE OF SPONTANEOUS EMISSION**  The characteristic of the radiation in all of the above examples is that the photons are emitted *incoherently*. This is in contrast to *coherent* radiation where sinusoidal components have specific phase relationships as in the Fourier-series examples of Chap. 2. In spontaneous emission, the population of the upper state decays exponentially with more photons emitted at the beginning than later on. The time of emission of any given photon is undetermined, being governed by the laws of statistics. There is thus no phase coherence between the various wave packets of radiation, and the light generated is made up of a random group of sinusoids spread over a band of frequencies which is the incoherent radiation referred to. The result may be of use if there is need for light energy within a band, but it does not behave in the same way as a highly coherent sinusoid of the type used in radio transmission. In particular, modulation and focusing are very different for coherent and incoherent waves. This explains the importance of the coherence that is a part of the laser principle to be discussed in Secs. 12.7 and 12.8.

## 12.6  photon coupling between semiconductor devices

Before turning to the matter of stimulated emission, we note the use of the spontaneous emission from semiconducting junctions to couple between devices. That is, the photon output from one junction device may be used to control a second semiconducting device. The advantage of photon coupling in relation to coupling through charge carriers in the solid is in the electrical isolation that may be obtained between output and input of the composite device. Devices using such photon coupling are called *optoelectronic* devices and have become important for practical applications only recently.

The general principle of photon coupling is illustrated in Fig. 12.13.

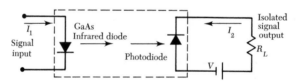

**FIGURE 12.13**  *Basic idea of photon coupling between semiconductor diodes.*

At the input, the recombination radiation at the junction of a diode is guided to a second diode, which acts as a photodiode as described in Sec. 12.4. A signal (an electrical current) is obtained in the output load resistance which is related to the input current of diode 1, and there is essentially no back coupling from the output diode to the input diode.

As a specific example, Fig. 12.14a shows a commercially available isolator followed by a transistor to provide gain. In this unit (hpa 4301) the radiating diode is constructed of GaAs. The infrared recombination radiation at the junction of this diode is guided by a dielectric "light pipe" to the photodiode, which is a *p i n* unit.[1] Figure 12.14b shows character-

---

[1] The *pin* unit has an intrinsic region between the *p* and *n* regions. It performs generally as a *pn* diode, but the usual depletion-layer electric field is spread out over the intrinsic region and the junction capacitance is reduced. The response of such devices is consequently very fast.

istic curves of the unit in which a 2N2857 transistor is incorporated. The complete device is applicable to electronic functions such as pulse couplers and choppers and has been especially important in electronic voltmeters

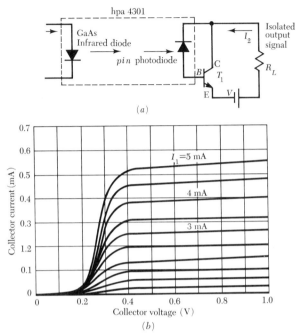

(a)

(b)

**FIGURE 12.14** (a) hpa 4301 *isolator driving a transistor;* (b) *characteristics of this combination with 2N2857 transistor.*

which are designed to produce negligible loading on the port being measured.

A second example is the optoelectronic multiplex switch shown in Fig. 12.15a. In this unit focusing of the light from the GaAs source is by means of a dome-shaped lens. The emitted radiation falls on two parallel silicon phototransistors as shown in the figure. The schematic of the unit is shown in Fig. 12.15b. The characteristic curves, shown in Fig. 12.15c, have the symmetrical, bilateral form shown. For sufficient input current to the emitting diode, switching is provided for either polarity of $V_2$. The isolation of the drive circuit from the output circuit is nearly complete, as in the first example.

## 12.7 stimulated emission of radiation: the laser principle

If an electromagnetic wave is impressed upon a system of atoms, as diagramed in Fig. 12.16, there may be *stimulated* or induced transitions in addition to the spontaneous transitions considered in Sec. 12.5. In a stimulated transition, the change is "triggered" by the incident wave and the phase of the photon process is related to the phase of the wave. Two stimulated processes are important. In one, the electromagnetic wave stimulates transitions from the lower state (Fig. 12.17) to the upper

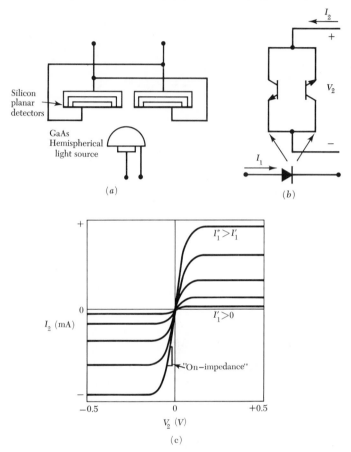

**FIGURE 12.15** (a) *Schematic of Texas Instruments optoelectronic switch [from J. R. Biard, E. L. Bonin, W. T. Matzen and J. D. Merryman, "Optoelectronics as Applied to Functional Electronic Blocks," Proc. IEEE,* **52,** 1529-1536 (1964)]*; (b) circuit diagram;* (c) *characteristic curves.*

state and gives energy to the atoms. Energy is then absorbed from the wave and the phenomenon is known as *stimulated absorption*. In the second process, the wave stimulates transitions from the upper level to the lower level so that energy is given from the atoms to the wave and the process is known as *stimulated emission*. For a system in thermal equilibrium, there are more electrons in the lower state than in the upper state so that stimulated absorption is greater than the stimulated emission and there is a net absorption. If one can "invert the populations" so that there are more particles in the upper state, there may be a net emission and the resulting power given to the wave can produce useful amplification or

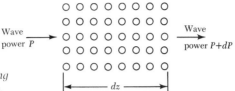

**FIGURE 12.16**  *Wave passing through a system of atoms.*

oscillation. This is the basis of the important laser principle. "Laser" is an acronym for *l*ight *a*mplification by *s*timulated *e*mission of *r*adiation.[1]

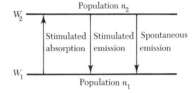

**FIGURE 12.17**  *Two-level system showing spontaneous emission plus stimulated emission and absorption.*

**EXAMPLE OF A HELIUM-NEON GAS LASER**    The gas laser, developed by A. Javan et al. in 1961, is one of the simplest to understand and to use. A typical arrangement is shown in Fig. 12.18 for use as an oscillator. A discharge

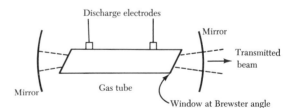

**FIGURE 12.18**  *Gas laser.*

is established in a tube containing one or more gases by a dc or high-frequency (rf) voltage source to provide the energy which inverts the population of electrons. This process is called "pumping" by analogy with the pumping of water to a high level for energy-conversion purposes. An electromagnetic resonant system is obtained using mirrors

---

[1] Most lasers are oscillators, not amplifiers, so should clearly be called "losers." The principle of amplification by population inversions was first demonstrated at microwave frequencies, and the name *maser* was coined by Gordon, Zeiger, and Townes for *m*icrowave *a*mplifier by *s*timulated *e*mission of *r*adiation. Although "maser" is considered by some as the generic term so that *optical maser* is used for the principle applied to light frequencies, "laser" is more common.

which are usually external to the tube. A spherical-mirror resonant system is shown since, with proper selection of dimensions, it is easy to align and has small diffraction losses. One of the mirrors has a finite transmission (typically 1/2 to 1 per cent) which provides the useful output beam energy. The actual tube which contains the gas has its end windows at the *Brewster angle*.[1] This angle provides transmission with zero reflection for one type of polarization of the light wave. The laser action in the gas provides gain, and if the gain exceeds the losses and useful output, oscillations will build up.

The first successful gas laser employed a mixture of helium and neon at pressures around 1 mm of mercury, and this type is still widely used. A number of laser lines have been observed from this system, with the red line at 6328Å most often used. The energy-level diagram for the 6328Å line is shown in Fig. 12.19. The energetic electrons of the dc or rf discharge

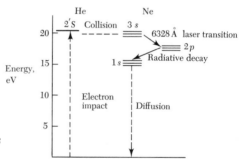

**FIGURE 12.19** *Energy-level diagram showing basic processes in He-Ne 6328 Å laser.*

excite both helium and neon atoms to higher levels, and a primary step in the pumping of this system is the excitation of a specific energy level of the helium atom, designated $2^1S$, as shown in the figure.[2] Energy is transferred by collision from this level to the 3s levels of neon, which is nearly of the same energy.

The 6328Å laser transition is from the $3s_2$ to $2p_4$ levels of neon. The lower $2p_4$ level decays by radiation to 1s levels, which are metastable and must be depopulated by collisions with the tube walls. Because of the mechanisms of pumping and depopulation of the 1s levels, the gas pressure, the relative proportion of the two gases, and the tube diameter are all important parameters in the design of this type of laser.

---

[1] See for example J. A. Richards, F. M. Sears, M. R. Wehr, and M. W. Zemansky, "Modern University Physics," p. 698, Addison-Wesley Publishing Company, Inc., Reading, Mass., 1960.

[2] Russel-Saunders notation is used here for helium and Paschen notation for neon. The reader need not be concerned with the specific significance of the notation. Those interested may see "American Institute of Physics Handbook," 2d ed., McGraw-Hill Book Company, New York, 1963, sec. 7. See Appendix C of this book for a review of electronic configurations of atoms.

**HISTORICAL DEVELOPMENTS**  We now return to the development and the fundamentals of stimulated emission. The process of stimulated emission was known as early as 1917 when Einstein developed its role, together with spontaneous emission, in establishing the equilibrium distribution of populations among energy states in a system of atoms. Attempts to invert populations for the narrowing of spectroscopic lines (i.e., confining the radiation from atomic transitions to a smaller range of frequencies) were made in the 30's and 40's, and the first successful demonstration of inverted populations was by E. Purcell and R. Pound in 1951. These workers also demonstrated the coherence of the stimulated emission with the stimulating radiation at microwave frequencies. This is a most important aspect of the process for use in amplification or oscillation, and in the ability to focus the light to very small spots. N. Basov, A. Prokhorov, C. Townes, and J. Weber independently recognized the importance of the process to microwave amplification around 1950. J. Gordon, H. Zeiger, and C. Townes in 1954 first demonstrated useful amplification. A. Schawlow and C. Townes in 1958 proposed the approach for extension of the process to optical frequencies, and T. Maiman demonstrated the first operating laser in 1960.

**STIMULATED AND SPONTANEOUS PROCESSES IN EQUILIBRIUM**  It is interesting to note first the interplay of the spontaneous and stimulated processes in a system which is in thermal equilibrium. Considering the two-level system of Fig. 12.17, we expect the equilibrium population of the two levels (i.e., the density of electrons in the two levels) to be related by the Boltzmann factor.

$$\frac{N_2}{N_1} = e^{-(W_2 - W_1)/kT}$$

(12.19)

This equilibrium is established by several processes. The first may be considered to be spontaneous emissions from level 2 to level 1 as shown in Fig. 12.17. These transitions deliver energy to the system, and the resulting electromagnetic fields stimulate transitions from 1 to 2 (absorptions) and from 2 to 1 (emissions). The three processes just balance in an equilibrium distribution.

For all three processes, the rate of change with time of the population density in state 2 is

$$\frac{dn_2}{dt} = -A_{21}n_2 - (B_{21}n_2 - B_{12}n_1)P$$

(12.20)

where $n_2$ and $n_1$ represent respectively the number of particles in states 2 and 1 per unit volume. $A_{21}$ is the transition probability for spontaneous emission discussed in Sec. 12.5, $B_{12}$ and $B_{21}$ are coefficients of stimulated absorption and emission, respectively, and $P$ is the power density in the wave. The latter must be included because the stimulated processes are understandably related to the power density of the stimulating process.

For an equilibrium process, $dn_2/dt = 0$. Einstein showed that for $P$ to have the proper spectral distribution for a thermodynamic system in equilibrium (i.e., that found by Planck for blackbody radiation), the coefficients $B_{12} = B_{21} = B$. Moreover, he showed that $B$ is related to $A_{21}$ as follows:

$$B_{12} = B_{21} = B = \frac{c^3}{4f^3 h} A_{21} \qquad (12.21)$$

where $c$ is the velocity of light, $h$ is Planck's constant, and $f$ is frequency.

**STIMULATED EMISSION FOR AMPLIFICATION PROCESSES**    Returning to Fig. 12.16, we now consider the net energy given to the incident electromagnetic wave in passing through a region containing atoms with inverted populations. We can neglect the incoherent spontaneous process in relation to the coherent stimulated processes since we anticipate a buildup or amplification of the coherent processes. For simplicity we take a one-dimensional system. We then write the rate of change of power in the electromagnetic wave moving through the material as the net energy given to it by the stimulated processes. This is the rate of stimulated emission times the energy per quantum. Thus the rate of change with distance $z$ is

$$\frac{dP}{dz} = -hfB\,(n_1 - n_2)\,P \qquad (12.22)$$

If $n_1$ and $n_2$ are assumed constant for the present, (12.22) shows that there is an exponential change of power with distance,

$$P = P_0 e^{-\alpha z} \qquad (12.23)$$

where $$\alpha = hfB\,(n_1 - n_2) \qquad (12.24)$$

The rate of change with distance represents an exponential decay when $n_1 > n_2$, as would be expected since there are then more particles for absorption than there are for emission. This is the case, for example, in the equilibrium distribution, (12.19).

To obtain a power growth or gain from (12.23), $\alpha$ of (12.24) must be negative. This is accomplished by making the population of the upper state greater than that for the lower state, $n_2 > n_1$. As noted at the first of the section, this is known as "inverting the populations." The early workers found it hard to accomplish this inversion, but now there are many successful ways of accomplishing it. A general model can be illustrated by considering the four-level system of Fig. 12.20. Suppose that electrons are excited from level 0 to level 3 by some process such as optical absorption, collisions in a dc or rf gas discharge, or introduction of chemical energy. The process of introducing energy from some external source to raise the atom to a high level of excitation is the pumping process mentioned in the example.

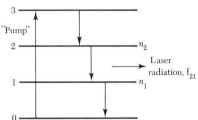

**FIGURE 12.20** *Generalized four-level system showing pumping from 0 to 3 and laser action from 2 to 1, for gain $n_2 > n_1$.*

We now suppose that the electrons at level 3 in Fig. 12.20 fall by some process to level 2, which we consider to be the upper laser level. That is, the wave for which amplification is desired is chosen to have a frequency

$$f_{21} = \frac{W_2 - W_1}{h} \qquad (12.25)$$

As noted above, there will be gain if $n_2 > n_1$. We can see that this is achieved by having the proper lifetimes in the various states. Lifetime is adjusted by choice of material, by impurities, and by control of collision processes. For a continuously operating system, the rate of transition of particles about the loop 0-3-2-1-0 is constant, but if the lifetime in state 2 is greater than that in state 1, a greater "reservoir" accumulates here and the desired population inversion is achieved. Still other mechanisms of population inversion are possible. Specific examples of continuous and pulse inversions are given in Sec. 12.8.

To this point, we have considered the interaction as though the transition frequency of all atoms is the same; that is, we assume that the line width is zero. In an actual system there is a finite line width, meaning that the atomic transitions are spread out over a finite frequency interval $\Delta f$. Line width arises from the spontaneous transitions (natural line width), collisions (collision or pressure broadening), thermal velocities of atoms (doppler broadening), or coupling to neighboring atoms. The last effect is especially important in solids. The gain formula, (12.24), is thus highly idealized and must be modified by introduction of the line width of the transition, $\Delta f$. The result is

$$\alpha = C_0 \frac{(n_2 - n_1) h f B}{\Delta f} \qquad (12.26)$$

where the constant $C_0$ depends upon the nature of the processes which produce the finite line width. We may also use (12.21) and (12.16$b$):

$$\alpha = \frac{C_0 (n_2 - n_1) c^3}{4f^2 \, \Delta f \, \tau_{21}} \tag{12.27}$$

Thus the gain of the laser increases with the inversion of population $n_2 - n_1$. It also increases with the narrowing of the line (with decrease in $\Delta f$); it increases with the decrease in spontaneous lifetime $\tau_{21}$ between the laser levels; and it decreases as the square of frequency.

There are additional complications in practical lasers, including degeneracies of the levels, transitions other than the laser transition between levels 2 and 1, etc. The above formula nevertheless gives the primary factors in laser amplification and the main elements in this basic and important process. Examples of specific lasers follow.

## 12.8   practical lasers

It was noted above that Gordon, Zeiger, and Townes first demonstrated the maser principle at microwave frequencies. The most interesting present applications are at optical frequencies. Lasers are used to amplify or generate coherent light of high intensity at wavelengths from hundreds of microns (tenths of millimeters) through the visible range and into the ultraviolet. Most present applications are for generators (oscillators). The coherence of the oscillation makes possible modulation, mixing, detection, and other electronic techniques of the type mentioned in Chaps. 1 and 2, so that lasers have potential in communication systems of high capacity.[1] Such communication systems have been utilized in the space program, but improvements in modulation techniques, propagation, and other aspects are necessary before the laser can achieve its promise for general communication purposes. The high intensity made possible by the focusing capabilities of the coherent beam opens applications to machining, welding, and medicine. The most important applications to date have been scientific ones, where the coherent, high-intensity source has made possible new physical and chemical experiments (e.g., in nonlinear optics and Raman spectroscopy).

**SOLID-STATE LASERS**   Maiman's first demonstration of laser action was in ruby. This crystal, which remains one of the best for high-power, pulsed laser action, has chromium ions in aluminum oxide ($Al_2O_3$:$Cr^{+++}$); the energy levels of concern are those of the chromium ions. An energy-

---

[1] This is because the available bandwidth is so high. For a center frequency of $10^{15}$ Hz, a bandwidth 0.1 percent of the center frequency yields $10^{12}$ Hz for the communication band. This value is more than the entire spectrum from dc through the microwave frequencies. The channel capacity formula, (2.29), shows that information capacity is proportional to bandwidth for a given signal-to-noise ratio.

level diagram is shown in Fig. 12.21. We need not be concerned here with the details of the spectroscopic designation of the levels, but note that optical pumping is used. That is, the $^4F_2$ and $^4F_1$ bands are in the

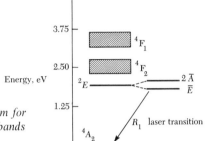

**FIGURE 12.21**   *Energy level diagram for ruby. The $^4F_1$ and $^4F_2$ absorption bands are based for optical pumping.*

green and blue, respectively. These can absorb energy from a bright lamp which has appreciable emission in these frequency ranges. After pumping, electrons cascade down from these upper energy bands to the upper laser level, here designated $^2E$. This is a degenerate level which is split into levels designated $2\overline{A}$ and $\overline{E}$. The so-called $R_1$ laser transition occurs from the lower of these to the $^4A_2$ level and produces red light at a wavelength of 6934 Å.

The physical configuration of a pulsed ruby laser is shown in Fig. 12.22. The flash lamp for optical pumping may be wound about the ruby rod in helical form. The ends of the crystal may be polished to form the reflectors for the resonant system, or external mirrors may be used. Figure 12.22 shows the former arrangement. The ruby laser is operated pulsed and

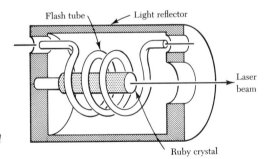

**FIGURE 12.22**   *Ruby laser with helical flash lamp for optical pumping.*

can give very high powers (megawatts) for short periods if the resonant system is suddenly adjusted after a period of pumping to achieve a maximum of population inversion.[1]

Other solid-state lasers (excluding the semiconductor type discussed below) utilize rare earth ions in various host lattices. Nyodymium ions

---

[1] This process is known as "$Q$-switching" or "giant pulsing."

in calcium tungstate and dysprosium ions in yttrium aluminum garnet are examples.

**GAS AND ION LASERS**    The helium-neon gas laser has been used as an introductory example of the principle in Sec. 12.7. The 6328Å line discussed provides a few milliwatts of power with a gain of a few percent per meter. The $1.15\mu$ line of the helium-neon laser (operating between the $2s_2$ and $2p_4$ levels of neon) yields somewhat higher powers and gain. The 3.39 $\mu$ line ($3s - 2p$) is a much higher gain line, giving gains of the order of 22 dB/m.

A variety of other gas lasers provide laser action from the far infrared to the ultraviolet ranges. One important class utilizes the energy levels of ionized gases. W. Bridges et al. in 1964 showed the richness of lines opened up in the green, blue, and ultraviolet by such ion lasers. One of the most useful of these is the 4880Å line in ionized argon. Ion lasers require high discharge currents and they provide relatively high powers (order of watts), although they are not of high efficiency.

Other gas lasers utilize molecular energy levels. An example is the $CO_2$ laser. The wavelength of this is in the 10 $\mu$ range with efficiencies of the order of 10 percent and with very high power output.

The gas laser field is in rapid transition. The above results are quoted only to show the variety and principles of such lasers and should not be considered as ultimate achievements.

**SEMICONDUCTING LASERS**    The recombination radiation at $pn$ junctions, discussed in Sec. 12.5, can also be made coherent, yielding radiation approximately corresponding to that of the energy gap at the junction. M. Nathan et al., R. Hall et al., and R. Rediker et al. observed this effect independently in GaAs at liquid nitrogen temperatures. In their experiments, pumping is by dc injection of the minority carriers to the high-potential side of the junction. Thus semiconducting lasers of this class are called *injection lasers*. Pumping in semiconducting lasers has also been accomplished by light and by electron beams.

The resonant system in the injection laser comes from internal reflection

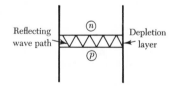

**FIGURE 12.23**    *Resonant reflections at junction of injection laser.*

of the waves within the depletion layer, as shown schematically in Fig. 12.23. (This is an oversimplified picture since the width of the depletion layer is small, and the discontinuity in dielectric constant is neither abrupt nor large. However, the sketch illustrates the nature of the resonance.) For the injection laser, the recombination radiation is incoherent for dc currents below a critical value; for currents above the critical value, oscillations may build up coherently. It has been difficult to achieve good spectral purity with the injection laser, but it is attractive because of its small size and high efficiency (of the order of 50 percent) and the ease of modulation. The frequency of most of the semiconducting lasers is in the infrared (for example, 0.84 $\mu$ for GaAs), but there has been extension into the visible. Useful GaAs lasers now also operate at room temperature and are the type most promising for space communication purposes for the near future.

### REFERENCES

R. L. Sproull, "Modern Physics," 2d ed., John Wiley & Sons, Inc., New York, 1963, chaps. 6, 12.

W. R. Beam, "Electronics of Solids," McGraw-Hill Book Company, New York, 1965, chap. 10.

B. A. Lengyel, "Introduction to Laser Physics," John Wiley & Sons, Inc., New York, 1966.

### PROBLEMS

**12.1**  Calculate the number of photons per second necessary to transmit 1 W of power at power-line frequency (60 Hz), radio frequency (1 MHz), microwaves (10 GHz), visible light (wavelength = 5000 Å), X rays (wavelength = 10 Å).

**12.2**  For a vacuum photodiode, plot the kinetic energy of emitted electrons versus frequency of light for the following materials:

| Material | Photoelectric work function, eV |
|---|---|
| Cesium on silver | 1.03 |
| Silver | 4.28 |
| Tungsten | 4.50 |
| Cesium on tungsten | 1.70 |

**12.3**  Because of the large cathode area, most vacuum photodiodes operate with emission limitation rather than space-charge limitation, except at very low voltages. Sketch the expected form of the $IV$ curves for a vacuum photodiode for different levels of illumination.

**12.4**  Repeat Prob. 12.3 for a gas-filled photodiode.

**12.5**  The average velocity of the secondary electrons emitted from a secondary emitter is low (corresponding to an energy of about 10 eV). Assume that the energy of primary electrons for maximum yield from a particular emitter is 200 eV. What potential should exist between dynodes of a secondary electron multiplier? For the crossed-field multiplier of Fig. 12.3*b*, explain qualitatively how this will modify the electron paths studied in Sec. 11.6.

**12.6** In a photoconductor, a voltage of 100 V is applied across a length of 1 cm. Mobility is 1350 cm²/V-s. Assume that there is a 10 percent chance of a photon ionizing an atom. Assume that the average time between trapping sites for the electron is $10^{-4}$ s and that there is an average lifetime of $10^{-3}$ s in such sites. How many electrons might be expected to flow to the electrodes per incident photon? If light intensity is suddenly changed, about how long does it take for the output current to respond to this charge? Discuss the relationship of this analysis to that of Prob. 8.7.

**12.7** A photodiode with reverse bias is used in the circuit shown, Assume that light falls on the photodiode.

(*a*) Sketch the distribution of minority carriers versus distance from the junction in both the *p* and *n* regions.

(*b*) The current voltage characteristic for such a diode is approximately

$$I = I_s(e^{V/V_T} - 1) - I_L$$

If the light is the output of an amplitude-modulated laser, the current $I_L$ can be described as

$$I_L = a + b \sin \omega_m t$$

Draw a small-signal circuit model and find the signal voltage appearing across $R_L$.

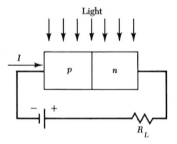

**Problem 12.7**

**12.8** A photodiode has the set of characteristics shown in figures *a* and *b*, where the polarities are as defined in figure *c*. This diode is placed in series with a dc voltage source and resistor as shown in figure *d*.

(*a*) The light intensity is increased from 2 to 8 mlm (millilumen). This causes the reverse voltage across the diode to change from $-80$ V to $-20$ V. (1) What is the source voltage $V_0$? (2) Show that $R = 1$ MΩ. (3) What is the corresponding change in diode current? (4) Draw the load line.

(*b*) The resistor is replaced by a second resistor of twice the value of the first. What is the change in diode current as the light intensity is increased from 2 to 5 mlm?

(c) The dc voltage source is shorted out, as shown in figure e. (1) What value of R will cause a diode current of $-5$ $\mu$A at an intensity of 0.5 mlm? (2) What power is dissipated in R? (3) Where is this power coming from?

(d) What voltage $V_1$ must be added (as shown in figure f) to maintain the current of $-5$ $\mu$A when the light intensity is increased to 1 mlm?

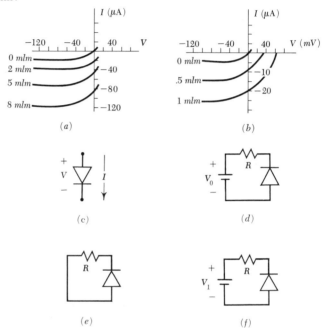

(a)

(b)

(c)

(d)

(e)

(f)

**Problem 12.8**

**12.9**  Show that the output current of an illuminated npn photo-transistor biased for active mode operation is

$$I_C = \beta_0 I_B + (\beta_0 + 1)(I_{CO} + I_L)$$

Compare this expression with that for reverse current of an illuminated photodiode. What is the output current if the base lead of the npn device is not connected?

**12.10**  A four-level system (Fig. 12.20) has the following average transition parameters:

$$A_{32} = 1 \text{ s}^{-1} \qquad A_{21} = 10 \text{ s}^{-1} \qquad A_{10} = 10^8 \text{ s}^{-1}$$

$$A_{31} = 0.2 \cdot 10^8 \text{ s}^{-1} \qquad A_{20} = 0.2 \text{ s}^{-1} \qquad A_{30} = 0.5 \cdot 10^8 \text{ s}^{-1}$$

Find the lifetime of excited electrons in each of the states 1, 2, and 3.

**12.11** For the circuit of Fig. 12.14a, $V = 0.9$ V and $R_L = 2$ kΩ. If $i_1(t) = (2.5 + 1 \sin \omega t)$ mA, find the operating point on the characteristics of Fig. 12.14b and give the approximate form of the collector current as a function of time.

**12.12** Utilizing the characteristic curves of Fig. 12.15c, explain the operation of the multiplex switch. Start with $V_2$ positive and note the effect of applying current $I_1$ to the GaAs source. Then repeat with $V_2$ negative.

**12.13** For two levels of energy (20 and 18.5 eV) in a particular material calculate the relative population density under thermal equilibrium conditions at 300°K. Repeat at liquid nitrogen temperature (77°K).

**12.14** For a four-level system, as in Fig. 12.20, assume that level 2 is at 20 eV and level 1 is at 18.5 eV with respect to level 0. Assuming only the transitions shown and continuous operation, estimate the ratio of lifetimes, $\tau_{21}/\tau_{10}$, in order to invert populations, making $n_2 \geqslant n_1$.

**12.15** For the gain formula of (12.27), estimate the constant $C_0$ by using typical values for a gas laser: $f = 3 \cdot 10^{14}$ Hz, $\Delta f = 1.5$ GHz, $\tau_{21} = 10^{-8}$, $(n_2 - n_1) = 10^{14}$ cm$^{-3}$ and $\alpha = 10^{-3}$ cm$^{-1}$. Point out the factors in the equation which would be affected by gas pressure, and explain why an optimum pressure might be expected.

**12.16** Utilizing the four-level system of Fig. 12.20, assume that there are transitions between all levels instead of just those shown. Explain which transitions might help the laser process and which might hinder it. Why do the "harmful" ones not completely prevent operation?

**12.17** A gas laser, as in Fig. 12.18, has a transmission through one of the mirrors equal to 0.5 percent, with transmission through the other negligible. Diffraction loss at each mirror is 0.1 percent of the incident power. Absorption in the gas and windows is 0.2 percent for each pass. What gain must the laser have for each one-way transmission to produce oscillation?

# appendix A

# COMPLEX NUMBERS

A complex number is an ordered pair of real numbers $a$ and $b$, written in the form

$$c = a + jb \qquad \text{(A.1)}$$

where $j$ is the imaginary number

$$j = \sqrt{-1} \qquad \text{(A.2)}$$

This complex number can be represented in a plane, called the complex-number plane (or simply complex plane), as illustrated in Fig. A.1. The first number $a$ of the ordered pair is taken as the distance along the $x$ or real axis, and the second $b$ as the

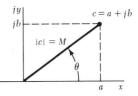

**FIGURE A.1** *A graphical representation of a complex number.*

distance along the $jy$ or imaginary axis.

The complex number may also be represented in polar form, with the coordinates given by the magnitude $M$ and angle $\theta$ of Fig. A.1. From the figure,

$$a = M \cos \theta \qquad \text{(A.3)}$$

$$b = M \sin \theta \qquad \text{(A.4)}$$

so that (A.1) may be written

$$c = M (\cos \theta + j \sin \theta) \qquad \text{(A.5)}$$

By the Euler identity, this is also

$$c = M e^{j\theta} \qquad \text{(A.6)}$$

423

The radius $M$ in the polar form is the magnitude of $c$ and $\theta$ is known as its phase angle. These quantities are related to $a$ and $b$, from (A.3) and (A.4) or by inspection of the figure, as

$$M = |c| = \sqrt{a^2 + b^2} \tag{A.7}$$

$$\theta = \tan^{-1} \frac{b}{a} \tag{A.8}$$

The polar form is also frequently written as $M \,\underline{/\theta}$, so that all of the following forms are equivalent:

$$c = a + jb = Me^{j\theta} = M \,\underline{/\theta} \tag{A.9}$$

The sum of two complex numbers $c_1$ and $c_2$ is

$$c_1 + c_2 = (a_1 + jb_1) + (a_2 + jb_2) = (a_1 + a_2) + j(b_1 + b_2) \tag{A.10}$$

As shown in Fig. A.2, this sum can be constructed in the complex plane

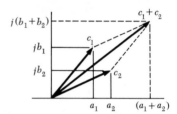

**FIGURE A.2**  *Sum of two complex numbers.*

by the rules for addition of two line vectors, so that $c_1 + c_2$ is just the diagonal of the parallelogram in the figure. Subtraction can be considered a special case of addition with the sign of the subtracted number reversed.

The product of two complex numbers is most easily obtained from the exponential forms of $c_1$ and $c_2$:

$$c_1 c_2 = |c_1| e^{j\theta_1} |c_2| e^{j\theta_2} = |c_1| \cdot |c_2| e^{j(\theta_1 + \theta_2)} \tag{A.11}$$

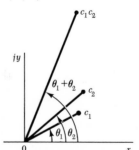

**FIGURE A.3**  *Product of two complex numbers.*

The result of the product is illustrated in Fig. A.3. The quotient of $c_1$ and $c_2$ is similarly

$$\frac{c_1}{c_2} = \frac{|c_1| e^{j\theta_1}}{|c_2| e^{j\theta_2}} = \frac{|c_1|}{|c_2|} e^{j(\theta_1 - \theta_2)} \tag{A.12}$$

# appendix B

# ATOMIC STRUCTURE

Let us consider an individual atom. It has a nucleus with positive charge which is surrounded by a number $Z$ of electrons orbiting around the nucleus; $Z$ is the atomic number of the element. In order to make the atom charge neutral to the outside, the positive charge of the nucleus must be equal to the total electronic charge, namely $Z$ times the charge magnitude $q$ of an electron. Each electron moves in its orbit without radiating energy, and it has an *energy state* which can be identified by a set of numbers called *quantum numbers*. Four different quantum numbers are needed to characterize each energy state.

Table B.1 shows the various quantum states, their identifying letters, and their possible values. The *principal quantum number* $n$ determines approximately the *total energy* of an electron. Frequently one speaks of shells in which the electrons orbit. There are $K$ shells, $L$ shells, $M$ shells, etc. These shells correspond to values of $n = 1, 2, 3, \ldots$, respectively. These shell labels have their origin in X-ray spectroscopy.

The *azimuthal quantum number* $l$ determines the angular momentum of the electron in orbit and depends on the electron mass $m$, its velocity $v$, and the electron's distance $r$ from the center of the nucleus. According to the values of $l$, one speaks of states of the electron, or of subshells. When $l = 0$, the subshell is labeled $s$ (meaning "sharp"); when $l = 1$, the label is $p$ (principal); when $l = 2$, the label is $d$ (diffuse); when $l = 3$, the label is $f$ (fundamental). These letter labels for the subshells were adopted for spectral analysis and are quite commonly used.

Any orbiting electron represents a moving charge, which has a magnetic field associated with it. Under the influence of

**TABLE B.1** *Quantum Numbers*

| PRINCIPAL $n$ | AZIMUTHAL $l$ | MAGNETIC $m_l$ | SPIN $m_s$ |
|---|---|---|---|
| Values of $n$: integers 1, 2, 3, . . . | Values of $l$: integers 0 to $(n-1)$ | Values of $m_l$: integers from $-l$ to $+l$ | Values of $m_s$: $+1/2$ and $-1/2$ |
| Determines total energy of an electron | Determines electron orbital angular momentum | Determines electron orbital orientation in external magnetic field | Determines electron spin direction |
| Nomenclature:<br><br>$n =$ 1  2  3  4<br>Shell K  L  M  N<br>Max. electrons<br>in *shell* 2  8 18 32 | Nomenclature:<br><br>$l =$ 0  1  2  3<br>State  s  p  d  f<br>Max. electrons<br>in *state* 2  6 10 14 | Permissible values: $(2l + 1)$ | |

**TABLE B.2** *Electronic Structure of Atoms†*

| PRINCIPAL QUANTUM NUMBER $n$ | | | | 1 | 2 | | 3 | | | 4 | |
|---|---|---|---|---|---|---|---|---|---|---|---|
| AZIMUTHAL QUANTUM NUMBER $l$ | | | | 0 | 0 | 1 | 0 | 1 | 2 | 0 | 1 |
| LETTER DESIGNATION OF STATE | | | | $1s$ | $2s$ | $2p$ | $3s$ | $3p$ | $3d$ | $4s$ | $4p$ |
| $Z$ | | ELEMENT | IONIZING POTENTIAL | | | | | | | | |
| 1 | H | Hydrogen | 13.60 | 1 | | | | | | | |
| 2 | He | Helium | 24.58 | 2 | | | | | | | |
| 3 | Li | Lithium | 5.39 | Helium core | 1 | | | | | | |
| 4 | Be | Beryllium | 9.32 | | 2 | | | | | | |
| 5 | B | Boron | 8.30 | | 2 | 1 | | | | | |
| 6 | C | Carbon | 11.26 | | 2 | 2 | | | | | |
| 7 | N | Nitrogen | 14.54 | | 2 | 3 | | | | | |
| 8 | O | Oxygen | 13.61 | | 2 | 4 | | | | | |
| 9 | F | Fluorine | 17.42 | | 2 | 5 | | | | | |
| 10 | Ne | Neon | 21.56 | | 2 | 6 | | | | | |
| 11 | Na | Sodium | 5.14 | Neon core | | | 1 | | | | |
| 12 | Mg | Magnesium | 7.64 | | | | 2 | | | | |
| 13 | Al | Aluminum | 5.98 | | | | 2 | 1 | | | |
| 14 | Si | Silicon | 8.15 | | | | 2 | 2 | | | |
| 15 | P | Phosphorus | 10.55 | | | | 2 | 3 | | | |
| 16 | S | Sulfur | 10.36 | | | | 2 | 4 | | | |
| 17 | Cl | Chlorine | 13.01 | | | | 2 | 5 | | | |
| 18 | Ar | Argon | 15.76 | | | | 2 | 6 | | | |
| 19 | K | Potassium | 4.34 | Argon core | | | | | | 1 | |
| 20 | Ca | Calcium | 6.11 | | | | | | | 2 | |
| 21 | Sc | Scandium | 6.56 | | | | | | 1 | 2 | |
| 22 | Ti | Titanium | 6.83 | | | | | | 2 | 2 | |
| 23 | V | Vanadium | 6.74 | | | | | | 3 | 2 | |
| 24 | Cr | Chromium | 6.76 | | | | | | 5 | 1 | |
| 25 | Mn | Manganese | 7.43 | | | | | | 5 | 2 | |
| 26 | Fe | Iron | 7.90 | | | | | | 6 | 2 | |
| 27 | Co | Cobalt | 7.86 | | | | | | 7 | 2 | |
| 28 | Ni | Nickel | 7.63 | | | | | | 8 | 2 | |
| 29 | Cu | Copper | 7.72 | | | | | | 10 | 1 | |
| 30 | Zn | Zinc | 9.39 | | | | | | 10 | 2 | |
| 31 | Ga | Gallium | 6.00 | | | | | | 10 | 2 | 1 |
| 32 | Ge | Germanium | 7.88 | | | | | | 10 | 2 | 2 |
| 33 | As | Arsenic | 9.81 | | | | | | 10 | 2 | 3 |
| 34 | Se | Selenium | 9.75 | | | | | | 10 | 2 | 4 |
| 35 | Br | Bromine | 11.84 | | | | | | 10 | 2 | 5 |
| 36 | Kr | Krypton | 14.00 | | | | | | 10 | 2 | 6 |

†From Charlotte E. Moore, "Atomic Energy Levels," vol. II, National Bureau of Standards Circular 467, Washington, 1952.

an external magnetic field the orbit can orient itself in different ways. These are characterized by the *magnetic quantum number* $m_l$. There are $2l + 1$ permissible values for $m_l$. Finally we note that the electrons are spinning and can do so in a clockwise or anticlockwise direction. This is characterized by the *spin quantum number* $m_s$, which has values of $+1/2$ or $-1/2$.

*Pauli's exclusion principle* states that no two electrons can occupy the same quantum state. Consequently the electrons must take on different orbits if the allowed states in a given orbit are filled. We will consider here the *ground state* of the atom only. In this state the electrons occupy those quantum states which result in an overall minimum of energy for the atom. Table B.2 shows the occupancy of the various shells and subshells for some of the atoms having different numbers $Z$. Note that according to Pauli's exclusion principle there can be at most two electrons in the $s$ state, at most six in the $p$ state, 10 in the $d$ state, etc. This corresponds, as an example, to a maximum of two electrons in the $K$ shell; the $L$ shell has $2 + 6 = 8$ electrons, the $M$ shell $2 + 6 + 10 = 18$, the $N$ shell $2 + 6 + 10 + 14 = 32$, etc. As can be seen from Table B.2, not all the outer orbits are filled with electrons. Also, when going from a given $Z$ number to the next, the electrons do not fill up available orbits in a regular fashion. These facts are important, because they affect the ability of the atom to bind itself to another atom of the same or of a different kind. It is typical of inert-gas atoms, for instance, that they have all the outermost orbits filled. It is known that such atoms do not enter easily into bonds with other atoms of the same kind. Such behavior is typical for atoms with completely filled outer shells. In contrast, atoms of metals typically do not have filled outermost orbits. Therefore the metals enter easily into bonds with other atoms. Table B.3 is a periodic table of the elements. The atoms with filled outermost orbits are on the right-hand side of the periodic table. These are the inert gases. Metal atoms are at the left of the table.

Radiation is emitted or absorbed when electrons change from one energy level to another (see Chap. 12). The selection rules for "allowed" transitions in a hydrogen atom are those in which the changes in quantum numbers $l$, $m_l$, and $m_s$ are given by

$$\Delta l = \pm 1 \qquad \Delta m_l = 0 \text{ or } \pm 1 \qquad \text{and} \qquad \Delta m_s = 0$$

Other transitions may occur, but with a much smaller probability. The above rules hold well for other elements with one outermost electron (called hydrogen-like atoms), but for more complicated atoms the total quantum numbers must be defined, and various kinds of couplings are dominant depending upon the atomic structure and the specific transition. See R. L. Sproull, "Modern Physics," *op. cit.*, Chap. 6, or "American Institute of Physics Handbook," McGraw-Hill, 1963 (2d ed.), Sec. 7d.

**TABLE B.3** *Periodic Table of the Elements*†

| | I | II | III | IV | V | VI | VII | VIII |
|---|---|---|---|---|---|---|---|---|
| 1 | H 1 1.0081 | | | | | | | He 2 4.002 |
| 2 | Li 3 6.940 | Be 4 9.02 | B 5 10.82 | C 6 12.01 | N 7 14.008 | O 8 16.00 | F 9 19.00 | Ne 10 20.183 |
| 3 | Na 11 22.997 | Mg 12 24.32 | Al 13 26.97 | Si 14 28.06 | P 15 31.02 | S 16 32.06 | Cl 17 35.457 | A 18 39.944 |
| 4 | K 19 39.096 | Ca 20 40.08 | Sc 21 45.10 | Ti 22 47.90 | V 23 50.95 | Cr 24 52.01 | Mn 25 54.93 | Fe 26 55.84  Co 27 58.94  Ni 28 58.69 |
| | Cu 29 63.57 | Zn 30 65.38 | Ga 31 69.72 | Ge 32 72.60 | As 33 74.91 | Se 34 78.96 | Br 35 79.916 | Kr 36 83.7 |
| 5 | Rb 37 85.48 | Sr 38 87.63 | Y 39 88.92 | Zr 40 91.22 | Cb 41 92.91 | Mo 42 96.00 | Tc 43 ...... | Ru 44 101.70  Rh 45 102.91  Pd 46 106.70 |
| | Ag 47 107.880 | Cd 48 112.41 | In 49 114.76 | Sn 50 118.70 | Sb 51 121.76 | Te 52 127.61 | I 53 126.92 | Xe 54 131.30 |
| 6 | Cs 55 132.91 | Ba 56 137.36 | La 57 138.92 | Hf 72 178.60 | Ta 73 180.88 | W 74 184.00 | Re 75 186.31 | Os 76 191.50  Ir 77 193.10  Pt 78 195.23 |
| | Au 79 197.20 | Hg 80 200.61 | Tl 81 204.39 | Pb 82 207.21 | Bi 83 209.00 | Po 84 ...... | At 85 ...... | Rn 86 222 |
| 7 | Fr 87 ...... | Ra 88 226.05 | Ac 89 ...... | Th 90 232.12 | Pa 91 231.00 | U 92 238.07 | | |

THE RARE EARTHS
[To go between La (57) and Hf (72)]

| Ce 58 140.13 | Pr 59 140.92 | Nd 60 144.27 | Pm 61 ...... | Sm 62 150.43 | Eu 63 152.0 | Gd 64 156.9 |
|---|---|---|---|---|---|---|
| Tb 65 159.2 | Dy 66 162.46 | Ho 67 163.5 | Er 68 167.64 | Tm 69 169.4 | Yb 70 173.04 | Lu 71 175.0 |

†The number to the right of the symbol for the element gives the atomic number. The number below the symbol for the element gives the atomic weight. This table does not include the synthetically produced elements above 92. Atomic weights are taken on the basis of oxygen as 16.00.

# appendix C

# CONTINUITY EQUATION

Figure C.1 shows a one-dimensional configuration in which current varies in the $x$ direction. The differential distance between planes at $x$ and at $x + dx$ is considered. The charge

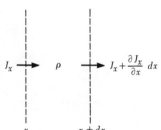

**FIGURE C.1**

in this region changes with time if there is a net flow out or in (represented by a different current at $x + dx$ from that at plane $x$), or if some charge is removed by recombination with free charges of the opposite sign.

The charge $Q$ between planes, for an area $A$, is

$$Q = A\rho \, dx \qquad (C.1)$$

where $\rho$ is charge density. If there is no loss of charge by recombination, $Q$ can change with time only because of a net current flow, and the rate of change is

$$\frac{\partial Q}{\partial t} = \frac{\partial}{\partial t}(A\rho) \, dx = A\left[J_x - (J_x + \frac{\partial J_x}{\partial x} \, dx)\right] \qquad (C.2)$$

or

$$\frac{\partial \rho}{\partial t} = -\frac{\partial J_x}{\partial x} \qquad (C.3)$$

430

Charge density may also be written as the particle density $p$ multiplied by the charge per particle $q$. (Holes are considered for convenience.)

$$\rho = qp \tag{C.4}$$

so that (C.3) is also

$$\frac{\partial p}{\partial t} = -\frac{1}{q}\frac{\partial J_x}{\partial x} \tag{C.5}$$

If there is also a net recombination rate of $r$ charges per unit volume per second, this adds an additional term which shows a negative rate of change with time of particle density:

$$\frac{\partial p}{\partial t} = -r - \frac{1}{q}\frac{\partial J_x}{\partial x} \tag{C.6}$$

This is the continuity equation for current in one dimension used in Chap. 5.

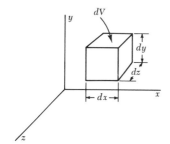

**FIGURE C.2**

A similar consideration of variations in three dimensions shows that total charge for a rectangular volume $dx\,dy\,dz$ as in Fig. C.2 is

$$Q = \rho\,dx\,dy\,dz \tag{C.7}$$

The rate of change with time of this charge is given by the recombination rate plus terms showing the net current flow out of the region. This latter contribution is obtained as in the one-dimensional example, except that there are contributions from changes in the three dimensions $x$, $y$, and $z$:

$$\frac{\partial \rho}{\partial t}\,dx\,dy\,dz = -qr\,dx\,dy\,dz + \left[J_x - \left(J_x + \frac{\partial J_x}{\partial x}\,dx\right)\right]dy\,dz$$

$$+ \left[J_y - \left(J_y + \frac{\partial J_y}{\partial y}\,dy\right)\right]dx\,dz + \left[J_z - \left(J_z + \frac{\partial J_z}{\partial z}\,dz\right)\right]dx\,dy \tag{C.8}$$

Division by $q\,dx\,dy\,dz$ yields the three-dimensional continuity equation:

$$\frac{\partial p}{\partial t} = -r - \frac{1}{q}\left(\frac{\partial J_x}{\partial x} + \frac{\partial J_y}{\partial y} + \frac{\partial J_z}{\partial z}\right) \tag{C.9}$$

The three-dimensional continuity equation is frequently written in terms of the *divergence* of current density. This is defined as the net current flow out of the infinitesimal volume, per unit volume and written div $\vec{J}$ or $\nabla \cdot \vec{J}$. By identification with terms above, we see that it is expressed in rectangular coordinates as

$$\operatorname{div} \vec{J} = \nabla \cdot \vec{J} = \frac{\partial J_x}{\partial x} + \frac{\partial J_y}{\partial y} + \frac{\partial J_z}{\partial z} \tag{C.10}$$

The continuity equation in terms of the divergence is then written

$$\frac{\partial p}{\partial t} = -r - \frac{1}{q} \nabla \cdot \vec{J} \tag{C.11}$$

In words, this states that *the rate of change with time of particle density at any point is the negative recombination rate per unit volume plus the negative of the net flow rate out of the unit volume, per unit volume.* For electrons of density $n$, the sign of the last term is reversed. See also R. B. Adler *et al*, "Introduction to Semiconductor Physics," *op. cit.*, Sec. 4.1.

# appendix D

# CATHODE-RAY TUBE PHOSPHORS

| DESIGNA-TION | COLOR | | SPECTRAL RANGE BETWEEN 10% POINTS IN ANG-STROMS | SPECTRAL PEAK IN ANGSTROMS | PERSISTANCE (APPROXI-MATE TIME TO DECAY TO 10% OF PEAK) |
|---|---|---|---|---|---|
| | FLUORESCENT | PHOS-PHORESCENT | | | |
| P 1 | Green | Green | 4900–5800 | 5250 | 20 ms |
| P 2 | Blue-green | Green | 4500–6400 | 5430 | 51 ms plus one long |
| P 4 silicate-sulfide | White | Yellow | 3300–6990 | 2 components: 5400, 4350 | 20 ms |
| P 7 | Blue-white | Yellow | 3900–6500 | 2 components: 5580, 4400 | 66 ms plus one long |
| P 20 | Yellow-green | Yellow-green | 4600–6490 | 5550 | 2 ms |
| P 22 | Tricolor | | 3900–6800 | 3 components: 6430, 5260, 4500 | One short two medium |
| P 31 | Green (high luminosity) | | | | 32 ms |

appendix **E**

# PREFERRED VALUES AND COLOR
# CODES FOR *R* AND *C* ELEMENTS

When for a given situation we obtain numerical values of resistors, we must consider such values in the light of the available
standardized values. The Electronics Industry Association uses
three broad groups of resistor values, corresponding to the
tolerances of $\pm 20$ percent, $\pm 10$ percent, or $\pm$ 5 percent.
Starting for each group with a value of 10, the next available
value will be approximately 40 percent higher for the 20 percent
tolerance group, only 20 percent higher for the 10 percent
group, and 10 percent higher for the 5 percent group. Table E.1
gives the basic values for each group in the range of 10 to 100.
It is to be understood that the base values given in Table E.1
can be multiplied by *decimal multipliers* for larger or smaller
values. The reason for this standardization is to reduce the
required stocks of resistor values to a reasonable minimum.
The designer of an electronic circuit must, of course, use these
standard values for a given application.

In many applications one can operate with the large tolerance
values of $\pm 20$ percent. If we wish to use a value of 6800 $\Omega$,
for example, which corresponds to the base value of 68 in
Table E.1, we would have a tolerance range of from 5440 to
8160 $\Omega$. Should we use a $\pm 5$ percent tolerance, the range would
be restricted from 6460 to 7140 $\Omega$. The resistor with the closer
tolerance is, however, more expensive and its use must be
justified by strong reasons.

434

**TABLE E.1**    *Preferred Values, Standard in the Electronics Industry*

| Tolerance | $\pm 20\%$ | $\pm 10\%$ | $\pm 5\%$ |
|---|---|---|---|
| Percent step size | 40 | 20 | 10 |
| Step multiplier | $\sqrt[6]{10} = 1.46$ | $\sqrt[12]{10} = 1.21$ | $\sqrt[24]{10} = 1.10$ |
| Preferred values | 10 | 10 | 10 |
| | — | — | 11 |
| | — | 12 | 12 |
| | — | — | 13 |
| | 15 | 15 | 15 |
| | — | — | 16 |
| | — | 18 | 18 |
| | — | — | 20 |
| | 22 | 22 | 22 |
| | — | — | 24 |
| | — | — | — |
| | — | 27 | 27 |
| | — | — | 30 |
| | — | — | — |
| | 33 | 33 | 33 |
| | — | — | 36 |
| | — | 39 | 39 |
| | — | — | — |
| | — | — | 43 |
| | 47 | 47 | 47 |
| | — | — | — |
| | — | — | 51 |
| | — | 56 | 56 |
| | — | — | 62 |
| | — | — | — |
| | 68 | 68 | 68 |
| | — | — | 75 |
| | — | — | — |
| | — | 82 | 82 |
| | — | — | 91 |
| | 100 | 100 | 100 |

The small size of resistors and capacitors for electronic circuits does not permit imprinting the values on them, and therefore a scheme of color coding is used. This gives all the pertinent information for a resistor, such as its resistance value in ohms and tolerance group. For the resistance values, the two first digits only and a multiplier are used. Table E.2 shows the typical coding scheme for fixed-composition resistors. Note that the first two color bands signify the ohmic-value digits. The third color band is the color code for the multiplier, and the last color band indicates the tolerance group (if the fourth color band is missing, it signifies tolerance $\pm 20$ percent). It is thus possible to verify the values of any such resistor by using the color code.

For ceramic tubular capacitances, a similar color code is used. Again the first two digits for the capacitance are given in the same code as for the resistors; the same applies for the multiplier values. In contrast to the resistor scheme, the first band on the left for a capacitor is a broad band as shown in Table E.3. This band signifies the temperature coefficient in parts per million per degree centigrade (ppm/°C). To the right of this band are the values and tolerance bands, as shown.

Years of practical use of this color-coding scheme have proven its extreme usefulness and simplicity, even to a person without any special technical training.

**TABLE E.2  Color Code for Resistors–Fixed Composition**

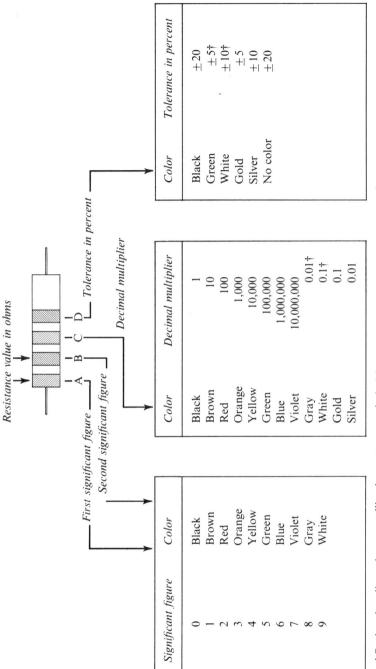

| Significant figure | Color |
|---|---|
| 0 | Black |
| 1 | Brown |
| 2 | Red |
| 3 | Orange |
| 4 | Yellow |
| 5 | Green |
| 6 | Blue |
| 7 | Violet |
| 8 | Gray |
| 9 | White |

| Color | Decimal multiplier |
|---|---|
| Black | 1 |
| Brown | 10 |
| Red | 100 |
| Orange | 1,000 |
| Yellow | 10,000 |
| Green | 100,000 |
| Blue | 1,000,000 |
| Violet | 10,000,000 |
| Gray | 0.01† |
| White | 0.1† |
| Gold | 0.1 |
| Silver | 0.01 |

| Color | Tolerance in percent |
|---|---|
| Black | ±20 |
| Green | ±5† |
| White | ±10† |
| Gold | ±5 |
| Silver | ±10 |
| No color | ±20 |

†Optional coding where metallic pigments are undesirable.

437

**TABLE E.3** *Color Code for Ceramic Capacitors*

| Color | Temp. coeff. ppm/°C |
|---|---|
| Black | 0 |
| Brown | −30 |
| Red | −80 |
| Orange | −150 |
| Yellow | −220 |
| Green | −330 |
| Blue | −470 |
| Violet | −750 |
| Gray | 30 |
| White | 500 |

| Significant figure | Color |
|---|---|
| 0 | Black |
| 1 | Brown |
| 2 | Red |
| 3 | Orange |
| 4 | Yellow |
| 5 | Green |
| 6 | Blue |
| 7 | Violet |
| 8 | Gray |
| 9 | White |

| Color | Decimal multiplier |
|---|---|
| Black | 1 |
| Brown | 10 |
| Red | 100 |
| Orange | 1000 |
| Gray | 0.01 |
| White | 0.1 |

| Color | More than 10 pF (in %) | Less than 10 pF |
|---|---|---|
| Black | ±20 | 2.0 |
| Brown | ±1 | |
| Red | ±2 | |
| Green | ±5 | 0.5 |
| Gray | | 0.25 |
| White | ±10 | 1.0 |

Temperature coefficient

First significant figure

Second significant figure

Decimal multiplier

Capacitance tolerance

# INDEX

# general physical constants – some probable values

| CONSTANT | SYMBOL | VALUE |
|---|---|---|
| electronic charge | $q_e = -q$ | $-1.602 \times 10^{-19}$ C |
| electronic mass (rest mass) | $m$ | $9.1085 \times 10^{-31}$ kg |
| electron charge to mass ratio | $q/m$ | $1.759 \times 10^{11}$ C/kg |
| proton mass | $M$ | $1.672 \times 10^{-27}$ kg |
| velocity of light in free space | $c$ | $2.998 \times 10^{8}$ m/s |
| dielectric permittivity of free space | $\varepsilon_0$ | $8.85 \times 10^{-12}$ F/m |
| magnetic permittivity of free space | $\mu_0$ | $1.257 \times 10^{-6}$ H/m |
| acceleration of gravity | $g$ | $9.807$ m/s$^2$ |
| Boltzmann's constant | $k$ | $1.380 \times 10^{-23}$ J/°K or $8.62 \times 10^{-5}$ eV/°K |
| Planck's constant | $h$ | $6.625 \times 10^{-34}$ J-s |
| Avogadro's number | $N_0$ | $6.025 \times 10^{23}$ molecules/mole |
| volume per mole | | $2.2421 \times 10^{-2}$ m$^3$ |
| mechanical equivalent of heat | | $4.1855$ J/cal |

*Source:* R. T. Birge, "A New Table of Values of the General Physical Constants," *Rev. Mod. Phys.* **13**:233-239 (October, 1941).